Chemical and Natural Control of Pests

E. R. de ONG
Consulting Entomologist
Agricultural Technologist

Formerly Assistant Entomologist
University of California

REINHOLD PUBLISHING CORPORATION
NEW YORK
CHAPMAN & HALL, LTD., LONDON

To Our
Granddaughter
Nishka Marta Yudnich

PREFACE

Maximum success in the control of pests, particularly insects and plant diseases, is possible only by understanding the value of natural control forces. These factors, when operating alone, seldom result in the degree of control satisfactory to our high standards of production. Hence it is often necessary to supplement natural control with chemical control. The purpose of this book is to assist manufacturers, research workers, instructors, and farmers in evaluating the two methods.

Excessive use of insecticides, especially the more toxic forms, may lead to the almost complete extinction of the beneficial insects present, the development of insect resistance to chemicals, and abnormally high chemical residues. It is for this reason that an introduction is given to the importance of weather, resistant plants, insect diseases, and insect parasites and predators in retarding the development of injurious insect populations and outbreaks of plant diseases.

For illustrative purposes, mention is made of many materials, both those in common use and in experimental procedure; but this is not to be taken as a final guide. The status of the various chemicals changes and so does their usage in different parts of the country. The State Experiment Station or local agricultural officers should be consulted for the latest procedure.

E. R. de ONG

Albany, California
April, 1960

CONTENTS

1. INTRODUCTION

Pest control is primarily natural control. The forces of nature, however, must be supplemented by the use of chemicals if the highest standards of protection are to be achieved. Pests—including insects, plant diseases, weeds, and rodents—are subject to adverse extremes of temperature and humidity, severe rains, flood, drought, high winds, and variable supplies of food. There is constant struggle between groups and among their members. Insect preys upon insect, while the plant-feeders attack every form of vegetation. Plants compete with each other for food, light, and moisture, while insects, fungi, and viruses attack each type of plant. It is only through struggle between the various groups that a natural balance is achieved. Although these forces war continually upon each other, extermination rarely occurs. A small percentage of each group persistently survives. Man must take up the struggle where nature's work ends.

We have but to remember the Irish famine in 1845 and 1846, when for two years the potato crop in that country was almost totally destroyed by late blight, to understand the terrible physical misery and desolation which plant disease can cause if unchecked. Millions of people either died from malnutrition or were forced to emigrate. A similar disaster struck the farmers in portions of the Mississippi Valley from 1874 to 1877 when great hordes of grasshoppers migrated from the Colorado foothills, devouring green vegetation, and forcing the settlers to leave their homes. There have also been the terrible scourges caused by disease-carrying insects—malaria, yellow fever, bubonic plague, and many others less well known. These diseases have been checked in part during recent years but still persist in large areas. Famine and wide destruction from pest attack is now rare, but losses ranging from 5 to 50 per cent of every crop, either in the field or storeroom, are not infrequent.

The farmer or commercial gardener does not willingly sacrifice 10 to 40 per cent of his crop to encroaching weeds, insect damage, or the ravages of disease. Substandard crops are unmarketable or at least unprofitable, but the demand for high-quality food is permanent.

The attacks of pests may be persistent but almost unnoticed—a few mice feeding in the storehouse, termites working in the basement, or a slight attack of rose mildew. Again, the attack may come in sweeping

1

waves of grain rust, as an outbreak of potato blight, or as an invasion of armyworms. Each form of attack means loss of food or fiber, or an injury to the garden. Cattle, attacked by swarms of biting flies, lose weight or lessen milk flow. A 10 per cent loss of the apple crop results from an infestation of codling moth and apple scab. Millions of bushels of corn are lost annually from the attack of the European corn borer. The world's growing demand for food and the increasingly higher standards of its quality can be met only by recognizing and co-operating with natural forces and the increased use of pesticides, together with trained people to direct the farmer in their use.

Insects

The term *pests*, as commonly used, includes not only the plant-feeding insects and those attacking man and livestock but also many of the lower forms of plants—fungi, bacteria, and viruses—together with the unwanted plants or "weeds" of field and garden, rats and mice of the storehouse, and ground squirrels and prairie dogs of the open fields.

As the growing of food crops became general, the conspicuous attack of insects soon led to their recognition as man's chief competitor. Their abundance, rate of reproduction, adaptability (learned through ages of development), and wide distribution are almost beyond comprehension. The number of known species in the world approaches one and a half million. The number of individuals within one of the larger species is beyond calculation. It has been shown that the offspring of a single aphid or a pair of flies would in one season, if unchecked, cover the earth to a considerable depth. Only the continuous force of natural control agents hold this potential mass of insects from burying the earth.

Very few of this great host of insects are known to be injurious, and many are beneficial. The former, or "pest" types, attack field crops, orchards, forests, gardens, livestock, and humans. The latter include the insect parasites and predators that attack the plant-feeding insects (see Chapter 2); the scavengers of field and forest—termites, flesh flies and springtails—that break down plant material and the bodies of animals; bees, flies, and moths that assist in pollinating the flowers; and even a tiny group that destroy certain weeds.

Injurious Insects. Injurious insects are divided into two groups: those with sucking mouth parts that feed on the fluids of plants and animals, and those with biting mouth parts that consume tissue.

Examples of the first group are the scale insects and their relatives the mealybugs. These are usually fixed in one position as adults, being attached to a leaf or twig by the sucking beak. Common examples are the San José scale and the European fruit scale. Scale insects are rated as among the most injurious insects, especially to orchard trees, but also to the oak, elm, and certain pines. Aphids (plant lice) attack almost every type of plant. They are even more prolific than scale insects, but are often held in check by their many enemies. Certain of the leafhoppers are carriers of serious plant diseases, such as curly top of beets and tomatoes.

Mosquitoes, because of their wide distribution, annoyance to man and other animals, and carrying of malaria and yellow fever, are generally recognized as dangerous enemies. Stable and horn flies of livestock and the black flies of running streams are also well-known examples of sucking insects. Fleas are pests of both man and beasts throughout much of the world. Besides the annoyance they cause, they are also known as carriers of bubonic plague.

The second group of insects are those with biting mouth parts in either the immature or adult form or both. Grasshoppers, beetles, roaches, and termites have similar feeding habits in both the adult and immature stage. Moths and butterflies are injurious only in the larval stage, because they then have biting mouth parts.

Grasshoppers are extremely destructive; their abundance and record of injury dates from Biblical times to the present. Even today great hordes of these insects develop in dry ground or in the foothills and migrate into the cultivated valleys, eating all vegetation unless checked by the application of insecticides.

Roaches (cockroaches) vie with man for food in his home. Termites are wood-destroyers. The subterranean form infests buildings and timbers exposed on damp soil. The dry-wood termite feeds on the dry lumber of the upper stories of buildings. The codling moth has for many years been the most persistent and injurious enemy of apples and, to a less extent, of pears, and is now attacking other fruits and the English walnut. In addition to moth enemies of growing crops, there are the destructive enemies of stored crops, the Indian-meal moth and the Mediterranean flour moth. These cause severe losses of stored grain and its products and of dried fruit and nuts.

The beetles include many well-known injurious species. The more prominent ones are the leaf-feeding forms, such as the Japanese beetle and the Colorado potato beetle. In addition to those which attack growing crops, there are others that feed on stored products—the grain and rice weevils, the flour beetles, and the saw-toothed grain beetle.

The above examples are only a few of the many insect species that are constantly preying upon crops and domestic animals. Variability in the feeding habits of the insect pests and in susceptibility to insecticides and to natural control presents a puzzling picture both to the chemical manufacturer and those directing the use of pesticides. Advances in the types and skillful use of insecticides, together with a better understanding of natural control, will lead to increased consumption of chemicals with a corresponding decrease in crop loss.

Beneficial Insects. Accumulated tree trunks, roots, and leaves would soon cumber the earth if they were not converted into their original compounds and elements. This is accomplished by the combined attack of various insects, supplemented by several types of bacteria and fungi. Dead bodies of insects and larger animals are attacked by flesh flies, burying beetles, hide beetles, and bacteria. The combined attack on vegetative and animal matter results in the formation of humus and various chemical compounds which serve as food for soil bacteria and plant growth.

The bees, both native species and the honey bee, together with many of the flies and moths, are important agents in the cross-pollination of flowers. Pollination (transfer of pollen from the flower's anthers to the pistil) is necessary before fertilization can take place. Many plants require the pollen of another type of plant to complete fertilization; others are self-pollinated. Many varieties of orchard trees and field crops, including alfalfa, clover, and cotton, are cross-pollinated and hence may require the help of pollinating insects. Cross-pollination and the development of hybrids have added much to our agricultural wealth and the beauty of our gardens (Vansell, 1952; Bohart, 1952; Green, 1957).

Weed-Destroying Insects. Two notable instances of weed control by means of introduced insects are those of the Klamath weed, or St.-Johnswort, on the northwestern ranges of the United States and those of the prickly pear cactus in Australia.

Klamath weed thrives where there is abundant winter moisture but the summer is dry. It spreads rapidly where overgrazing weakens the native growth. Desirable grazing plants are now reoccupying the range as the Klamath weed is checked. Besides displacing valuable food plants, the weed itself is somewhat poisonous to livestock. Animals feeding upon it become scabby, sore-mouthed, and unthrifty but are seldom killed (Sampson and Parker, 1930).

Klamath weed (*Hypericum perforatum*) is a native of Europe which was introduced into Australia and our northwestern states. Chemical control of the weed is impractical because the infestation extends over hundreds of thousands of acres of low economic value (Holloway and Huffaker, 1952).

Australia first attempted control of this weed through the use of beetles introduced from Europe. Many years of investigation are required to establish successful colonies because there must first be careful preliminary work to determine the possibility of an introduced plant-feeder attacking valuable crops. Two species of leaf-feeding beetles, *Chrysolina hyperici* and *C. gemellata*, were established in Australia and from this source taken to California. In 1946, preliminary feeding tests on economic plants were completed and the species *C. gemelleta* has since been widely established (Holloway and Huffaker, 1952).

Cactus plants, commonly known as prickly pear, were introduced into Australia about 1787 to be used in culturing the cochineal insect as a source of red dye. Unguarded plants spread quickly in the absence of natural enemies and by 1925 had affected 60 million acres, making much of it valueless. After many introductions of insects from North and South America, the original home of these cacti (Hamlin, 1924), a moth (*Cactoblastis cactorum*) from Argentina was found to be successful in checking the spread. Seven years after the moth was first introduced, the dense growth of prickly pear was destroyed and the land again brought into production. The total cost of introducing and successfully establishing the moth amounted to less than one penny per acre (Bishopp, 1952).

These quiet insect friends are working continuously around us, usually unrecognized, to benefit the soil, increase our crops, and protect us against injurious insects.

Plant Diseases

Disease is a broad term referring to any cause which checks growth and normal functioning. Plant disease may refer to infection by a pathogenic organism or to stunted growth caused by an unfavorable environment. Any agent which seriously disturbs the natural growth of our crops is a factor with which we must contend. Symptoms of disease include wilting, spotted foliage, fruit decay, cankers, and stunted or distorted growth.

In the early stages of agriculture, few crops were grown and an outbreak of disease such as potato blight or wheat rust might destroy the food crop over a large area, becoming a veritable scourge followed by starvation or migration. The increased use of pesticides, resistant crops, and greater variety in cropping now prevent such tragic losses.

The parasitic form of plant disease is caused by infection with organisms such as fungi, bacteria, and viruses. The nonparasitic form is caused by conditions unfavorable to growth or by irregular nutrition. The latter may arise from a lack of food elements and of minor nutrients, such as copper or borax. Drought or "water stress" is a common disturbance, either from a lack of soil moisture or from a soil so dense that roots cannot penetrate it. In the southwestern areas, alkaline soils render large acreages barren or at least unprofitable for production.

Fungi are a form of plant life that lack the green pigment, chlorophyll, by which the higher forms of plants produce sugar. They are forced to draw food from the plant or other host upon which they feed. The parasitic form of fungi penetrates the cellular structure of leaves, stems, and roots of living plants, absorbing food from the host plant and even breaking down the tissue. Enormous numbers of these fungi occur, for they attack practically every known plant and even living animals. They are known to develop new forms readily, apparently by mutation, as it is called in the case of the higher plants. The new forms, as found among those causing grain diseases, also show variability in susceptibility to chemicals, which increases the difficulty of control. Nonparasitic fungi (saprophytes), which feed on dead vegetation and other substances, are not included among the causes of plant diseases.

Fungi reproduce by means of spores (seed-like bodies), which are released in enormous numbers and drift about in air currents, sometimes being carried great distances. The fruiting bodies from which the spores are released vary in size, shape, and color and are used as a means of identification.

Among the better-known diseases caused by fungi are apple scab, caused by the fungus *Venturia inaequalis,* tomato anthracnose caused by *Colletotrichum phomoides,* peach brown rot caused by *Monilinia fructicola,* and wheat leaf rust caused by *Puccinia rubigo-vera tritici.*

Bacteria are microscopic vegetative organisms which multiply by fission and spore formation. Like fungi they depend upon other organisms or substances for food. Those attacking living organisms are known as *parasites.* One hundred and seventy forms of bacteria are recognized as attacking flowering plants (Riker and Hildebrandt, 1953)—a very much smaller number than that of fungus enemies.

Bacterial infection of plants may occur through the stomata (breathing pores of the leaf), lenticels, opening flowers, or wounds. Bacteria are distributed by the sap stream and through broken tissue. Infection usually causes recognizable symptoms such as retarded growth, wilting, decay, and the formation of galls. Well-known examples of bacterial diseases are crown gall of the stone fruits, caused by the bacterium *Agrobacterium tumefaciens,* and fire blight (pear blight) of the apple and pear. The bacteria that attack living plants are of a selective type, infecting only closely related forms. The condition and state of growth of the host plant may determine the possibility of infection. Fire blight, for example, usually invades during the blooming season and period of greatest growth.

Viruses are to an increasing extent being recognized as the cause of many plant diseases, as well as those of the higher animals and of insects. Only within recent years, and especially since 1900, have virus diseases of plants been identified as causing severe crop damage. This is in part due to a wider distribution of plants and to the extremely small size of the virus itself, which hinders identification. The largest recognized form of plant virus is smaller than any bacterium now known. It was only through the development of the electron microscope that the particles of certain of the disease-producing viruses could be seen and identified (Bennett, 1953).

Transmission of virus-infected diseases may be caused by means of cuttings from infected plants. The use of buds and scions, even though showing no visible signs of disease, may infect the nurseries and orchards where they are used. Virus diseases are also in many cases carried by sucking insects such as leafhoppers and aphids. A well-known example of this form of transmission is that of the curly top disease of the sugar beet. Other well-known virus diseases are aster yellows, tobacco mosaic, and peach yellows.

Weeds

From ancient times to this day, "the ground has brought forth thorns and thistles." Weeds (which are plants out of place) are a continuous drain upon our growing crops and gardens. They occupy some of our most fertile soil. Under the favorable growing conditions found in many river-bottom lands, weeds have become such pests that, were it not for the newly developed herbicides, the fields would be lost to cultivation. Perennial weeds such as Johnson grass (*Sorghum halepense*) and bindweed or wild morning glory (*Convolvulus arvensis*) are found in our orchards and fields and on the banks of irrigating canals absorbing vital supplies of moisture and plant food. Our grain fields and pastures are often giant flower beds of hardy weeds. The tremendous cost of row crop cultivation is largely due to the necessity of weed control. Any farmer or gardener knows the toll that weeds take and the effort required to control them.

Introduced plants such as the Klamath weed (described by Sampson and Parker, 1930), the Russian knapweed (*Centaurea repens*) of the Pacific Coast, and the prickly pear of Australia are examples of the danger of introduced pests. Such introductions frequently assume serious proportions before their potential danger is recognized, thus necessitating heavy expense in their control.

The value of weeds in certain situations, however, should be recognized. They may check erosion, conserve soil nitrates, or act as cover crops and as soil conditioners. Following brush fires in the western semiarid districts, black mustard, (*Brassica niger*) is sometimes seeded on steep hillsides to aid in holding the soil and to prevent severe erosion during the winter rainy season. Mustard seeds germinate quickly and soon form flat rosettes that are effective in checking runoff. Weedy growth following harvest absorbs available nitrates and thus prevents their loss by leaching during heavy rains. The weeds, when plowed under, soon decompose and release the nitrates for the following crop. Mallow or cheese weed (*Malva*) is an example of a common deep-rooted weed that assists in breaking up plow sole and withdraws soluble plant food from the subsoil to replenish the surface soil.

Rodents

These animals in various forms range from the Atlantic to the Pacific Coasts and from Canada to Florida. They are in our fields, or storehouses, and our homes. No district is entirely free from them. In addition to our native rats, mice, gophers, ground squirrels, and rabbits, we have three species of rats and the house mouse introduced from the old world. The latter are the ones usually found in our homes and warehouses. The most common and by far the most destructive is the brown or Norway rat (*Rattus norvegicus*). The roof rat (*Rattus rattus alexandrinus*) and the black rat (*Rattus rattus rattus*) are of less importance. The house mouse (*Mus musculus*) is very widely distributed throughout our country (Storer, 1952). A number of native species of mice and the wood rat of the foothills and the mountains are also troublesome. Since the rats and mice found about buildings have been known to carry disease, it is very desirable to exclude them from the grounds.

The plains and foothills of the western states are often populated by numerous forms of ground squirrels and prairie dogs. These are destructive to grain fields and the range alike. The pocket gopher (*Thomomys*) is another common rodent in the western states infesting alfalfa, cultivated fields, and orchards. They feed principally on roots and hence are very destructive.

NATURAL CONTROL AGENTS

Weather

Weather and variable food supplies are two of the most important factors in checking the potential increase of plant diseases and of insects. The latter are also subject to heavy attacks by parasitic and predaceous members and by insect diseases.

Weather comprises rain, snow, dew, atmospheric humidity, temperature, cloudiness, sunlight, wind, and evaporation. One or more of these agents may affect the growth and distribution of insects and the diseases caused by fungi, bacteria, and viruses. Soil temperature and moisture absorption is affected by soil composition and texture, which also influence the plants it supports and soil-inhabiting insects. Weather varies from hour to hour and from day to day, and the averages of these conditions constitutes the climate. Crop areas are limited largely by the distribution of temperature and moisture (Miller, 1953).

The insect world, dormant during the winter, responds to the warmth of the early spring days. Hibernating moth eggs hatch, and young caterpillars attack the opening leaf buds. Other forms, safely hidden under sheltering leaves, are stimulated into activity, development being regulated largely by temperature. Grasshoppers are especially susceptible to their environment. The eggs, enclosed in a watertight capsule, are laid in hard, dry soil in small openings made by the female grasshopper. These, being near the surface, readily absorb the warmth of the sunshine and may hatch before settled weather arrives. Prolonged rain, snow, and hail chill the tiny hoppers, or they are swept away in floods. Many of the eggs are destroyed by birds and predaceous flies and beetles; if from any cause the capsule is broken, the eggs are exposed to attack by fungi.

Aphid development and growth are directly related to rising temperature and possibly to the degree of moisture present. Reproduction is rapid at maximum temperatures of 60° to 70°F for only a few hours a day, and if this persists for three or four weeks, the increase may be enormous. However, a rapidly rising temperature also stimulates the parasites and predators which attack the aphids and may bring the former out in such numbers as to hold the latter in control. Hence a prolonged cool spring usually results in a heavy population of aphids, until the higher temperatures of early summer check the rate of reproduction or their enemies develop in sufficient numbers to check them.

The attack of parasitic fungi on crops starts in the early spring with rising temperatures and, with continued favorable weather, may develop into a severe outbreak. Dry weather and yet higher temperatures may check an incipient attack before it assumes alarming proportions. Moisture is also a dominating factor in the development of a fungus attack, as well as in maintaining growth. The spores of some fungi require the presence of free or liquid moisture for germination. Others may germinate at about 99 per cent relative humidity, while still others develop at a much lower dgeree of moisture in the air. The contrast between the prevalence of fungus and bacterial diseases of plants in the humid areas of the Atlantic Coast and central West, and their relative absence in the semiarid West, is a further demonstration of the effect of summer rains and high humidity in the former.

Well-known examples of the influence of the weather on the spread of fungus-caused plant diseases are evident in the cases of potato late blight, blue mold of tobacco, cereal stem rust, and apple scab.

Potato late blight attacks in cool, moist weather. The earlier in the season the outbreak begins, the greater the possibility of a severe attack, provided weather conditions are satisfactory and susceptible plants are present. The very conditions that favor the spread of the fungus may also hinder the application of a fungicide and thus make control doubly difficult. The severity of the attack by blue mold (downy mold) on tobacco is influenced by the prevailing temperature in January. High temperature in this month stimulates early infection, while low temperature retards development. The spread of grain rusts is also recognized as dependent on favorable weather conditions (Miller, 1953). Apple scab is a very serious disease in the northeastern states, where cloudy, rainy weather prevails during the early growth of buds and leaves. By contrast, the apple-growing districts of California are almost free from this disease, except in portions of the fog belt along the Pacific Coast.

Food

The abundance and suitability of food for quick growth and development is second only to the weather in its influence on the insect population. The plant-feeding insects are largely restricted to one, or at least related, species of plants and refuse to attack other forms. There are a number of exceptions to this statement, such as in the cases of the green peach aphid (*Myzus persicae*), which attacks orchard trees and vegetables as well as numerous weeds. Most aphids and other sucking insects, however, are quite definitely limited to a few hosts. The cabbage aphid (*Brevicoryne brassicae*) is found on cabbage, cauliflower, radish, and related species. The squash bug (*Anasa tristis*) attacks squash, melons, and pumpkins. The Douglas-fir beetle (*Dendroctonus pseudotsugae*) prefers the Douglas fir but also attacks big-cone spruce and the western larch. The lodgepole pine beetle (*D. murrayanae*) attacks both the lodgepole pine and the Engelmann's spruce (Essig, 1926).

It should be noted, however, that although many types of insects feed on a variety of plants, there may be differences in the rate of growth and development or in the number of viable eggs laid depending on the food eaten.

Parasitic and Predatory Insects

Parasitic insects are closely restricted to a limited number of species as host insects. This is shown in the biological control of insects, where it has been found that an introduced form of injurious insect is quite rarely attacked by native parasites and predators; rather, these must be imported from the country of origin of the host insect.

Plant Disease Organisms

Fungi, bacteria, and viruses which attack plants are subject to a restricted food supply. The familiar powdery rose mildew (*Sphaerotheca pannosa*) does not attack the snapdragon, nor is the rust of the latter plant found on the rose. Certain fungi even require alternate hosts for their complete development; for example, the white pine blister rust completes one stage of its growth in a species of wild currant or of gooseberry (*Ribes* spp.). Spores developed on the latter host then carry the infection to the pine tree.

The grain rusts also attack numerous grass hosts but are not found on broad-leaved plants. Blight of the Persian or English walnut is caused by the bacterium *Xanthomonas juglandis*. The severity of its infection varies, some seedlings being quite resistant, while a number of the cultivated varieties are decidedly susceptible. The virus causing curly top of the sugar beet is one of the most severe diseases of that crop, but of little importance to the table beet. The disease is also found on the tomato in some regions and also on a number of common weeds.

CROP LOSSES FROM INSECTS, PLANT DISEASES, AND WEEDS

Despite the natural control forces and the use of pesticides, the annual losses from pests in the United States is estimated at from 11 to 12 billion dollars. Damage from insect attack is placed at 3.6 billion dollars, with an added 400 million dollars for control measures (Staff, 1956). Plant diseases and weeds each add a 3-billion dollar loss, with rodent damage amounting to at least another billion dollars.

Cotton continues to be one of the most seriously crops damaged by insects, not only because of its large acreage, but on account of the number and severity of attacks by cotton-feeding insects. The National Cotton Council reports that in 1953 the loss from cotton insects was 1,430,000 bales (500 pounds each) of cotton and 585,000 tons of cottonseed valued at 261 million dollars. In 1952, however, the loss had been 289 million dollars. A trend in reduction has been evident for a number of years (Staff, 1956). Comparing these losses with that for 1950 of 908 million dollars—the highest in history—shows encouraging progress with the new organic insecticides and the handling of crop residues (Haeussler, 1952).

Grasshoppers of 14 states in 1936 caused an estimated crop damage of 102 million dollars. The value of crops saved by control measures in that same year is placed at 26 million dollars. During the next three years, the annual crop losses from grasshoppers ranged from 49 to 66 million dollars. The value of crops saved by control measures, however, ranged from 102 to 176 million dollars. From 1940 to 1950, inclusive, annual crop damage ranged from 13 to 17 million dollars in 18 to 23 states, but the saving by control measures ranged from 7 to 72 million dollars (Haeussler, 1952).

The European corn borer (*Pyrausta nubilalis*) entered this country about 1915 and by 1939 was causing an estimated annual loss of almost

4 million dollars. The figures climbed until, in 1948, the loss was estimated at 103 million dollars and, in 1949, it was placed at almost 400 million dollars (Haeussler, 1952). By 1956, however, the estimated loss was placed at about 119.5 million dollars (Dorward, 1957).

The corn earworm (*Heliothis zea*) loss in 1945 is placed at 140 million dollars. Loss from the hessian fly (*Phytophaga destructor*) in 1944 was 47 million. The pea aphid (*Macrosiphum pisi*) caused loss to alfalfa in 1944 of 31 million, and lygus bugs (*Lygus* spp.), to the alfalfa seed crop, 16 million. Estimates of average annual losses to livestock from the attack of cattle grub, flies, lice, ticks, and mites runs over 400 million dollars for the years 1940 to 1944 (Haeussler, 1952).

Protecting our crops of corn, wheat, rice, and grain sorghums during storage on the farm and in the warehouse is often more difficult than during the growing season. This is especially true in the southern states, where insect infestation often starts in the field and continues in storage throughout the winter. The value of stored grain lost annually in this country through insect-feeding has been estimated at 300 million dollars. This includes not only loss of weight but also that of quality. Grain that is even slightly contaminated by insects or rodents is considered unfit for human consumption and is degraded to feed-grain. Leaf tobacco, during the long storage of the curing season, is also subject to serious losses from insect-feeding.

Clothes moths (*Tinea*) and the carpet beetle (*Attagenus piceus*) are estimated to cause annual losses in the United States ranging from 200 to 300 million dollars. They attack wool, mohair, hair, bristles, and furs in the form of carpets, upholstery, and woolen garments (Staff, 1954).

Our forests are other fields where insect damage is increasing. Forestry officials estimate the annual killing of standing timber by insects and disease equals—if not exceeds—that from fire loss. Injury results both from defoliation and the work of bark beetles, which kill the tree by feeding just beneath the bark. An estimated 70 to 90 per cent of the mature balsam, fir, and spruce forests in Minnesota and Maine were killed, from 1910 to 1920, by the spruce budworm (*Choristonatura fumiferana*). An outbreak of the Engelmann's spruce beetle (*Dendroctonus engelmanni*) in Colorado from 1940 to 1946 destroyed about 20 per cent of the timber (Haeussler, 1952). Hemlock, heavily defoliated in 1953 by the gypsy moth (*Porthetria dispar*), showed little or no new needles in 1954 (Blaisdell, 1954).

Annual losses from 1940 to 1944 to our apple crop from the attack of the codling moth (*Carpocapsa pomonella*) were placed at an average of 15 per cent of the crop, or 25 million dollars. An additional 25 million dollars was spent in control work. Following the introduction of DDT as

(*Courtesy United–Heckathorn*)
Figure 1. Spraying for Spruce budworm in Montana.

a control for this insect, the annual average loss from 1944 to 1948 was reduced to about 4 per cent of the crop value, or 9 million dollars (Haeussler, 1952). This saving has been partly offset by the need of additional insecticides to check certain insects and mites that increased in number despite frequent or heavy dosages of DDT. The plum curculio (*Conotrachelus nenuphar*) still causes losses to peach growers in the eastern and central United States of 8 million dollars a year.

Quarantine Protection

A review of the cost due to insect attack would be incomplete without reference to quarantine measures used in preventing the introduction and establishment of injurious foreign insects here. Elaborate quarantine measures are enforced by federal officers at the principal entry points of sea and air traffic. Search is made of baggage and suspicious freight packages, especially from regions known to harbor dangerous insects not known to be present in this country. This effort will be understood when it is realized that many of our most destructive insects were introduced years ago from abroad. Not having the natural checks that are effective in their native land, the pests frequently assume alarming proportions. Occasional entrances of the more dangerous types of fruit and vegetable flies and the gypsy moth, and more recently the Khapra beetle (*Trogoderma granarium*), in the New England states are examples.

Once a dangerous insect is introduced, efforts are made to eradicate the infestation, especially if it feeds on a limited number of host plants. Infested areas are determined by thorough inspection and control measures applied as needed over the entire area under suspicion. Usually, under California conditions, "a period of three annual consecutive treatments without the finding of a live individual of the species against which the measures are being directed, is advisable in all eradicative projects." Financial costs of eradicative projects usually exceed $250,000. The cost of the Mexican bean beetle (*Epilachna varivestis*) control project in California has already totaled $840,000 and is as yet incomplete (Armitage, 1954).

Plant Disease Losses

The effects of plant diseases are less conspicuous than insect attack and are often confused with the effects of weather or a soil deficiency. Hence it is difficult to make estimates of the damage they cause and to identify the organism responsible for the infection. Many serious outbreaks of diseases have been recorded during the past hundred years, and it is certain that without our present control measures their severity would continue. The outbreaks of potato late blight in Ireland in 1845 and 1846 have already been mentioned. Since then there have been other serious outbreaks—notably in Germany in 1917—and now the disease is firmly established in many potato-growing regions. The tomato is also subject to a similar form of disease. Recent losses have been greatly reduced through the use of organic fungicides and Bordeaux mixture and other copper compounds.

Wood (1953) reviews the 1935 outbreak of stem rust on wheat in Minnesota and six adjoining states that caused almost a 60 per cent loss of the wheat crop. Ergot, a disease caused by the fungus *Claviceps purpurea*, attacks rye in particular but also barley, wheat, and some of the grasses. In the Middle Ages, when rye was the common bread cereal, severe attacks of ergot caused many serious epidemics in Europe. Once the cause of the disease was established a tolerance was set up for ergot in rye that was to be used for bread.

Seed-borne and soil-borne diseases of the cereal grains cause heavy annual losses in our country, much of which could be avoided by planting resistant varieties, crop rotation, and chemical seed treatment. One of the best known grain diseases is bunt, or stinking smut, of wheat. Loss results both from a decrease in weight and by degrading because of discoloration and the foul odor. Annual losses amount to about 20 million dollars. Loose smut of wheat caused by the fungus *Ustilago tritici,* is responsible for another 7.5 million bushels loss (Leukel and Tapke, 1954).

"Barley diseases reduce the annual yield by at least 5 per cent or about 15 million bushels." Covered smut, caused by the fungus *Ustilago hordei,* destroys 0.5 to 4 million bushels of barley annually in the United States. Two other barley smuts, nigra loose smut and nuda loose smut, are of minor importance (Leukel, 1954).

The rusts of wheat, oats, barley, and rye are caused by the fungi *Puccinia,* which are again made up of numerous races. Outbreaks of rusts have frequently caused severe losses, but are less injurious since the development of resistant varieties (Martin and Salmon, 1953). A number of other fungus- and virus-caused diseases also produce mild to severe outbreaks on the principal grains and grasses.

All clovers, both *Trifolium* and *Melilotus* are subject to attack from root to flower by fungi, bacteria, and the viruses. The root and crown diseases of clover are considered the most destructive and have been known to kill 45 per cent of the stand the first season. Stem diseases, including the northern anthracnose caused by the fungus *Kabatiella caulivora,* and the southern anthracnose, caused by the fungus *Colletotrichum trifolii,* are serious in the districts indicated. Losses of up to 50 per cent of a crop have been noted (Hanson and Kreitlow, 1953). Snap beans and lima beans are subject to a great many diseases, with losses ranging as high as 15 million dollars (Zaumeyer and Thomas, 1953). A list of the common vegetables shows that almost every type of plant grown throughout the country is subject to infestation.

Orchardists also experience severe losses from diseases caused by fungi, bacteria, and viruses. Apple scab has already been mentioned. Apple blotch is a disease of the foliage and the fruit which later develops into canker of the twigs and fruit spurs. Fruit infestation causes a corky, cracked area through which secondary fungi may enter and cause decay (Dunegan, 1953). Rust diseases of the apple, the best known being the cedar-apple rust and powdery mildew, and a number of minor disorders of the apple require constant vigilance to prevent loss.

Brown rot of the peach and other stone fruits is a serious disease in the eastern states and to a less extent in the West. The attack is aggravated by the presence of the plum curculio. The punctures made by the insect when feeding or ovipositing furnish ideal points of entry for fungus spores.

The peach fruit itself is attacked, and in warm rainy weather one-half or more of a crop may be destroyed within a few days (Dunegan, 1953).

One of the most destructive fruit diseases is that of powdery mildew, caused by the fungus *Uncinula necator*. It attacks wine, table, and raisin grapes drying up the berries on the vines and, if unchecked, may destroy the entire crop.

Loss from Weeds

A survey of hays in New Jersey "showed that 23 per cent contained more than 5 per cent weeds and 12 per cent had more than 10 per cent weeds. Weed content exceeding 5 per cent lowers the hay grade and indicates lower feeding value." Such weed content reduces the yield of hay and establishes the various species as of permanent contamination. "Yield and hay quality are reduced on an estimated 2 million acres." Pastures seeded to mixtures of legumes are especially difficult to treat because of the varying susceptibility of the different types of plants. The productivity of the Northeast's 12 to 15 million acres of pasture is reduced by the growth of woody plants, wild onion, dock, thistle, plantain, and many others. Corn is another major crop of this district that suffers from encroaching weeds. "Annual weeds are by far the biggest problem but certain perennials may be more damaging in the areas where they occur." (Aldrich, 1956)

Many weed problems, especially with the deep-rooted perennials, are just as serious in the North Central States now as before the advent of 2,4-D. Canada thistle and sow thistle (*Cirsium* spp.) are generally distributed in this region, but progress is being made in their control by the use of chemicals and by crop rotation. Field bindweed, leafy spurge (*Euphorbia esula*), and other perennials are only *controlled* by 2,4-D, eradication being impracticable. Resistance to the effect of this compound is also developing among a number of weeds. Annual weeds in small grain fields are checked by 2,4-D, but in soybeans only pre-emergence application of the contact-type of herbicide is practical. Broad-leaved weeds in beet fields are not controlled with available chemicals. Quackgrass (*Agropyron repens*) and Johnson grass (*Sorghum halepense*) are serious pests in many districts and even interfere with reforestation (Grigsby, 1956).

Weed control in the North Central States, from the standpoint of public health, has had but little attention. It is estimated that 40 per cent of the agricultural land in the area could be profitably sprayed as a preventive for the drifting weed pollen that causes hay fever and as a check on poison ivy in park and resort areas (Grigsby, 1956).

The Pacific Coast has largely adopted 2,4-D as a control for wild mustard (*Brassica arvensis*) and wild radish (*Rapponus sativus*) in the fields of small grains. Wild oats, however, are an increasing problem both in grain fields and among dry peas. The perennial bindweed and Russian knapweed offer serious problems in control. Range-land control of various brushes offers the greatest potential market for chemicals cheap enough to handle the problem on low-value land (Harvey, 1956).

The southern states' greatest weed problem is that involving cotton. Since 1952, the total cotton treated with pre-emergence herbicides has ranged between 180,000 and 250,000 acres, and post-emergence oils have been used on about half this acreage. "Ultimately, herbicides could possibly be used to good advantage on as much as 10 to 12 million acres of the cotton grown in the United States." Other potential markets for herbicides include 4 million acres of soybeans and 22 million acres of oats, wheat, and rye, besides large acreages of vegetables (Ennis, 1956).

REFERENCES

Aldrich, R. J., *J. Agr. Food Chem.*, **4**, 308 (1956).

Armitage, H. M., *J. Econ. Entom.*, **47**, 6 (1954).

Bennett, C. W., "1953 Yearbook," Washington, D.C., U.S. Dept. Agr., 1953.

Bishopp, F. G., *ibid*, 1952.

Blaisdell, H. L., "1954 Annual Report," Washington, D.C., U.S. Dept. Agr., 1954.

Bohart, G. E., "1952 Yearbook," Washington, D.C., U.S. Dept. Agr., 1952.

Clausen, C. P., *U.S. Dept. Agr. Technical Bull.*, **1139** (1956).

Dorward, K., *Agr. Chem.*, **12** (6), 62 (1957).

Dunegan, J. C., "1953 Yearbook," Washington, D.C., U.S. Dept. Agr., 1953.

Ennis, W. B., *J. Agr. Food Chem.*, **4**, 314 (1956).

Essig, E. O., "Insects of Western North America," New York, The Macmillan Co., 1926.

Flanders, S. J., *J. Econ. Entom.*, **50**, 171 (1957).

Green, H. B., *ibid.*, **50**, 318 (1957).

Grigsby, B. H., *J. Agr. Food Chem.*, **4**, 310 (1956).

Haeussler, G. J., "1952 Yearbook," Washington, D.C., U.S. Dept. Agr., 1952.

Hamlin, J. C., *J. Econ. Entom.*, **17**, 447 (1924).

Hanson, E. W., and Kreitlow, K. M., "1953 Yearbook," Washington, D.C., U.S. Dept Agr., 1953.

Harvey, W. A., *J. Agr. Food Chem.*, **4**, 312 (1956).

Holloway, J. E., and Huffaker, C. B., "1952 Yearbook," Washington, D.C., U.S. Dept. Agr., 1952.

Leukel, R. W., and Tapke, V. F., *U.S. Dept. Agr. Farmer's Bull.*, **2069** (1954).

——, *ibid.*, **2089** (1955).

Martin, J. H., and Salmon, S. C., "1953 Yearbook," Washington, D.C., U.S. Dept. Agr., 1953.

Miller, P. M., *ibid.*

Peterson, G. D., *J. Econ. Entom.*, **49**, 786 (1956).

Riker, A. J., and Hildebrandt, A. C., "1953 Yearbook," Washington, D.C., U.S. Dept. Agr., 1953.

Sampson, A. W., and Parker, K. W., *Calif. Agr. Exp. Sta. Bull.*, **503** (1930).

Staff, *J. Agr. Food Chem.*, **4**, 221 (1956).

————, *U.S. Dept. Agr. Home & Garden Bull.,* **24** (1954).

Storer, T. I., *Calif. Agr. Exp. Sta. Cir.,* **410** (1952).

Vansell, G. H., "1952 Yearbook," Washington, D.C., U.S. Dept. Agr., 1952.

Wood, J. I., *ibid,* 1953.

Zaumeyer, W. J., and Others, "1953 Yearbook," Washington, D.C., U.S. Dept. Agr., 1953.

<h2 style="text-align:center">GENERAL REFERENCES*</h2>

Assoc. American Pesticide Control Officials, Inc., Pesticide Chemicals Official Compendium (1958).

Martin, Hubert, "Guide to the Chemicals Used in Crop Protection," 1957.

U.S. Dept. Agr., "Agriculture Handbook No. 120," 1959.

Calif. Agr. Exp. Sta. Leaflet, **69–81** (1959); Mim. Vegetable and Crop Pest Control (1958).

Univ. Calif. Citrus Exp. Sta. Spray Program—Citrus Fruits (1958).

---

* These references are also applicable to other chapters. The first two will serve as a check list for the spelling of pesticidal terms used throughout this book.

Part I
Natural Control of Pests

2. INSECT PARASITES AND PREDATORS: EFFECT OF PESTICIDES

Plant-feeding insects are under continuous attack by some form of parasite or predator. This may occur during every stage of the host insect or it may be confined to the egg, larva, pupa, or the adult form. For many species of insects, it may be the most important agent of natural control. Recognition of this value, coupled with careful selection and use of pesticides, will give the best protection against loss.

The *parasite* feeds within or on the body of the host insect without causing immediate death. The *predator* kills the prey at the time of attack either by sucking out the body fluids or, like the hornet, storing their paralyzed prey or tearing the larger bodies into pieces to stock the nest for the young.

Parasites and predators are both widely distributed but are generally selective in their feeding, the former, especially, usually confining their attack to closely related forms. Glen (1954) sums up the relative value of the two groups of control agents as follows: "In general, parasites are most effective at densities of the pest species that are higher than can be tolerated economically, whereas general predators may be relatively influential at lower pest densities." For example, the attack of the parasitic wasp is usually made on dense colonies of aphids that are causing serious injury. By contrast, the ground beetle and dragonfly seek their prey over a wide range, capturing any insect that may come near them.

The attack of entomophagous (insect-feeding) insects is decidedly influenced by weather conditions and availability of the necessary food to bridge the gap from one generation to another of the host insect or to survive during a long, cold winter. Hence the cycles of relative abundance of parasites or predators and the host insect vary widely. The natural agencies of beneficial insects, unfavorable weather, and varying food supplies tend to reduce the population of injurious insects to a point where man can survive but is faced with a dangerous remnant. Should this remnant be of sufficient size to cause economic loss, then it must be checked by the use of chemicals or other control measures or the consequences be suffered (Decker, 1956; Hagen and Smith, 1958).

21

PARASITES

With a few exceptions, the important parasites attacking other insects are members of the order Hymenoptera (bees, ants, and wasps). The most abundant ones are the tiny wasps which attack and develop within or on the bodies of caterpillars, scale insects, and mealy bugs, or even in the eggs of leafhoppers, katydids, and other insects. The wasps range in size from 0.3 to 2 mm in length to that of the giant tarantula hawk (*Pepsis formosa*), 20 to 40 mm long (Essig, 1926). The parasitic wasps, although but slightly known, are more abundant than ants, bees, and the large predaceous wasps, yellow jackets, and hornets.

The reproductive rate of the parasitic wasp is very rapid. The development period (life history) from egg to adult insect may not be more than six to ten days. This makes possible a number of generations in one season, providing a continuous supply of food is available. With the rapid increase comes the danger of an intermittent supply of available food. If such shortage develops, then the later generations may perish without an opportunity of ovipositing. Reproduction among some of the parasitic wasps is also favored by the development of a number of individuals from a single egg. Division of the egg into two may be repeated until a very large number of individuals have arisen from one egg. A number of species are known to deposit several hundred eggs a day, with a final total of 1,000 to 1,500. With the short life history, it is possible for the offspring of a single wasp to number a million or more in one season (Bishopp, 1952).

Parasitic Control of Insects

A number of the parasitic wasps attack aphids. One species, *Aphelinus mali*, is well known from its attack on the wooly aphid (*Erisoma lanigerum*). This aphid is a native of the northeastern portion of the continent. With the extension of apple-growing into the western areas, the aphid was also introduced. The parasite was first left behind but is now established and assists in the control of the aphid (Clausen, 1956a).

Scale insects attacking citrus trees are subject to attack by a number of parasites. Muma (1955) found that under Florida conditions the purple scale (*Lepidosaphes beckii*), the most common scale insect, is attacked in large numbers by two eulophids, *Aspidiotiphagus citrinus* and *A. lounsburyi*. These two species associated with entomophagous fungi and predators show a high degree of control, especially in the summer, "but control is not comparable to that attained with insecticides." Florida red scale, *Chrysomphalus aonidum*, is attacked by a number of parasites but only four—three eulophids and one encyrtid—are important. "Natural control of Florida red scale is apparently maintained by insect parasites with parasitic fungi and predators being of secondary importance." The degree of control of this scale in unsprayed groves is usually adequate, and comparable to that obtained with insecticides. In a later paper (1959) Muma states that "Florida red scale was adequately controlled by natural factors." Parasitic hymemoptera are indicated as the critical factor in natural control, although all parasites and predators have not been thoroughly evaluated. Neither has the direct effect of weather on the scale itself nor the scale's food supply been studied. A number of predators have been studied, but predation is not considered a critical natural factor. The parasite *Pseudomalopoda prima*, which attacks mature female scales is considered the critical parasitic species.

Flanders (1942) states that "the parasitic fauna of the citricola scale, *Coccus pseudomagnoliarum*, [on orange] in California prior to 1937 consisted of certain species that are primarily parasitic upon the soft brown scale [*Coccus hesperidum*]." Of these, the most important is *Metaphycus luteolus*. The latter is very effective when associated with the black scale (*Saissetia olea*) and the soft brown and citricola scales, because this offers a continuous food supply.

Bartlett (1953) in a further study of the citricola scale on orange in California, stated that the natural control agents of climate and parasitic populations are the dominant factors in the economic importance of the scale. Both central California (Fresno and Tulare Counties) and the interior of southern California are subject to hot, dry weather (110°F and above) during summer, particularly so in the central district. Such extremes of temperature have "in a number of cases studied, caused mortalities of 60 to 97.5 per cent." Reduction in host-insect populations to that degree greatly increases the possibility of parasitic control where a sufficient population is present. Because of the larger number of parasitic species and the number of alternate host scales in southern California, the parasites can bridge the gap when the single-brooded citricola scale is not available or lacking physiologic suitability. In central California, however, where the effective parasite *Aphycus helvolus* does not occur, the parasites are relatively inefficient and give control only in regions of marginal abundance.

English and Decker (1954), in a review of the current situation of scale control on elms, state that "several chalcid parasites have been found to be an important factor in the control of Putnam scale, *Aspidiotus ancylus*, under natural conditions." A recent increase in the population of the scale was apparently related to the use of DDT in the control of bark beetles that disseminate the disease fungus *Ceratostomella ulmi*, which attacks the elm. A revised spray program is being developed in an effort to avoid injury to the chalcids.

A number of native egg parasites have been recorded as attacking the eggs of katydids, moths, and leafhoppers. Tashiro and Schwardt (1953) found that the eggs of the horse flies (*Tabanus* and *Chrysops*) were being heavily parasitized by *Telenomus* and *Trichgramma*. One egg mass of the horse fly *Tabanus stratus* produced 430 tabanid larvae and 371 adult parasites. Only a single adult parasite emerged from each parasitized egg. Mulla (1956) found two mymarid egg parasites, *Anagrus epos* and *A. armatus nigriceps*, active in the control of the leafhoppers *Typhlocyba prunicola* and *T. quercus*. Under California conditions, *A. epos* overwinters as a larva and pupates inside the host's eggs. Parasitism of the eggs of *T. prunicola* may run as high as 95 per cent in September. These two parasites are very tiny, being only about 0.3 mm long.

Caterpillars, the larvae of moths and butterflies, are hosts to a large number of parasitic wasps and also several species of tachinid flies. Since many of our injurious caterpillars are introductions from foreign fields, their parasites were left behind until they were imported and bred in large numbers for release. In a very few instances, native parasites have attacked the foreign pests and been helpful in control. A notable contribution of this type is that of the native parasite, *Macrocentrus ancylivorus*, normally feeding on the strawberry leaf roller, turning to the introduced pest, the Oriental fruit moth (*Grapholitha molesta*). Colonization of the parasite in infested orchards on the Atlantic Coast reduced infestation as much as 80 per cent. This was the principal means for control of the fruit moth until the introduction of DDT and other organic insecticides (Clausen, 1952).

Thompson and Steinhaus (1950) discuss the value of the parasite *Apanteles medicaginis*, which attacks the alfalfa caterpillar (*Colias philodice eurytheme*), as a carrier of the disease-producing virus, *Borrelina campeoles*. Their conclusions were that the infection of the caterpillar may occur by stinging with the contaminated ovipositor or by mechanical contact of the parasite body.

The above records serve to illustrate the work of a few of the better-known parasites of pest insects which attack growing crops. The caterpillars feeding on stored crops (grain, nuts, and dried fruit) are also attacked by a widely distributed parasite, *Bracon* (*Microbracon*) *hebetor*. Morrill (1942) while at Fresno, California, worked out the life history of this parasite as it fed on the larvae of the raisin moth (*Ephestia figulilella*) and the Indian-meal moth (*Plodia interpunctella*). The average egg-to-adult period ranged from 28 days at a mean of 65°F for the period of January 31 to March 13, to 9.5 days for the period of July 10 to August 1 at a mean of 86°F. The average number of eggs deposited per female parasite ranged from 71 to 153.

Tachinid flies have long been recognized as important parasites, but little effort has been made to synchronize the use of insecticides with the activities of these insects. Studies by Taylor (1954) of the parasitization of the salt-marsh caterpillar (*Estigmene acrea*), showed four tachinid flies and one ichneumonid to be important. Tachinid flies also attack certain beetles and grasshoppers, but are not recognized as very important in this field. Dietrick and others (1957) report the successful rearing and distribution of the tachinid fly, *Trichopoda pennipes,* a parasite of. the squash bug.

PREDATORS

By contrast with the restricted distribution of the parasite group, predators are found to be scattered throughout almost the entire insect world. Being more conspicuous, they are also better known to the public. There is no insect more striking in appearance and feeding habits than the dragonfly (mosquito hawk). These abound near swamps and shallow water, where their larvae carry on the same war in the water that the adults do in the air. These and their relatives, the damselflies, may be seen through the warmer seasons of the year taking their prey of flies, midges, and mosquitoes on the wing. Dragonflies have four net-veined wings, similar in size and shape and showing iridescent colors. The large head is composed almost entirely of the enormous compound eyes and the mouth parts. The eyes are made up of thousands of facets, each capable of showing a complete image. The dragonfly is thus able to see in almost all directions at once. The prey is taken in the large basket-like legs and devoured on the wing. In size, the dragonfly ranges from 1 to 2½ inches in length, with wing spreads of 1½ to 3½ inches.

Relatives of the dragonfly are the nerve-winged insects, the green-winged lacewing (*Chrysopa*), the brown lacewing (*Sympherobius*), and the dusty wings (*Conwentzia hageni*), all of which are important feeders on plant pests. They are, however, restricted in numbers because of the attacks of parasitic wasps. The larva of *Chrysopa* is especially noted as a feeder on aphids and plant-feeding mites.

Fleschner (1950) found the larvae of *Chrysopa* to be very active in their search for prey, much more so than the larvae of lady beetles and that of the dusty wings. Location of their prey was by physical contact and apparently without any indication of perception by the senses. For this reason, once contact was lost from a colony of aphids or plant mites, the predator wandered about blindly in search of further prey. One *Chrysopa* larva was found to consume 9,500 citrus mites during the last instar (period between molts).

Adults of *Conwentzia hageni* did not survive when fed on a diet of mites or scale insects alone. A diet of mites, scale insects, and honey prolonged the life of the adult and increased egg production. The larvae did not develop on a diet of mites alone but thrived on a combination of scale insects and tuberworm moth eggs. Dusty-wing larvae were quite susceptible to the action of acaricides (Fleschner and Ricker, 1953).

Green lacewing larvae are reported "practically immune" to the action of Systox (Ahmed and others, 1954). They also have been found "relatively tolerant" to the insecticides DDT and toxaphene (Van den Bosch and others, 1956).

Sucking bugs (Hemiptera) include a large number of predators which feed by piercing the bodies of their victims and drawing out the fluids. They range in size from the big-eyed bug, *Geocoris pallens*, 2 or 3 mm long, to the giant water bug, *Lethocerus americanus*, 45 to 60 mm long. The former is a common form that feeds on aphids, thrips, and plant mites (Gaines, 1954; Glick and Lattimore, 1954; Smith and Hagen, 1956).

(Photograph, F. E. Skinner)

Figure 2. Adult lady beetle, *Hippodamia convergens*, Guérin, feeding on spotted alfalfa aphids on alfalfa.

Bartholomi (1954) found the flower bug, *Orius insidiosus, feeding* on the eggs of the European corn borer, while Glick and Lattimore (1954) list the bug as an important feeder on the eggs of the bollworm (*Heliothis zea*) on cotton.

Beetles include many of the most beneficial predators because they feed on certain caterpillars, fly larvae, grasshopper eggs, snails, and many of the sucking plant-feeders, including aphids, thrips, scale insects, and the mealybugs. There are two large groups of predaceous ground beetles, the first, the carabids, feed by night and hide during the day under stones and boards; the second group is largely comprised of day feeders which hide at night. Both groups have large, heavy mandibles with which they grasp their prey and suck out the body fluids. Another common enemy of aphids is the leather-winged beetle (cantharids), which may be seen in our gardens searching for their prey. Their size ranges from 6 to 20 mm in length, the head and prothorax are yellow and the wing covers, black, with a fine white pubescence. The bark beetles of the pine trees also have beetle enemies. The clerids or checkered beetles are 7 to 12 mm long, and brown or black in color, with yellow spots and bars. This beetle feeds

(*Photograph, F. E. Skinner*)
Figure 3. Larva of ladybeetle, *Coccinella novemnotata, franciscana* Casey, feeding on winged adult spotted alfalfa aphid.

on the bark-beetle adult, and its larva attacks the larvae and pupae of the pest beetle in their galleries beneath the bark.

The most abundant and best known of the beetle predators are the lady beetles, or coccinellids. These are small, quasihemispherical shaped, brightly colored beetles, shiny black with red spots or red wing covers and varicolored thorax with white markings. Another group is a light tan color. The entire family with one exception, the introduced Mexican bean beetle, is predaceous both as adults and as larvae. The latter are slow-moving, warty- or spiny-appearing "worms" which crawl over the leaves searching for aphids, mites, scale insects and mealybugs. The bright yellow eggs are laid in clusters on the underside of the leaves. Because of their distribution and voracious appetites, the larvae are very efficient in holding in check many injurious forms of insects. The larvae of certain species of lady beetles are in turn attacked by parasitic wasps.

A number of species of lady beetles have been introduced into this country to feed upon some of the more injurious scale insects and mealy bugs. These will be discussed in the section on biological control.

Flies

A number of species of the syrphid flies, also known as flower and hover flies, feed in the larval stage on aphids and scale insects. The adult fly of the predator group is usually banded across the abdomen, thus resembling yellow jackets (wasps) or one form of the honey bee. Their coloring, and the habit of hovering over flowers and in searching for aphid colonies, makes them quite conspicuous. Their eggs are deposited singly near or in the midst of a colony of aphids. The larva is slug-like, moving about blindly in search of its prey. Once an aphid is located, it is held up from the twig upon which it was feeding and the body fluids sucked out.

Wasps and Hornets

Besides the many species of parasitic wasps, described above, there are a number of tiny predaceous wasps that sting their prey and carry it away to stock their nests. These are located in a sandbank or in the pithy stems of bamboo, *Bambusa*, willow, *Salix*, and wild rose (*Rosa canina*). These small predators attack and paralyze their victims by stinging them. Their prey consists of aphids, leafhoppers, and very small caterpillars. A lack of suitable nesting sites near abundant prey limits their value (Janvier, 1956).

The hornets and yellow jackets, *Vespula*, with their coarse paper nests, are well-known members of the large-predator group. They are 9 to 15 mm long, with white or yellow bands across the abdomen. Some wasps feed principally on flies; others, on caterpillars. Whatever the insect preyed upon, the usual procedure is to cut the victim into small pieces and use these for stocking the cells of the developing young.

The wasp *Polistes* is an active predator on the tobacco hornworm (*Protoparce sexta*). Rabb and Lawson (1957) found that wasp colonies located near tobacco fields depended largely upon the two annual broods of the hornworm as food both for the adult and for stocking the nests. The alternate host, taken largely between the two hornworm broods, was the green cloverworm, *Plathypena scabra*, feeding on soybeans. While procuring prey, the female wasp kills the hornworm larva with her mandibles and feeds on the body fluids. The first instar larva may be eaten on the spot or rolled in a ball and carried away to the nest. The second-, third-, and fourth-stage larvae are killed and torn apart and the pieces carried to the young in the nest. "Predators, chiefly species of *Polistes*, killed 68 per cent of the hornworm larvae in the experimental areas, but along with other natural enemies, failed to reduce the population below the economic level" (Rabb and Lawson, 1957).

Thrips

The "banded-winged" thrips, *Aeolothrips*, attack the plant-feeding thrips and other small insects and mites. Many of the species are single-brooded, the larvae dropping to the ground where they lie quiescent, pupating later in the year. For this reason, they are easily disturbed by cultivation and irrigation and hence do not become abundant (Bailey, 1951).

The six-spotted thrips, *Scolothrips sexmaculatus*, is a widely distributed predator noted as a control of a number of plant-feeding mites.

Mites

A problem of increasing importance is the control of the cyclamen mite (*Tarsonemus pallidus*) on the strawberry. Cultural methods and the application of acaricides have thus far proven ineffective. Parathion applications have but little effect on the cyclamen mite, but kill many of the predaceous laelaptid mite (*Typhlodromus reticulatus*) (Huffaker and Spitzer, 1951). The problem is further complicated by the necessity of controlling the two-spotted mite *Tetranychus telarius* (*bimaculatus*), which is a serious pest of the strawberry. A selective acaricide is sought that will preserve the balance in favor of the predaceous mite (Huffaker and Bennett, 1953). Muma (1955) found two parasitic fungi, predatory mites, and a predatory thrips to be the important factors in the control of the purple scale.

Increased populations of plant-feeding mites on apple, following the use of DDT, its analogues and sulfur mixtures, has been noted in West Virginia apple orchards by Clancy and McAlister (1956). The rise in mite population was associated directly with a reduction in number of predaceous mites.

Spiders

The best known of any predator is probably that large group of insect relatives known as spiders. They are occasionally mentioned in surveys of beneficial agents, but since they are not recognized as general feeders on the more injurious plant-feeding insects, their value seems limited.

BIOLOGICAL CONTROL OF INJURIOUS INSECTS

The term *biological control* is usually taken to mean the finding and introduction of beneficial parasites and predators not native to a particular location, and their artificial growth and distribution. The establishment in the United States of any introduced parasite or predator within the range of the pest insect may reduce the latter to the approximate level found in the country of origin. This, however, may not be sufficient to avoid economic loss; in which case, chemical or some other method of control would be required, perhaps at a lower cost or by the use of a less toxic agent. If the parasite introduction is sufficiently effective to lower the population of the pest insect below the level of economic injury, then large annual savings are possible by avoiding the cost of chemical application, fumigation, or other control practice (Clausen, 1956b). In addition to the potential value of lowered pest-control costs, other advantages include the avoidance of chemical residues, reducing the danger of developing resistant strains of pest insects, and pesticide injury to the host plant. The substitution of natural or biological control for one or more chemical applications, particularly for an entire season, would be extremely helpful in preventing the danger of developing insect resistance.

The first successful importation of a parasite, *Apanteles glomeratus*, in 1884, was for the control of the imported cabbage worm. The parasite was established, but did not succeed in controlling the pest. In 1888, the Vedalia beetle (*Rodolia cardinalis*) was imported from Australia in an effort to control the cottony-cushion scale (*Icerya purchasi*). The beetle became established, and within two years the scale was under control in the citrus-growing districts of California.

There are now 95 species of imported parasites and predators established in continental United States. Many of these were brought from Europe to control the gypsy moth, the brown-tail moth (*Nygmia phaeorrhoea*), and other forest insects, the European corn borer, and the alfalfa weevil. A large number of parasites and predators have been introduced from Australia and South Africa, but only a few from South America. Of the established species, 81 are parasites and 14 predators. Thirty-two species of the parasites are largely for use against scale insects and mealy bugs in California. The tachinid flies are for use principally against forest and shade-tree insects. Practical biological control (without the use of insecticides) has been attained against the cottony-cushion scale, black scale (limited), nigra scale, citrophilus mealybug, long-tailed mealybug, alfalfa weevil, and grape skeletonizer (Clausen, 1952, 1954, 1956b).

Biological control of the fruit flies—Mediterranean fruit fly (*Ceratitis capitata*), melon fly (*Dacus cucurbitae*), and Oriental fruit fly (*D. dorsalis*)—has received much attention in Hawaii since 1912. Three species of the larval parasite *Opius* have been introduced and established. Various species of *Opius* have become dominant at different times. Field parasitization from 1914 to 1933 averaged 42.3 per cent for all fruits, varying with the depth of the pulp. A combined program of parasitization and chemical spraying is now in use for mangoes and guavas (Clausen, 1956a).

Economical production of great numbers of parasites and predators has been a large factor in the success attained in biological control. By this means, effective numbers can be built up ready for annual colonization in districts infested by pest insects. A noted example is the introduction from Australia and growing of great numbers of the lady beetle (*Cryptolaemus montrouzieri*), which feeds on the citrus mealybug (*Pseudococcus citri*). The latter can be grown on potato sprouts, which offers a cheap and convenient method of supplying food for both the lady beetle and the parasite. The mealybugs and their enemies are held in specially constructed houses under optimum growing conditions. One ton of potatoes, handled in this way, will produce 125,000 or more *Cryptolaemus* and even much larger numbers of internal parasites (Smith and Armitage, 1931).

Following the introduction of the Oriental fruit moth in California in 1942, a method of mass-rearing the parasite *Macrocentrus* on the larva of the potato tuberworm was developed. This made possible economical production of the parasite for release to infested orchards (Flanders, 1943, 1945; Finney, 1944; Smith, 1945). Another record of similar type is that of York and others (1955), in which the native parasites attacked the European corn borer. Brunson and Allen (1954), after comparing the results of control of the Oriental fruit moth with insecticides and that with parasites, concluded that "under conditions such as occurred during the period of this experiment, satisfactory control of the . . . moth in ripe . . . peaches can be obtained from mass liberation of parasites and one preharvest application of insecticide." Another well-known instance of the introduction of parasites is that for the European corn borer (*Pyrausta nubilalis*).

The parasites and predators of four species of mealybugs found on citrus trees in California are listed by Bartlett and Lloyd (1958), as is their relative effectiveness.

EFFECTS OF PESTICIDES ON PARASITES AND PREDATORS

In the early days of pest control, the arsenicals were the principal stomach poisons. Contact sprays included the plant derivatives, nicotine, pyrethrum, and rotenone, supplemented by dormant sprays of unrefined petroleum-oil fractions. Residual activity of the three plant extracts is comparatively short. Application of any one of these contact sprays or dusts would probably drive many of the larger predators out of the treated areas, only to have them return gradually and feed upon the pest insects that had escaped the toxicant. During their more susceptible stages, the predators might be killed. Adult parasites would probably be susceptible to the contact agent. The egg, larva, or pupa, often enclosed within the body of the host insect, would probably develop and emerge as an adult after the residual stage of the toxicant had passed. They would then be ready to oviposit on the pest insect that had escaped the application.

The arsenicals—once considered a menace to natural control—are now recognized as being but slightly hazardous to either parasite or predator. The latter feed upon living insects, and only contact the toxicant by accident or through feeding on a newly killed caterpillar. Winged predators may be driven away, just as with the contact spray, but return to feed upon the pest escaping the application. Adult parasites are also largely immune to arsenicals, except through accident. Bartlett (1956) states that "pest control through the use of stomach poisons often establishes an advantage to internal parasites, since attack by an internal parasite commonly stops or slackens further feeding by the host, while unparasitized hosts continue feeding until killed by the toxicant. This results in earlier dominance by the parasite, as well as better reservoirs to check pest resurgence."

The fungicides, Bordeaux mixture and other copper compounds, are largely harmless to beneficial insects. An exception is the effect of copper on the parasitic fungi which attack certain scale insects in Florida. The use of sulfur as a miticide (mite control) and fungicide has been recognized in some situations for several years as reducing the number of susceptible predaceous mites (Cutright, 1944).

The introduction and use of DDT and related compounds with extended periods of residual activity have, with certain orchard crops and in some instances with cotton, increased the degree of control of pest insects (Newcomer and Dean, 1953); in other instances, they have apparently reduced the natural control, thereby causing outbreaks of minor pest insects

(Newton and List, 1952; Mills and La Plante, 1951). The tiny adult parasite, being quite susceptible to such compounds as DDT and dieldrin, usually succumbs. The persistent residue of these two compounds bridges the time when the larvae and pupae are buried in the body of the host insect, and when the adult insect emerges, it also is killed. The larger and stronger predators, such as many of the lady beetles, are less susceptible and may survive. Repeated heavy applications, however, may kill almost all natural enemies, including spiders (Gaines, 1954).

The organic phosphate compounds parathion and malathion are hazardous to beneficial insects. This is especially true of parathion with its residual action of 10 to 12 days. These and many other phosphate compounds are quite toxic to all types of insects and in some instances have been known to kill the parasite larva within the host insect.

Such danger can be reduced in two ways: first, by the use of the lowest effective dosage of the toxicant and avoiding unnecessary repeat applications; second, by selection of the type of pesticide showing the least hazard to beneficial insects and by the development of selective types of pesticides for specific pests of certain crops.

Glen (1954) states that "Under conditions prevailing in Nova Scotia (apple) orchards, DDT, parathion and sulfur drastically reduce the numbers of natural enemies; nicotine, lead arsenate, summer oil, Ovotran, Phygon, and ferbam are lethal to some beneficial species and not to others, whereas cryolite, glyodin (Crag Fruit Fungicide 341), Tag 331 (phenyl mercury salts in mixture) and copper fungicides are relatively harmless to all important parasites and predators." A later list of chemicals that harmonize chemical and biological control includes glyodin, captan, Bordeaux, and mercury eradicants as fungicides; and nicotine, lead arsenate, and ryania as insecticides. "The virtual elimination of sulfur, dormant oils, dinitrocresol, the chlorinated hydrocarbons and the organophosphates from the program has brought about a remarkable reduction in some of the more important apple pests" (Pickett, 1955). These recommendations are not to be taken in their entirety as applying generally, but are for use under the economic conditions of this particular district (Nova Scotia) and for those pest and beneficial insects concerned.

The use of chemicals in pest control is a broad subject which must be reviewed from the standpoint not only of the interrelationship of injurious and beneficial insects, but also of public health and the protection of wildlife.

The use of DDT at the rate of 1 pound in 1 gallon of oil per acre is effective in the control of the spruce budworm (*Choristoneura fumiferana*), and superior to a number of other insecticides tested against this insect (Secrest and Thornton, 1959). Bark beetles, whose damage may equal that from fire, are being controlled by chemical applications. The herbicides 2,4-D and 2,4,5-T, when used against the alternate host, *Ribes*, protect white pine against blister rust. With these many enemies, it becomes a problem deciding when direct control is necessary (Benedict, 1958).

The control of the imported fire ant is another complex problem, not only as to the injury the insect causes, but as to difficulties of control by heptachlor and dieldrin applications and protection of wildlife from these (Blake and others, 1959).

EFFECTS OF CERTAIN PESTICIDES ON BENEFICIAL INSECTS AND VERTEBRATES

Aldrin residue on foliage dissipates more rapidly than does that of DDT, which places the former in the class of chlorinated hydrocarbons less hazardous to beneficial insects (Decker, 1957).

Aramite was the least toxic acaricide to the predaceous mite *Typhlodromus fallacis*, but was ovicidal "and had residual toxicity at higher levels." (Ristich, 1956)

Arsenicals, including Paris green, calcium arsenate, and lead arsenate, as used in the orchard, alfalfa and cotton fields, and wherever they are applied to blooming crops, have caused serious losses to bees and, in varying degree, have reduced the number of predators present. Todd and Mc-Gregor (1952) state that the application of calcium arsenate by aircraft to cotton has been especially dangerous to the bee industry. Atkins and Anderson (1954) listed calcium arsenate as of medium toxicity to the honey bee. Changing to the organic type of insecticide has in many instances not reduced toxicity to beneficial insects but sometimes increased it.

Benzene hexachloride (BHC) was found to reduce the number of lady beetles and predaceous bugs that were feeding on pest insects in cotton (Newsom and Smith, 1949; Gaines, 1954, 1955). It is considered moderately toxic to game and fish (Rudd and Genelly, 1956).

Captan is listed by Pickett (1955) as one of the more desirable fungicides for apples in Nova Scotia. Ristich (1956) found it moderately toxic to the predaceous mite *T. fallacis*. Anderson and others (1957) found it comparatively safe to honeybees under the conditions of their experiments. Captan is not considered dangerous to wildlife.

Chlordane is listed as one of the more dangerous insecticides to bees (Todd and McGregor, 1952; Atkins and Anderson, 1954). It has also been found quite dangerous to predators in cotton fields (Glick and Lattimore, 1954). "Chlordane is less toxic to fishes than is DDT but is nonetheless able to induce significant mortality at field application rates." Chickens, ring-necked pheasants, and bobwhite quail are quite susceptible to medium dosages (Rudd and Genelly, 1956). DeLong (1954) made a number of experiments to determine the toxological effect of chlordane on vertebrates. In addition to feeding experiments with contaminated food, rabbits, guinea pigs, white rats, mice, and poultry were exposed to fog applications of 7 per cent chlordane. The fog remained as a smoke-like haze in the experimental room for more than an hour; yet, "no injury was caused to any of these animals and no apparent reactions were observed." It was concluded that no evidence was found "that either the vapors or the resulting residues would be harmful to man or animals, even if food materials were exposed and contaminated with insecticidal residues." The author then subjected himself to confined vapors of 7 per cent chlordane for 15-minute exposures at 3-day intervals for a period of 12 weeks for 2 years in succession. Repeated, thorough medical examinations have shown no toxic effects whatever from this exposure to chlordane.

Chlorobenzilate is listed by Atkins and Anderson (1954) as of moderate toxicity to the honey bee, while Ristich (1956) found it generally toxic to the predaceous mite *T. fallacis.*

Chlorthion was found to be highly toxic to the honey bee (Atkins and Anderson, 1954).

Cryolite is stated by Glen (1954) to be "relatively harmless" to all important parasites and predators in Nova Scotia apple orchards. Atkins and Anderson (1954) found it to be of moderate toxicity to bees, while Todd and McGregor (1952) state that "the arsenicals are some 50 times more toxic to bees than cryolite."

Cuprous and cupric compounds are relatively harmless to all parasites and predators. Pickett (1955) lists Bordeaux mixture as one of the recommended fungicides for apple orchards in Nova Scotia. Atkins and Anderson (1954) found that Cunilate (copper 8-hydroxyquinolate) was quite safe for the honey bee.

CS-708 has been found by Johansen (1954) and Atkins and Anderson (1954) as being but slightly toxic to the honey bee.

DDT, because of its long persistence as a toxic residue, has been found to be so dangerous to many parasites and predators as to require supplementary sprays for injurious insects and mites, which with previous spray programs had been of minor importance. Bartlett (1957) has found that the natural enemies of the citrus mealybug (*P. citri*) are being killed by the drift of DDT from adjoining treated areas. Linsley and MacSwain (1947) have shown the repelling action of DDT to the honey bee, while acting as a pollinator of alfalfa bloom. Early application of necessary dusts of DDT is stressed, and further dustings are to be avoided if practical. This compound has been found of moderate toxicity to bees by Atkins and Anderson (1954).

The following typical records have been noted of applications which showed injury to parasites and predators from somewhat indiscriminate use of DDT, and the consequent disturbance of natural control: that of Glen (1954); Gaines (1954, 1955); Bartlett (1953); Baker (1952); English and Tinker (1954); English (1955); and Harries and Valcarce (1955).

It must not be assumed, however, that the use of DDT has been generally harmful; on the contrary, it is one of our most beneficial insecticides, both in agriculture and in public health. Longer experience with this material has shown the possibility of its use even in districts where much dependence is placed on the value of parasites and predators (DeBach, 1955; van den Bosch and others, 1956). A dosage of 0.5 pound of DDT per acre, applied in the early morning, as a spray but not as a dust, has been found safe to honeybees (Lieberman, 1954). Quail and pheasant chicks are somewhat susceptible to 100 to 150 ppm of DDT in the feed. The viability of eggs was affected from birds receiving 100 ppm in the feed throughout growth, maintenance, and reproduction (DeWitt, 1956).

Demeton: see Systox.

Diazinon is reported to be similar in toxicity to other phosphates to the convergent lady beetle, but less so to the striped collops (*Collops vittatus*) (Harries and Valcarce, 1955).

Dichlone, a fungicide, has been found by Clancy and McAlister (1956) to be moderately toxic to the predaceous mites in West Virginia.

Dieldrin at 1.5 per cent combined with 5 per cent DDT and 40 per cent sulfur was found by Gaines (1954) to show a slight increase in beneficial insects between applications of dust mixtures on July 7 and 28. Further applications of the dust mixture at 12 pounds per acre, on August 1 and 5, practically eliminated all beneficial insects and spiders from the cotton field. In laboratory tests with a large number of pesticides on the predaceous mite *T. fallacis,* Ristich (1956) found that dieldrin, ryania, and lead arsenate were the least toxic to the predator. Todd and McGregor (1952) state that dieldrin is very toxic to the honey bee and because of the persistent residue is unsafe for a week following an application. Field experiments by Shaw (1959) in Massachusetts showed that residues of 0.25 pound of actual dieldrin per 100 gallons of spray may be highly toxic to honey bees for at least up to 96 hours after application. At a 12-minute interval between application and exposure of the bees, 88.3 per cent were dead after 24 hours.

This material when present in the food at the rate of 10 ppm had an adverse effect on quail and pheasant chicks. Available data indicate that dieldrin is a hundred times more toxic to quail chicks and at least twenty times more toxic to pheasant chicks than is DDT fed under similar conditions (DeWitt, 1956). The material is also known to be quite toxic to fish.

Dinitro compounds are listed by Pickett (1955) as detrimental to the pest-control program for apples in Nova Scotia. Atkins and Anderson

(1954), in work with the honey bee, found dinitro-o-sec-butyl phenol (DNOSOBP) to be the most toxic chemical tested of a large list of organic insecticides, including the organophosphate compounds. Dinitro-o-cyclo-hexyl phenol (DNOCHP), however, was found to be more moderate in its toxic action on the bee.

DMC (Dimite) was found by Ristich (1956) to be the most toxic to the predaceous mite *T. fallacis* of a number of chlorinated hydrocarbons.

Dormant oils are known to reduce the number of parasites present in scale insects on apple and other orchard trees. Pickett (1956) also recog-izes them as detrimental for apple orchard application in Nova Scotia.

Endrin has been found to be of moderate toxicity to predators by Harries and Valcarce (1955), and van den Bosch and others (1956). It is stated by Atkins and Anderson (1954) that endrin is one of the most dangerous of any of the insecticides to the honey bee. DeWitt (1956) found it to be detrimental when included even in very small amounts in the breeding diet of quail and pheasant. It is also hazardous to fish.

EPN was found by Atkins and Anderson (1954) to be one of the most toxic to the honey bee of any organic insecticide.

Ferbam (Fermate) has been found injurious to some beneficial insects of the apple, but not to others (Glen, 1954). It gave erratic results against the predaceous mite *T. fallacis* with apparently some toxic action to both eggs and larvae (Ristich, 1956). Slight injury was noted to bees by Ander-son and others (1957) from ferbam applications under the conditions of their experiments.

Glyodin is recommended as a fungicide in Pickett's list (1955) of safe compounds for use in Nova Scotia apple orchards. Glen (1954), Clancy and McAlister (1956), and Garman (1956) all speak favorably of this material for some phase of orchard spraying. Anderson and others (1957) found but slight injury to the honeybee from the use of this material.

Heptachlor at 2.5 per cent concentration was found by Harries and Valcarce (1955) to be less toxic than most organophosphate compounds to the striped collops beetle (*C. vittatus*) and to lady beetles. Ristich (1956) found that at 0.5 per cent concentration it was very toxic to *T. fallacis*. Atkins and Anderson (1954) list heptachlor at 2 per cent concentration as one of the most dangerous of insecticides to the honey bee. Lieberman and others (1954) states that heptachlor at the minimum dosage of 0.25 pound per acre is even then too dangerous for bees. Rudd and Genelly (1956) rates the toxicity of heptachlor to fish as between that of chlordane and aldrin. Heptachlor is considered slightly more toxic than chlordane.

Kelthane "did not seriously affect natural enemies of the mites on English walnut (European red mite and Pacific spider mite) except" to deprive them of food (Michelbacher, 1956).

Lindane at a concentration of 1.5 per cent has been found by Atkins and Anderson (1954) to be one of the most dangerous insecticides to honey bees. This finding is confirmed by Todd and McGregor (1952). Ristich (1956) found it very dangerous to *T. fallacis,* even at a concentration of 0.02 per cent of the active material.

Lime-sulfur solution, applied at monthly intervals to citrus trees in Texas, resulted in large increases of California red scale (*Aonidiella aurantii*), compared with the unsprayed trees (Clark and Friend, 1932). The present custom is to depend more on parasites as a control for this insect (Dean, 1955). Cox (1942) found that orchard trees sprayed with lime-sulfur solution had very few parasites of scale insects while in unsprayed orchards they were abundant.

Malathion was severely toxic to the adult and larva of the lady beetle (*Hippodamia*) where it was being used as a control of the spotted alfalfa aphid (*Therioaphis maculata*). It was also more toxic than a number of chlorinated hydrocarbon compounds to the striped collops beetle (*C. vittatus*) and the lady beetles, *H. convergens* and *Coleomegilla maculata* (Harries and Valcarce, 1955). Malathion is listed as highly dangerous to the honey bee, both by Atkins and Anderson (1954) and Lieberman and others (1954).

Mercurial fungicides. Anderson and others (1957) report data from various sources to the effect that the Puratized compounds (phenyl mercury lactate and phenyl mercury acetate) have, in some experiments, shown little effect on bees, either as contact or residual applications; in other reports the acetate compound was quite toxic.

Mercuric chloride is highly toxic to fish even at a fraction of parts per million. The toxicity of the seed fungicides, Ceresan (methoxyethyl mercurisilicate) and Ceresan M [N-(ethylmercuri)-P-toluene sulfonanilide], is similar to mercuric chloride. Treated seed is very dangerous to livestock and poultry (Rudd and Genelly, 1956).

Nicotine has one of the shorter periods of residual toxicity of any of the insecticides, it being but 18 to 24 hours for certain aphids (de Ong, 1923). This short period offers little danger to parasitic wasps, even those with life histories as short as 6 to 10 days. Adult predators, which may be driven from the field during spraying or dusting, usually begin returning within 36 hours and feed in safety on the pest insects which may have escaped the nicotine.

Nicotine is stated by Pickett (1955) to be a satisfactory insecticide for Nova Scotia apple orchards, although Glen (1954) lists it as lethal to some beneficial insects. Newsom and Smith (1949) found that calcium arsenate plus 2 per cent nicotine was less hazardous to the predaceous bugs *Geocoris punctipes* and *Orius insidiosus* than BHC or toxaphene. Michelbacher (1954) found that 14 per cent nicotine dry concentrate gave slightly better control of the walnut aphid (*Chromaphis juglandicola*) than did BHC, parathion, malathion, or TEPP. He attributed the superiority of nicotine to its slight toxicity to natural enemies. Atkins and Anderson (1954) found nicotine to be the least hazardous to the honey bee of any of the common insecticides, including pyrethrum, rotenone, and also calcium arsenate.

Ovex (Ovotran) is reported by Glen (1954) to be harmful to some species of beneficial insects, but not to others. Ristich (1956) found it to be moderately toxic to *T. fallacis*. Atkins and Anderson (1954) found it to be one of the safer compounds for the honeybee.

Parathion and methyl parathion were found by Atkins and Anderson (1954) and Todd and McGregor (1952) to be very toxic to the honey bee. Glen (1954) stated that parathion drastically reduced the numbers of natural enemies. Bartlett (1953) showed that parathion at a dosage of 6 pounds of 25 per cent concentrate eliminated *Metaphycus luteolus,* a principal parasite of the citricola scale, for from one to three months. Harries and Valcarce (1955) found it to be very toxic to lady beetles and to the striped collops beetle. The long residual period makes these two compounds especially dangerous to the parasitic wasps.

Phygon is listed by both Glen (1954) and Pickett (1955) as an effective fungicide for apple orchards in Nova Scotia and safe for most parasites and predators, although the former states that it is lethal to some species. Garman (1954) found that Phygon, combined with lead arsenate and DDT, resulted in an improvement of the flavor of the apple over that from other combinations. When used as a control of algae and other aquatic plants, it showed no visible effect on fish or aquatic invertebrates (Rudd and Genelly, 1956).

Rotenone, having but a moderate length of residual activity, is to that degree safer to beneficial insects than insecticides which persist for a longer time. Atkins and Anderson (1954) list it as one of the safest insecticides from the standpoint of the honey bee. Rotenone is very toxic to fish, and drift of spray or dust to waters containing fish should be avoided. It is now being used in fish management control to increase the population of sport fishes.

Ryania has been found by Pickett (1955) to be one of the safest insecticides for Nova Scotia apple-growers to use in codling-moth control, from the standpoint of safety to beneficial insects. Clancy and McAlister (1956), working in West Virginia apple orchards, found that a combination of ryania and glyodin gave outstanding control of a severe codling-moth infestation in both abandoned and commercial orchards, compared to that usually obtained with DDT. The predaceous mites were unharmed by the pure ryania, but populations were seriously reduced by repeated application of an activated form. Hamilton and others (1954) and Madsen (1956) found ryania to be a promising material for codling-moth control. Ristich (1956) and Garman (1956) both report favorably on the use of ryania as being harmless to certain predaceous mites and not detrimental to apple flavor.

Sabadilla in laboratory tests at 20 per cent concentration was found by Atkins and Anderson (1954) to be highly toxic to the honey bee. Further laboratory tests reported by Anderson and Atkins (1958) show a similar high toxicity in applications of 20 per cent concentration, but dusts of 1 per cent and 5 per cent concentration were nontoxic to the bees. The 5 per cent dust at 30 pounds per acre is about double the sabadilla alkaloid dosage on citrus trees.

Schraden, a selective insecticide, is toxic to aphids feeding upon sprayed plants, but has little or no effect on their predators or parasites (Ripper, 1957).

Sevin. During field tests in Massachusetts, Shaw (1959) found that 1 pound of actual Sevin per 100 gallons was highly toxic as a contact poison to honey bees. The residue was very toxic for 24 hours following application, but diminished after a period of 96 hours.

Strobane has been found to be similar in toxicity to DDT and toxaphene, but less toxic than the phosphate insecticides (Harries and Valcarce, 1955). Pheasant and quail chicks were somewhat injured when more than 50 ppm of strobane were included in the diet (DeWitt, 1956).

Sulfur and sulfur-bearing compounds have been found by Bartlett (1956) to be more injurious to natural enemies than are the newer types of fungicides. An increase in the population of the purple scale on citrus trees resulting from the residue of wettable sulfur is reported by Griffiths and Fisher (1949). Cutright (1944) found that the use of sulfur as a fungicide on apple trees reduced the population of the predaceous mite *Seius*, with a consequent increase in the number of European red mites. Clancy and McAlister (1956) also report high toxicity to the predaceous mite *Iphidulus*, on apple trees, when treated with sulfur. Glen (1954) and Pickett (1955) both stress the danger to natural enemies from the use of sulfur on apple trees in Nova Scotia. Atkins and Anderson (1954) and Anderson and others (1957) place sulfur as one of the safer pesticides for use with bees.

Systox at a dosage of 1 and 2 ounces per acre gave a good initial kill of the alfalfa aphid, with moderate toxicity to the parasitic wasp *Praon palitans,* and held aphids migrating into the treated field to a low level. The parasites which escape the low dosage of Systox reduce the number of aphids which escape the insecticide and thus lower the threat of developing resistance (Stern and others, 1958). Systox was found by Lieberman (1954) to be safe for honey bees when applied in the morning at the rate of 6 ounces of the active material per acre. Atkins and Anderson (1954) list Systox (demeton) as one of the safer materials for bees.

TEPP at 1 per cent concentration has been found to be very toxic to bees when first applied, but dissipates rapidly and thus is lethal only near the time of application (Atkins and Anderson, 1954). These findings are confirmed by Lieberman and others (1954) who list evening sprays of 6 ounces of TEPP per acre as being safe to bees. This compound is highly toxic to the higher animals. Such toxicity is confined to the time of application, there being no residual hazard (Rudd and Genelly, 1956).

Toxaphene "practically eliminated" the beneficial insects and spiders from cotton with three dust applications of 10.9 or 12.6 pounds per acre. The eight applications were made from July 15 to August 24. Included in the formulas was one mixture of 20 per cent toxaphene and 40 per cent sulfur (Gaines, 1955). Similar results were found by the same author (1954) with this formula. Glick and Lattimore (1954) found that a toxaphene-sulfur dust applied to cotton after two early-season (May 28, June 8) toxaphene-DDT sprays gave the lowest population of injurious insects and the highest population of beneficial insects. Van den Bosch and others (1956), working on the control of cotton insects in California, state that a dust mixture of DDT and toxaphene "is severely toxic and should be used only where the effect on predators is not a consideration." Toxaphene at a dosage of 1.5 pounds per acre was found by Lieberman (1954) to be one of the safest insecticides to be used in relation to bees and should be chosen when necessary to apply during flowering. Todd and McGregor (1952) and Atkins and Anderson (1954) list toxaphene as of moderate safety to bees.

Toxaphene is very toxic to fish, and care should be used to avoid drift to fish-bearing waters. Instances have also been reported of killing several ducks, geese, and pheasants. Bobwhite quail and mourning doves are apparently less sensitive to the compound (Rudd and Genelly, 1956).

Warfarin when used as a rodent poison around buildings may cause secondary poisoning of dogs and cats. Birds are apparently not affected by field-baiting of rodents and carnivores (Rudd and Genelly, 1956).

Zinc phosphide. This is a hazardous material but, with careful handling, may be used with safety to wildlife. It is quite toxic to poultry, pheasants, and geese. Secondary poisoning has also occurred due to eating poisoned rodents (Rudd and Genelly, 1956).

REFERENCES

Ahmed, M. K., and Others, *J. Econ. Entom.,* **47,** 445 (1954).
Anderson, Jr., L. D., and Atkins, Jr., E. L., *ibid.,* **51,** 103 (1958).
Anderson, Jr., L. D., and Others, *ibid.,* **50,** 570 (1957).
Atkins, Jr., E. L., and Anderson, Jr., L. D., *ibid.,* **47,** 969 (1954).
Bailey, S. F., *Hilgardia,* **21,** 43 (1951).
Baker, H., "1952 Yearbook," Washington, D.C., U.S. Dept. Agr., 1952.
Bartholomi, C. W., *J. Econ. Entom.,* **47,** 295 (1954).
Bartlett, B. R., *ibid.,* **46,** 25 (1953).

———, *ibid.*, **50,** 753 (1957).

———, *Agr. Chem.*, **11** (2), 42 (1956).

———, and Lloyd, D. C., *J. Econ. Entom.*, **51,** 90 (1958).

Benedict, W. V., *Agr. Chem.*, **13** (12), 28 (1958).

Bishopp, F. C., "1952 Yearbook," Washington, D.C., U.S. Dept. Agr., 1952.

Blake, Jr., G. H., and Others, *J. Econ. Entom.*, **52,** 1 (1959).

Brunson, M. H., and Allen, H. W., *ibid.*, **47,** 147 (1954).

Campbell, W. V., and Hutchins, R. E., *ibid.*, **45,** 828 (1952).

Clancy, D. W., and McAlister, E. J., *ibid.*, **49,** 196 (1956).

Clark, S. W., and Friend, W. H., *Texas Agr. Exp. Sta. Bull.*, **455** (1932).

Clausen, C. P. "1952 Yearbook," Washington, D.C., U.S. Dept. Agr., 1952.

———, *J. Agr. Food Chem.*, **2,** 12 (1954).

———, *J. Econ. Entom.*, **49,** 176 (1956a).

———, *U.S. Dept. Agr. Tech. Bull.*, **1139** (1956b).

Cutright, C. R., *J. Econ. Entom.*, **37,** 499 (1944).

Dean, H. A., *ibid.*, **48,** 444 (1955).

———, and Newcomer, E. J., *ibid.*, **47,** 936 (1954).

DeBach, P. J., *ibid.*, **48,** 584 (1955).

Decker, G. C., *Bull. Entom. Soc. America*, **2** (1), 2 (1956).

———, *Agr. Chem.*, **12** (2), 39 (1957).

———, *J. Agr. Food Chem.*, **6** (2), 98 (1958).

DeLong, D. M., *J. Econ. Entom.*, **47,** 1056 (1954).

de Ong, E. R., *ibid.*, **16,** 486 (1923).

DeWitt, J. B., *J. Agr. Food Chem.*, **4,** 863 (1956).

Dietrick, E. J., and Others, *J. Econ. Entom.*, **50,** 627 (1957).

English, L. L., *ibid.*, **48,** 279 (1955).

———, and Decker, G. C., *ibid.*, **47,** 624 (1954).

———, and Tinker, M. E., *ibid.*, **47,** 858 (1954).

Essig, E. O., "Insects of Western North America," New York, The Macmillan Co., 1926.

Finney, G. L., and Flanders, S. E., *J. Econ. Entom.*, **37,** 61 (1944).

Flanders, S. E., *ibid.*, **35,** 830 (1942).

———, *ibid.*, **36,** 807 (1943).

———, *ibid.*, **38,** 323 (1945).

Fleming, W. E., *U.S. Dept. Agr. Bur. Entom. & Plants Quarterly*, **E-737,** (1947).

———, and Maines, W. W., *J. Econ. Entom.*, **46,** 445 (1953).

Fleschner, C. A., *Hilgardia*, **20,** 233 (1950).

———, and Maines, W. W., *J. Econ. Entom.*, **46,** 445 (1953).

Gaines, R. C., *ibid.*, **47,** 543 (1954).

———, *ibid.*, **48,** 477 (1955).

Garman, P., *ibid.*, **49,** 521 (1956).

Ginsburg, J. M., and Reed, J. P., *ibid.*, **47,** 467 (1954).

Glen, R., *ibid.*, **47,** 398 (1954).

Glick, P. A., and Lattimore, W. B., *ibid.*, **47,** 681 (1954).

Griffiths, Jr., J. T., and Fisher, F. E., *ibid.*, **42,** 829 (1949.

Hagen, K. S., and Smith, R. F., *Agr. Chem.*, **13** (7), 30 (1958).

Hamilton, D. W., and Others, *ibid.*, **47,** 768 (1954).

Harries, F. H., and Valcarce, A. C., *ibid.*, **47,** 768 (1955).

Huffaker, C. B., and Spitzer, C. H., *ibid.*, **44,** 519 (1951).

Huffaker, C. B., and Kennett, C. E., *ibid.*, **46,** 802 (1953).

Janvier, H., *ibid.*, **49,** 202 (1956).

Johansen, C. A., *ibid.,* **47, 715** (1954).

Lieberman, F. V., *ibid.,* **47,** 316 (1954).

Linduska, J. P., and Surber, E. W., *U.S. Dept. Int. Fish and Wildlife Service Circular,* **15** (1948).

Linsley, E. G., and MacSwain, J. W., *J. Econ. Entom.,* **40,** 358 (1947).

Madsen, H. F., *ibid.,* **49,** 467 (1956).

Michelbacher, A. E., *ibid.,* **47,** 192 (1954).

———, *Calif. Agr.,* **10** (7), 4 (1956).

Mills, W. D., and LaPlante, A. A., *Cornell Agr. Exp. Sta. Bull.,* **812** (1951).

Morrill, Jr., A. W., *J. Econ. Entom.,* **35,** 593 (1942).

Mulla, M. S., *ibid.,* **49,** 438 (1956).

Muma, M. H., *ibid.,* **48,** 432 (1955).

———, *ibid.,* **52,** 577 (1959).

Newcomer, E. J., and Dean, F. F., *ibid.,* **46,** 414 (1953).

Newsom, L. D., and Smith, C. E., *ibid.,* **42,** 904 (1949).

Newton, J. H., and List, G. M., *ibid.,* **45,** 643 (1952).

Packard, C. M., "1952 Yearbook," Washington, D.C., U.S. Dept. Agr., 1952.

Pickett, A. D., *Agr. Chem.,* **10** (6), 36 (1955).

Rabb, R. L., and Lawson, F. R., *J. Econ. Entom.,* **50, 778** (1957).

Ripper, W. P., *Agr. Chem.,* **12** (2), 36 (1957).

Ristich, S. S., *J. Econ. Entom.,* **49,** 511 (1955).

Rudd, R. L., and Genelly, R. E., *Calif. Dept. Fish & Game Bull.,* **7** (1956).

Secrest, J. P., and Thornton, D. G., *J. Econ. Entom.,* **52,** 212 (1959).

Shaw, F. R., *ibid.,* **52,** 549 (1959).

Smith, H. S., *ibid.,* **38,** 316 (1945).

———, and Armitage, H. M., *Calif. Agr. Exp. Sta. Bull.,* **509** (1931).

Smith, R. F., and Hagen, K. S., *Calif. Agr.,* **10** (4), 8 (1956).

Stern, V. M., and Others, *ibid.,* **12** (1), 4 (1958).

Tashiro, H., and Schwardt, H. H., *J. Econ. Entom.,* **46,** 680 (1953).

Taylor, E. A., *ibid.,* **47,** 525 (1954).

Thompson, C. G., and Steinhaus, E. A., *Hilgardia,* **19,** 411 (1950).

Todd, F. E., and McGregor, S. E., "1952 Yearbook," Washington, D.C., U.S. Dept. Agr., 1952.

Van den Bosch, R., and Others, *J. Econ. Entom.,* **49,** 359 (1956).

York, G. T., and Others, *ibid.,* **48, 765** (1955).

3. INSECT DISEASES

Insects are subject to infection by the same types of disease-causing organisms as are the higher animals and plants, namely, bacteria, viruses, fungi, protozoa, and nematodes. Great numbers of insects die of disease annually but are rarely noticed unless serious outbreaks (epizootics) occur. The organisms that attack insects are very seldom the same as those attacking the higher animals or plants.

Recognized diseases of the silk worm date back thousands of years. The germinal nature of one of these diseases, known as *muscardine*, was first shown by the Italian, Agostino Bassi. He found that the disease was caused by a "vegetable" parasite which is now known as the fungus *Beauveria bassiana*. Bassi demonstrated that the fungus could be killed by disinfecting with lye or wine and by boiling or burning. It is his work with the infectious diseases of insects that has become the principal basis for the use of microorganisms to control harmful insects (Steinhaus, 1956).

The disease of the silkworm known as *jaundice* is now recognized as being caused by a polyhedral form of the virus of the genus *Borrelina*. This form of infection also attacks the larva of the gypsy moth, the alfalfa caterpillar, and the larva of the European spruce sawfly. The polyhedra found in the body of diseased insects are crystal-like bodies from which the virus particles may be released by treating with a weak alkali. The particles are visible with the electron microscope (Steinhaus, 1952, 1956).

Another group of diseases dating back into antiquity are those infecting the larvae of the honey bee. These are now commonly known as *foulbrood*. The pathogen causing European foulbrood (*Bacillus alvei*) was described in 1885. The one causing American foulbrood, (*B. larvae*) was not discovered until 1904.

Sacbrood of the honey bee (*Apis mellifera*) is caused by a virus, while the Nosema disease of the honey bee is caused by a microsporidian (Steinhaus, 1952).

MICROORGANISMS USED IN INSECT CONTROL

A number of attempts have been made in the latter part of the nineteenth and early part of the twentieth century to develop methods for utilizing disease-producing organisms in the control of pest insects. One of the first

44

attempts was directed against the chinch bug (*Blissus leucopterus*), followed by work on grasshoppers, the brown-tail moth, (*Nygmia phaeorrhoea*), and the citrus whitefly (*Dialeurodes citri*). Unfortunately these experiments were all with fungi, the propagation and distribution of which are largely dependent upon weather conditions; hence it was difficult to evaluate their efficacy in the field (Clausen, 1954).

Dissemination of Pathogenic Organisms

Fungus diseases of insects are dependent upon favorable conditions of atmospheric moisture and temperature such as are commonly found in Florida. Hayslip (1953) states that "aphid populations are often materially reduced by some of these organisms [fungi] during warm, humid weather. . . . Grasshoppers are frequently affected by various fungi of the genera *Empusa, Entomophthora,* and *Sporotrichum.*" Insects infected with organisms of these types are a common sight in Florida. Muma (1955) notes a number of instances of parasitic fungi aiding in the control of citrus pests. By contrast with Florida conditions, the citrus districts of California, being in a semiarid climate, place no reliance on disease as a control of citrus insects. However, with the opening of the rainy season in California, flies killed by fungi are occasionally seen clinging to building walls.

Bacteria, viruses, and protozoa are not so dependent as are fungi on a high relative humidity for growth and dissemination. They may be ingested with food or carried accidentally by host insects, predators, and parasites, or by wind, rain, and irrigation water. Temperature and relative humidity are, however, important in developing the necessary population densities of the host insect (Thompson and Steinhaus, 1950). Evidence of a "latent" infection of the gypsy moth (*Porthetria dispar*), by a polyhedrous virus which was transmitted from generation to generation, has been shown by Wallis (1957). The incidence of the polyhedrosis remained low during a period of low relative humidity, but increased rapidly with a rise in humidity. It is suggested that relative humidity may be an important factor in the outbreak of the disease among gypsy moths under existing conditions in Connecticut.

Diseases of the Japanese Beetle (*Popillia japonica*)

In 1933, a number of the larvae of this beetle, present in New Jersey fields, were found to be enlarged and filled with a milky white fluid teeming with bacterial spores. These were identified as *Bacillus popilliae*. Type-B milky disease is caused by the bacterium *Bacillus lentimorbus* (Tashiro and White, 1954). Grubs infected by this disease die, and the spores are left in the soil to infect other grubs feeding on grass roots. The spores are very resistant to dryness, moisture, cold, and heat and may live in the soil for years. As the beetle-grub population enlarges, the possibility of infection increases.

The United States Bureau of Entomology and Plant Quarantine has developed means of growing great numbers of infected grubs. When properly developed, the grubs are refrigerated until ready to use, then ground up. Powdered or other dust base is then added and the mixture standardized at one billion spores per gram. The powder is then ready for packaging. Great quantities of the spore dust are produced and distributed through the areas infested with the Japanese beetle.

The powder may be mixed with fertilizer or certain of the insecticide powders and distributed over the ground, or placed alone in piles of about 2 grams each at distances of 3 to 10 feet apart. After the dust is distributed over the surface, it is washed in by rain or lawn sprinklers. Spore dust prepared in this way is in commercial distribution for insect control and is for sale at many garden-supply stores in beetle-infested areas (Hawley, 1952).

Infection by the milky disease spore develops slowly, the first symptoms appearing in 6 to 9 days at 86 F, but at longer periods at lower temperatures. For this reason and because the dead bodies distintegrate quickly, a sampling of grub-infected soil seldom shows a high degree of infection. Milky disease organisms will not develop at temperatures above 97 F° or near this point. Therefore they cannot infect warm-blooded animals with higher bodily temperatures (Hawley, 1952; Polivka, 1956).

The European chafer (*Amphimallan majalis*) has a similar life history and feeding habits to the Japanese beetle and hence seemed to offer possibilities of susceptibility to the same disease. Tashiro and White (1954) have tested three possible strains of milky disease organisms. Two of them were the regular type-B and type-A strains of *Bacillus lentimorbus* and *B. popilliae*. "An organism tentatively called the type-B *Amphimallon* strain and one called the type-A Stanton strain were also used." Two methods of infection, injection and ingestion of the spores, were tried. "The regular type-B strain of *lentimorbus* exhibited low pathogenicity to chafer larvae by both methods of infection. Type-B *Amphimallon* and the type-A strains were highly pathogenic by both methods."

Diseases of the Alfalfa Caterpillar (*Colias philodice eurytheme*)

Infectious diseases of the alfalfa caterpillar have been recognized since about 1888. Diseased larvae were noted occasionally in the Imperial Valley through 1911 to 1915, but identification of the causative organism as a polyhedral virus occurred first in Kansas (Dean and Smith, 1935). This was confirmed by Steinhaus in California (1945), where the disease has

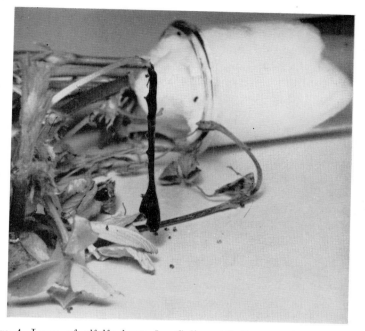

Figure 4. Larva of alfalfa butterfly, *Colias philodice eurytheme Bdv.* dead of polyhedrosis used in sprays. Note how fluid contents of body fluids have gravitated to anterior end of the insect. (Test tube and cotton plug at right.)

since been under continuous observation. Infection by the virus *Borrelina campeoles* usually requires from five to seven days to reduce a population of caterpillars below the economic level. Soon after death, the body of the caterpillar breaks down into a disintegrating, decaying mass. The dead insects are usually attached to an alfalfa stalk, so that the liquid discharge runs down over the leaves. Where these decaying larvae are very abundant, the hay may be rendered unpalatable to cattle. Infected pupae show a dark, mottled appearance. The butterfly is not known to be affected. The virus has been found in the topsoil and surface debris of all the alfalfa fields studied. This infection is found throughout the year, but disease outbreaks do not usually occur until midsummer or later (Steinhaus, 1948).

"Natural epizootics [outbreaks] of polyhedrosis, in general, cannot be depended upon to occur regularly enough to give satisfactory economic control of the caterpillar." Population density is apparently one of the most significant factors in the increase of the disease. Temperature seems to have little effect on the susceptibility of the insect to infection, but does affect the incubation period, it being shorter at higher temperatures.

Relative humidity apparently has little effect on the susceptibility of the host to infection. The importance of humidity appears to be largely in its effect upon the health and growth of the host caterpillar. Optimum conditions of temperature and relative humidity are important, however, in the development of insect populations, and this indirectly leads to the breaking out of an epizootic (Steinhaus, 1950).

An initial supply of virus material may be assembled in two ways. Healthy larvae may be brought in from the field and infected in the laboratory. The second method is to collect dead and dying larvae in the field, break up this material, and dilute and distribute it as needed. In the latter method, additional supplies may be secured by continual collecting in fields where infected larvae are found. Where supplies are maintained for long periods of time or over winter, the use of refrigeration will retard the action of the putrefying bacteria and make the material more pleasant to handle (Steinhaus, 1950).

Bacterial Disease of the Alfalfa Butterfly

A spore-forming bacterium known as *Bacillus thuringiensis* was first reported in Germany as attacking the Mediterranean flour moth (*Anagasta* (*Ephestia*) *kuhniella*). This is now recognized as a strain of *Bacillus cereus* which causes a septicemia in the southern army worm (*Prodenia eridania*). The bacterium *B. thuringiensis* has been found to cause infections in a number of different lepidoptera larvae but, because of its virulence to the alfalfa caterpillar, extensive experiments have been made with the latter. No virulence to vertebrates has been found with this organism (Steinhaus, 1951).

B. thuringiensis grows readily on ordinary nutrient agar* without loss of virulence, thus making possible the preparation of sufficient quantities for field-testing.

The spore powder in the following experiments was prepared in the laboratory and applied with a five-gallon hand sprayer. Two gallons of the spore suspension was applied to plots varying in size from 12 by 48 to 30 by 48 yards, with similar-size control plots. Better distribution is

---

* Spore material grown on nutrient agar is placed in six-liter Povitsky bottles. Because of the offset neck, the medium is confined safely when the bottle is placed on its side. The medium in each bottle is sprayed with a 24- to 48-hour diluted culture of the bacillus, using a small hand atomizer. The bottles are incubated for about seven days—although little is to be gained by longer incubation than three days. After incubation is complete, the agar can be washed with 100 ml of sterile, distilled water. The suspension is washed once by centrifugation, filtered through cheesecloth, and poured in flat enameled pans to dry. The dried deposit is scraped out and ground to a fine powder with mortar and pestle. Each lot of powder is stored in a large glass vial and held in a dry place at room temperature. Dried spores retained their viability for a year or longer. Yields averaged about 0.2 to 0.3 grams per flask (Steinhaus, 1951).

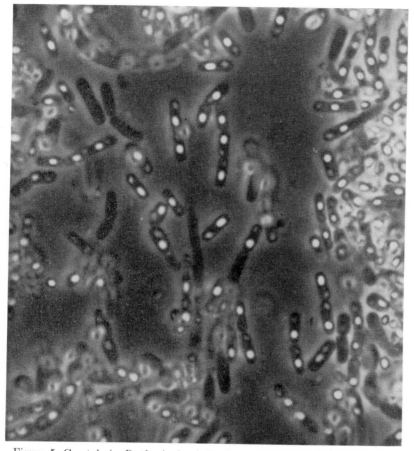

Figure 5. Crystals in *B. thuringiensis* Berliner, taken by light microscope.

obtained by shaking glass beads in the tank just before application. The approximate number of spores applied per plot ranged from 7 to 13 billion. The age of the spores ranged from 1½ to 12 months. Within 24 to 48 hours after application, the typical symptoms of sluggishness, diarrhea, discoloration, and flaccidity appeared, while larvae were dying in large numbers. In seven of the nine plots sprayed with spore suspensions of the bacillus, the larval population was brought below an economic level (twenty larvae per two sweeps of a collecting net), while in the control plots, the population remained at a destructive level (Steinhaus, 1951).

Comparative Effectiveness of Bacillus and Virus

On the conclusion of the tests to date, it has been found that *B. thuringiensis* may reduce a destructive population of alfalfa caterpillars to a point below which no economic damage to the crop may occur. It does not, however, consistently reduce the population to as low a point as does the virus. In the control of the alfalfa caterpillar, the bacillus is effective within 2 to 3 days, compared with 5 to 6 days for the virus. The bacillus is also cleaner because the bodies of the caterpillars it kills usually drop to the ground without breaking open. The bodies of those killed by the virus, however, break open and smear the foliage, thus lowering the palatibility of the crop.

The ease with which the bacillus is grown on artificial media may offer advantages over the polyhedrous virus, which may be cultured only in the living tissue of the host insect. The bacillus is easily produced in quantity and the product stored indefinitely. Under field conditions, however, the virus may be collected simply by sweeping up infected caterpillars in insect nets and storing them under refrigeration. The combination of the two agents might be advantageous because it would give the quick action of the bacillus and the persistent thoroughness of the virus. Further experimentation is necessary to develop preventive measures for handling both organisms (Steinhaus, 1951).

Extended Uses of Insect Diseases

The European spruce sawfly (*Diprion hercyniae*) was accidentally introduced into eastern Canada and has since spread over large areas. A virus disease, apparently also accidentally introduced, has been recovered and is being disseminated by the Canadian Department of Agriculture. For about eighteen years, during which this investigation has been conducted, there has been no evidence of increasing resistance to the disease.

The European pine sawfly (*Neodiprion sertifer*) entered the United States about the same time that the spruce sawfly was found in Canada. This epidemic of sawflies has been checked by a virus disease brought in from Sweden. In an outbreak in Indiana, an application of virus suspension was applied by airplane at the rate of a gallon per acre. Counts made 23 days later showed an average kill of 89 per cent (Staff, 1956). Epidemics of the Virginia pine sawfly and of the white fir sawfly have also been checked by a polyhedrous-type virus application (Beal, 1956; Dowden and Girth, 1953).

Under conditions in Hawaii, the armyworm *Pseudaletia unipuncta* was found susceptible to both a polyhedrous and a granulosis virus. First- and second-instar larvae were highly susceptible to both viruses, but the last four instars were much more resistant. A mixture of the two viruses, when fed to the more resistant last four instars, resulted in a high mortality from virus infection (Tanada, 1956a). The same author (Tanada and Beardsley, 1957) reports a second infection of an armyworm, *Spo-*

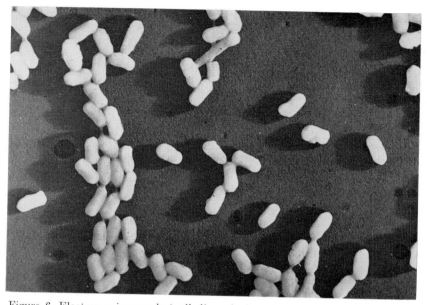

Figure 6. Electron micrograph (palladium-shadowed preparation) of the granular inclusions characteristic of the granulosis of the omnivorous looper, *Sabulodes caberata* Gn.

doptera maurita, by a polyhedrous virus "slightly more than 2 years after the armyworm was first found in Hawaii." Tanada (1956b) also reports effective control of the imported cabbageworm (*Pieris rapae*) by a granulosis virus, *Bergoldia virulenta,* and the bacterium *Bacillus thuringiensis.* He states that "the bacterium offers more promise than the virus in the control of the cabbageworm because it kills the cabbageworm in a shorter period—2 to 4 days as compared to 4 to 8 days for the virus." The larva of the diamondback moth (*Plutella maculipennis*) seemed more resistant to the bacterial spray than did the imported cabbageworm. The cabbage webworm (*Hellula undalis*) and the cabbage looper (*Trichoplusia ni*) were decidedly more resistant to *B. thuringiensis* than were the diamondback moth and the imported cabbageworm. Hall (1957) describes experiments with a polyhedrous virus collected from larvae of the cabbage looper. The virus was developed on living larvae and applied to looper larvae on lettuce. Three concentrations of the virus material were used (10 million, 5 million and 1 million polyhedra per milliliter) on replicated plots. High dosages of the virus were found more effective than low dosages in causing almost 100 per cent death of the larvae attacking the lettuce. Infected larvae were killed more quickly at temperatures of about 72° F than at lower temperatures.

Other well-known diseases are the virus-caused "wilt" of the gypsy moth (*Porthetria dispar*); infection of the European corn borer by the microsporidian, *Perezia pyraustae* (Zimmack and Others, 1954); and the virus disease of the tent caterpillar (*Malacosoma fragilis*) (Clark and Thompson, 1954).

A fungus (*Myiophagus*) has been found by Fisher (1950) to be a factor in the control of purple and Florida red scale on citrus in Florida. Muma (1955), in a review of natural control of citrus insects in Florida, states that there are two important parasitic fungi attacking the purple scale, but that fungi are less important than parasitic insects in the control of the Florida red scale. He also found that parasitic fungi are important in the control of the citrus rust mite and the citrus red mite.

The spotted alfalfa aphid (*Therioaphis maculata*) has been attacked in California by a number of parasitic fungi*. Three species, *Entomopthora exitialis, E. virulenta,* and *E. oronata,* are being grown on selected media and distributed throughout the principal alfalfa-growing regions of the state. Recommended sites for the release of infected aphids are fields under standard irrigation practice, with alfalfa 16 to 20 inches high, plots left uncut for one crop, and no insecticides to be applied to the plot during the inoculation attempt. In addition to the artificial distribution, natural movement of the insect is doing much to distribute the various fungi (Hall and Dunn, 1958).

In a review of the fungus-caused disease of the potato aphid (*Macrosiphum solanifolii*), Shands and Others (1958) state that the introduced fungus (*Acrostalagmus*) was recovered from dead specimens of the aphid three weeks after the plants had been sprayed with laboratory-cultured spores. Locally occurring species of the fungus *Empusa* were also noted as killing the potato aphid.

Advantages and Disadvantages of Microbial Control

The possibility of growing and distributing disease-producing organisms for insect control has as yet been restricted to a very few forms of insects. The organisms are restricted to a very narrow field of effectiveness—either to a single species or closely related forms. Further expansion of the use of fungi for destroying insects consists not in finding such organisms, for there are many known species, but rather in learning how

---

* It has been found by Hall and Dunn (1959) that laboratory tests show "that certain insecticides and fungicides are toxic to the vegetative stages of some of the fungi that attack the spotted alfalfa aphid, *Therioaphis maculata* (Buckton). Most susceptible to these materials was *Entomophthora exitialis* Hall and Dunn, the dominant pathogen of the aphid in California. Further tests have indicated that the insecticides do not kill the resting spores of *E. virulenta* H. & D., although germination is retarded to some extent."

to produce, store, and distribute infectious material so as to produce insect epizootics at will.

Pathogenic insect organisms as control agents are not supplanting the use of insecticides, but rather supplement the chemical program. This gives an alternative way of control that operates without dangerous residues or building up of resistance. (No tendency to insect resistance has thus far been noted to any pathogenic organism.) The microorganisms causing insect disease are not a threat to the higher animals or plants in any but rare instances. Neither are the organisms thus far cultured dangerous to parasites or predators or to the pollinators (Steinhaus, 1952).

"On the basis of theoretical considerations, as well as experimental evidence, there appears to be little reason to believe that crystalliferous *Bacillus thuringiensis* Berliner and its close varieties as they occur in properly prepared microbial insecticides are likely to mutate spontaneously into forms pathogenic for vertebrates. Similarly, on the basis of our present-day understanding of bacterial genetics, it appears that such mutations are not very likely with most of the truly entomogenous bacteria. At least, the possibilities in this regard do not appear to be sufficient to preclude the use of adequately tested entomogenous microorganisms for pest-control purposes. Nevertheless, safeguards should be maintained to detect such events should they occur." (Steinhaus, 1959)

The possibility of microbial control of insects offers a new field to pesticide manufacturers, either in manufacturing and distributing the product or to act as distributors for biological and fermentation houses. This is a natural field for agricultural chemical houses because many pathogens are compatible with a number of pesticides and fertilizers, and in some instances they are being applied together.

The microbial pesticide *B. thuringiensis* will be permitted to be manufactured and distributed under an experimental permit for one year by the Department of Agriculture. The material will be used against the cabbageworm, imported cabbageworm, alfalfa caterpillar, and others of this type of insects. If no question arises and the material proves practicable, the manufacturer will be allowed to ask clearance for general use. Marketing will be permitted under a temporary exemption from the requirement of a Food and Drug Administration tolerance.

This is the first use of such type of pesticide directly on food crops. The milky disease bacteria used against the Japanese beetle is applied to the soil and not directly to crops.

Insect Pathology Laboratory

A laboratory of insect pathology—the first of its kind—was established in 1945 at the University of California, under the direction of Edward A.

Steinhaus. The laboratory has five main functions: first, basic research on the diseases of insects and the organisms that cause them; second, the effects of diseases on insect populations in nature; third, assisting nature in killing off pests; fourth, the diagnosis of diseases of dead and dying insects, as received from all parts of the country and abroad; fifth, the teaching of students and the training of visiting scientists.

Those desiring the services of the Laboratory should obtain shipping instructions by writing to the Laboratory of Insect Pathology, Division of Biological Control, University of California, Berkeley 4, California (Clausen, 1954).

REFERENCES

Beal, J. A., *Bull. Ent. Soc. America,* **2** (2), 2 (1956).

Clark, E. C., and Thompson, C. G., *J. Econ. Entom.,* **47,** 268 (1954).

Clausen, C. P., *J. Agr. Food Chem.,* **2,** 12 (1954).

Dean, G. A., and Smith, R. C., *Kansas State Bd. Agr. Biennial Rpt.,* **29,** 202 (1935).

Dowden, P. B., and Girth, H. B., *J. Econ. Entom.,* **46,** 525 (1953).

Fisher, F. E., *ibid.,* **43,** 305 (1950).

Hall, I. M., *ibid.,* **50,** 551 (1957).

———, and Dunn, P. H., *ibid.,* **51,** 341 (1958).

———, *ibid.,* **52,** 28 (1959).

Hawley, I. M., "1952 Yearbook," Washington, D.C., U.S. Dept. Agr., 1952.

Hayslip, N. C., and Others, *Fla. Agr. Exp. Sta. Bull.,* **534** (1953).

Knipling, E. F., *Agr. Chem.,* **11** (10), 52 (1956).

Muma, M. H., *J. Econ. Entom.,* **48,** 432 (1955).

Polivka, J. B., *ibid.,* **49,** 4 (1956).

Shands, W. A., and Others, *ibid.,* **51,** 184 (1958).

Staff, *J. Agr. Food Chem.,* **4,** 195 (1956).

Steinhaus, E. A., *J. Econ. Entom.,* **41,** 859 (1948).

———, *Hilgardia,* **19,** 411 (1950).

———, *ibid.,* **20,** 359 (1951).

———, "1952 Yearbook," Washington, D.C., U.S. Dept. Agr., 1952.

———, *Hilgardia,* **26,** 107 (1956a).

———, *J. Agr. Food Chem.,* **4,** 676 (1956b).

———, *J. Econ. Entom.,* **50,** 715 (1957).

———, *ibid.,* **52,** 506 (1959).

Tanada, Y., *ibid.,* **49,** 52 (1956a).

———, *ibid.,* **49,** 320 (1956b).

———, *ibid.,* **50,** 118 (1957).

Tashiro, H., and White, R. T., *ibid.,* **47,** 1087 (1954).

———, *ibid.,* **50,** 350 (1957).

Thompson, C. G., and Steinhaus, E. A., *Hilgardia,* **19,** 411 (1950).

Wallis, R. C., *J. Econ. Entom.,* **50,** 580 (1957).

Zimmack, H. L., and Others, *ibid.,* **47,** 641 (1954).

4. RESISTANT PLANTS

The ideal way of protecting crops from disease and insect injury is by growing resistant varieties. The expense of sprays and dusts, the hazard of chemical residues, and the danger of developing resistance to chemicals are thus all avoided. The discovery, breeding, and selection of plants is a continuous process. Plant disease resistance is not a fixed condition. The environmental factors of rainfall, temperature, fertility, planting dates, and soil reactions may all influence the degree of resistance shown to a crop disease. Added to this is the continuous changing and developing of new races of dangerous fungi, such as the oat smut fungus (*Ustilago kolleri*). About twenty-five races of this fungus are now recognized in the United States, and all commercial varieties of oats grown are susceptible to one or more races of smut. The Victoria oat, because of its known resistance to smut for fifteen years, was used as a source of smut resistance for breeding new varieties. Now, various races of smut are attacking varieties derived from victoria throughout the southern United States (Holton and Tapke, 1953). Such variability as is found among races of fungi may also act in reverse, for a single variety of a cereal grain may be resistant to many races of a parasitic fungi.

Resistance of plants to disease occurs in varying degrees. A plant may be "slightly susceptible," "moderately susceptible," or "extremely susceptible." Immunity means either complete resistance to disease or not subject to attack. There are no variations in degree of immunity.

A plant may escape infection by maturing before the season of disease infection occurs. Thus, early maturing varieties of potatoes may escape late blight disease unless they are planted in mid- or late summer.

Disease endurance may be due to a vigorous growth that permits a plant to mature despite disease attack. Hardier structure or drought resistance may also be a factor enabling a plant to resist infection. Some varieties of hard spring wheats are but slightly resistant to rust and can withstand moderate attacks, but not an epidemic, of the disease (Wingard, 1953).

"True resistance to disease ... depends on some structural or physiological characters of the plant that prevent successful invasion of the parasite." (Winkard, 1953) It is a function of the genes, which are located on, and transmitted by, the chromosomes and give the hereditary characteristics of the plant. True resistance is a natural development by evolution which may be further developed by the plant-breeder.

The presence of resistant plants that have been exposed through long association to a given disease or insect pest has led to the belief that such resistance has been developed by the natural selection of evolution. A similar procedure in reverse may give rise to severe outbreaks if a parasite is introduced into a new environment and finds host plants lacking the necessary resistance to protect them against this same parasite, even though they may be immune to other disease-producing organisms or pest insects (Coons, 1953). A good example is the root aphid, *Dactylosphaera* (*Phylloxera*) *vitifoliae*, a native of the eastern United States, which feeds on the roots of grapes. Native grapes are but slightly affected by the attack of the insect; however, when it was accidentally carried to France, it nearly destroyed the French vineyards. Resistant varieties of grapes were developed by grafting European stocks on American resistants that had developed in *Phylloxera* districts. These types of resistant grapes are in use both in France and in the vineyards of California.

Another well-known example is the common practice in California of grafting English (Persian) walnut on various species of black walnut. The latter are resistant to attacks by the soil fungus, *Armillaria mellea*, while the English-walnut root is very susceptible. Graft unions made a foot or more above the soil surface, so as not to be covered by soil, give the best protection against *Armillaria* and also against crown-rot infection by the fungus *Phytophthora cactorum* (Smith, 1941).

DEVELOPMENT OF DISEASE RESISTANT PLANTS

Resistant plants frequently show improvement in yield and quality as a result of a more nearly normal growth, irrespective of the factor of resistance. The improved varieties that have been accepted in commercial production have given greater stability to the growing of many types of grain, potatoes, sugar beets, alfalfa, and a number of vegetables and fruit crops. This has led to permanence in the agricultural program of our area and the increased security that comes from the reduction of hazards in crop production (Coons, 1953).

Plant-breeding includes many phases of research. A world-wide search has been made within the groups of cultivated crops that are subject to serious disease for breeding material that offers possibilities of disease resistance. The early parents of cultivated plants have been sought for strains which, through natural selection, might show characteristics useful in the developing of resistant strains. Then comes the patient work of the plant-breeder, skillful in hybridizing and selecting plants showing desired qualities. Repeating the work over and over is needed until these factors have been firmly fixed and commercial production is begun. It is this type of work, carried on for many years by the United States Department of Agriculture, Division of Plant Pathology, that saved the sugar-beet industry of the West, the sugarcane culture of the Gulf States, protected the citrus industry from the *tristeza* disease, and developed many of our most successful types of cultivated crops (Coons, 1953).

Grain Smuts

The small grains, wheat, oats, and barley, are subject to attack by various types of smuts. Infection and development being somewhat similar for the various small grains, as is the use of resistant varieties, wheat diseases alone will be discussed.

Wheat is subject to a number of diseases caused by fungi. Stinking smut or bunt is carried by the fungi *Tilletia caries* and *Tilletia foetida*. Infection occurs both at threshing time, when spores are carried over the seed wheat and also blown to the fields. In the latter case, the spores lie dormant until fall in the Pacific Northwest and germinate with fall-sown grain. Control of bunt is possible by chemical treatment of the seed grain and the use of resistant varieties.

Seed treatment is desirable for resistant types also because new races of smut are constantly developing and no variety of wheat is immune to all. The breeding of smut resistance in wheat is a continuous struggle with the evolution of new races of bunt (Leukel and Tapke, 1954; Holton and Tapke, 1953).

Loose smut of wheat, caused by the fungus *Ustilago tritici*, is another serious disease. Infection occurs in the wheat flower and develops within the kernel. Hot-water treatment is the only one of value for treating seed grain. Resistance to loose smut is uncertain in many of the important varieties of wheat because of the number of races of smut (Leukel and Tapke, 1954).

Corn and Sorghum Diseases

Corn (maize) is attacked by both common corn smut and head smut. The smut galls of the former may develop on any part of the plant where young tissue is exposed. Leaves, tassels, and ear are attacked through feeding punctures of insects or through other wounds. The smut galls range in size up to 6 inches in diameter. When the gall breaks open, the spores scatter over the soil and trash and overwinter in this stage. The following summer, they provide small spores which are carried by wind currents to the growing corn. No chemical-control measures are practical, but dependence is placed on sanitation and the growing of resistant types of hybrid corn (Leukel and Tapke, 1954).

Head smut develops similarly to the common corn smut, but attacks the tassel and ear. Resistant varieties of corn and crop rotation are the chief methods of protection against this disease (Leukel and Tapke, 1954).

The sorghums, including sweet sorghum, grain sorghums, broom corn, and Sudan grass, are subject to three types of smut diseases—covered kernel smut, loose kernel smut, and head smut. The first two types of smut may be checked by growing resistant varieties and also by treating the seed with the disinfectant types of fungicides. Those varieties having persistent glumes (seed hulls) should be treated with a volatile mercury type of fungicide (examples: Ceresan M, Panogen). Seed without glumes may be treated with nonvolatile fungicides, for examples, Arasan and Phygon (Leukel and Tapke, 1954).

Leaf Blights

Leaf blights of corn vary in their attack and degree of injury. Those that attack seedlings may kill the plant. Infection later in the development stage of the plant injures the leaves to varying degrees and thus reduces the production of plant food. The blights include both fungus and bacterial forms of disease. Resistant types of inbred lines have been developed and are being used to develop commercial types of hybrids (Robert, 1953).

Rusts

The development over a period of sixty years of wheat varieties resistant to stem and leaf rust has been one of the outstanding results of plant-breeding. Many new varieties of wheat with varying degrees of resistance have been developed and grown for a period of years only to be supplanted by more successful types. Plant-breeding offers the most satisfactory approach toward rust control because chemical treatment is seldom practical. The problem is complicated by reason of the number of species of rust fungi concerned, and the movement of infecting spores from north to south, and the reverse, in the spring. Spores from rusts growing in the northern United States are carried by winds into the warmer belt of southern states and Mexico. Here the rust grows through the winter on grasses and volunteer grain. Then with the coming of spring, the spores are carried northward by air currents, starting new infections in Oklahoma and Kansas, and finally reaching the North Central States and Canada. Wherever the spores fall on a wheat leaf, they germinate in from one to several hours, depending on temperature and humidity. The germ tube growing out of the spore penetrates the stomata (breathing pore) of the leaf or stem. The invaders feed in the plant tissue for a week or more, until the rust pustule bursts, filling the air with spores. These short generations are repeated over and over as the disease sweeps northward over the grain-producing states (Martin and Salmon, 1953).

Northern wheat is also exposed to a form of stem rust that develops on the common barberry (*Berberris vulgaris*). An overwintering form of spore is produced on rust-infected wheat which remains on the straw, germinates in the spring, and infects the barberry. Yellow spots develop within a few days, and, from these, spores are erupted that infect other grains and grasses (Martin and Salmon, 1953).

Wheat varieties vary in their resistance to the ten or fifteen races or strains of stem rust that are active through the season. The parasitic organisms causing rust may be presenet in a region one year and absent another. A variety of wheat may thus be resistant one year and susceptible another year (Martin and Salmon, 1953).

The breeding varieties of wheat resistant to rusts began about 1900, using varieties of durum wheat and emmer as parents. These are not intended as flour-producing wheats, but are used as parents for rust-resistant varieties and form the basis for the commercial varieties of wheat grown in the northern states and Canada. In addition to the value for plant-breeding, the growing of early-maturing varieties through the central West has been found to be helpful as it shortens the time of growth during which infection is possible (Martin and Salmon, 1953).

Stem rust of the oat is smiliar in life history and spread to that of wheat stem rust. Crown or leaf rust of oats is very destructive, not only to grain but to many species of grasses. "The life history of crown rust is similar to that of stem rust except the cluster-cup stage develops on buckthorn, *Rhamnus*, instead of on barberries." (Martin and Salmon, 1953)

Barley is subject to attack of both stem and leaf rust. The former is caused by the same fungus that attacks wheat and rye. The same alternate host, the European barberry bush, is required in northern districts to carry the overwintering spores from grain into the infective stage for barley in the spring. As with other grains, the planting of rust-resistant varieties is also the recommended measure of protection. Since 1953, the Goliad variety of barley has been released as resistant to both stem and leaf rusts (Leukel and Tapke, 1955).

Two entries from barley world collections (Modjo, C.I. 3212 and C.I. 3212-1) have been found resistant to all strains of barley stripe-mosaic virus. This suggests that tolerance of stripe mosaic might be transferred from these strains to commercial varieties of barley (Sisler and Timian, 1956).

Resistance in Nongrain Plants

Forage Plants. Alfalfa is subject to a number of diseases including those caused by various fungi, viruses, bacteria, and nematodes. The development and growth of resistant types offers the most favorable method of protection.

Bacterial blight is one of the most widely distributed of alfalfa diseases. It is most serious in northern and central parts of the United States, diminishing in severity in the southern states. Symptoms may appear in the second crop year, but the disease does not usually become severe until the third year. Four resistant varieties have been developed for various areas: Ranger, for the northern states; Buffalo, for the central district; Caliverdi, derived from California common, for use in California; and more recently Vernal, from the Wisconsin Station (Jones and Smith, 1953; Stanford and others, 1954).

In addition to the above, there are a number of stem and leaf diseases, root rots, and nematode infections of various degrees of importance, and for which plant-breeding is the most promising control.

The clovers are subject to a great variety of diseases, including those caused by fungi, bacteria, and viruses. The development of resistant strains offers the greatest promise of control, although in a few instances seed disinfection with suitable fungicides may be useful. Red clover is subject to attacks caused by anthracnose. No strain of this clover is immune to the disease, but decided differences in resistance are shown among European and American strains. Southern anthracnose, caused by a different fungus than the northern form of the disease, is especially destructive. A resistant variety, known as *Kemland,* is available (Hanson and Kreitlow, 1953).

Cotton. The wilt disease of cotton is found wherever American cotton is grown in acid alluvial soils. The caustive organism, the wilt fungus (*Fusarium oxysporum, F. vasinfectum*), is carried inside the cotton seed. The susceptibility of cotton to the disease is increased by the feeding of nematodes on the roots. The injury caused by nematodes gives additional entry points for the fungus as it spreads throughout the woody portion. This results in poor stands, stunted plants, and small bolls with poor-quality lint. The fungus lives in the soil and produces spores which infect the cotton plant's roots. Losses from the wilt disease were so heavy, before the introduction of resistant varieties, that cotton acreages were reduced in many areas (Smith, 1953).

Control measures to protect against the wilt disease are directed both against the soil fungus and nematodes. Resistant varieties of cotton and the use of a balanced fertilizer help to control *Fusarium* wilt.

Nematode-resistant crops, rotation, and soil fumigation are all used against nematodes. The Rivers type of wilt-resistant sea-island cotton was developed and distributed about 1900, followed by a resistant type of upland cotton. These types were developed by selecting individual plants growing in infested soil. The following year, seeds from the selected plants were again grown in infested soil and the most desirable plants chosen. This was later followed by hybridization. A certain degree of resistance to root-knot nematode has been attained, but as yet it is not as successful as that against wilt disease (Smith, 1953).

Sugar Cane (Saccharum). This crop, wherever grown throughout the world, is subject to serious diseases caused by viruses, fungi, and bacteria. Root diseases, caused by various fungi, but especially a species of *Pythium*, led to a careful study of the various disease organisms concerned. The growing of seed cane, instead of reproduction by ratoons (sprouts from a bearing crop), and the development and use of a number of types of varying resistance, have been the means of maintaining production. Since the various types of disease organisms are constantly changing by mutation, the plant-breeder must meet these by new types of improved resistant varieties (Abbott, 1953).

Sugar Beets. These are a standard crop of western agriculture which produce about 20 per cent of our sugar for national consumption. The importance of the crop has led to a great effort in protecting it against destructive diseases. Curly top, a virus disease, is carried by the beet leafhopper (*Circulifer tenellus*). The insect must first feed on a diseased plant, after which it can carry the virus for the rest of its life. Young plants that are infected become stunted and make little further growth. Infection late in the growing season has but little effect, especially on resistant varieties. A number of resistant varieties have been developed, one of the most satisfactory being U.S. 22 (Coons, 1953; Sylvester and Severin, 1955).

Another newly bred type of the sugar beet, U.S. 216, is resistant to the black-root-disease complex. This is a fungus-caused disease associated with other damping-off organisms. Black root may kill so many seedling beets as to make the crop unprofitable.

Tobacco. This crop has been the subject of a most intensive search for strains resistant to serious diseases. For over fifty years, scientific tobacco-breeding has been in progress and is now expanded to cover resistance to many diseases, including the attack of root-knot nematode. "The goal is to breed varieties that resist all major diseases." (Clayton, 1953)

The black-root rot disease is caused by a variety of races of varying degrees of virulence. Progress in developing immunity to this disease comes from species native to Australia. Other species of the tobacco genus, *Nicotiana*, from Central America have shown strong resistance to root-knot-nematode disease, but as yet this has not been bred into commercial varieties of tobacco. Black shank, a fungus-carried disease, is receiving much attention in the developing of resistant types because this is the sole method of control. Granville wilt, *Fusarium* wilt, blue mold, and the bacterial leaf-spot disease show response to the development of resistance that can be transferred to commercial varieties of tobacco.

Beans. Beans are subject to a great variety of diseases. No part of our country is entirely free from bean disease. Fortunately, practical methods of reducing such injury have been developed. Such provisions include the growing of seed beans in districts that are almost free of bacterial infections, sulfur applications for bean rust, the use of commercial varieties tolerant of infections, and the development of resistant races (Zaumeyer and Thomas, 1953).

Bacterial blights of beans attack the foliage and the growing pod and infect the seed. If infected seeds are planted, the plant is infected internally, from which point the bacteria spread, stunting and killing the plant. Protection lies in the use of bean seed grown in the semiarid districts of the drier intermountain regions and in the Pacific States.

Mosaic disease of beans reduces the yield and quality of the product. The annual losses in the United States amount to several millions of dollars. Prevention comes only through the use of resistant varieties, of which there are several available (Zaumeyer and Thomas, 1953).

Peas. Diseases of the pea known as *wilt* and *near-wilt* are caused by soil-inhabiting species of the fungus *Fusarium*. It attacks the central core of the water-conducting vessels and produces a toxin that wilts, and may kill, the plant. Resistance to pea wilt has been developed and established in the varieties of canning peas. The resistant type, Delwich Commando, is the first introduced variety that is field-resistant to wilt and near-wilt (Schroeder, 1953).

Lettuce. Lettuce is subject to many diseases, but resistance, at this time, has been developed only for one of the common ones, downy mildew. A number of varieties are resistant to one or more strains of the downy-mildew fungus. The varieties Imperial D and F were once considered resistant, but are now known to be susceptible (Grogan and others, 1955).

Cucumber. Cucumber mosaic tends to dwarf both the vine and the fruit, the latter being distorted in shape. Insect carriers of the disease breed on such a variety of weeds that control with insecticides is of little value. The breeding and distribution of resistant varieties offers the best means of protecton (Middleton and Bohn, 1953).

All commercial varieties of cucumber grown on the Atlantic Coast are susceptible to downy mildew. A variety from China, introduced and developed locally, and another from India have been found very resistant to the disease and have been used in developing resistant varieties for use in this country (Thomas and Zaumeyer, 1953). A variety named S C-50 has been developed in South America from the Puerto Rican stock which is resistant to both mildew and anthracnose (Barnes and Epps, 1956).

Watermelon. These are subject to two diseases, anthracnose and *Fusarium* wilt, which are held in check by resistant varieties and spacing the crops two or more years (Thomas and Zaumeyer, 1953).

Muskmelon (Cantaloupe). These are subject to attack by powdery mildew, especially in the southwestern areas where the fungus overwinters. The disease may be controlled by applications of dusting sulfur or weak concentrations of lime-sulfur solution. Unfortunately, many varieties are very susceptible to sulfur injury, which has led to the development of sulfur-resistant types of cantaloupe (Middleton and Bohn, 1953; Reed and Doolittle, 1955).

Cabbage. Cabbage is subject to a serious disease known as *yellows*. A resistant variety, Wisconsin Hollander, was released in 1916 and is still grown (Walker, 1953). A new variety, Badger Ballhead, has recently been developed from a cross of Wisconsin Ballhead and Wisconsin Hollander. The new variety is quite resistant to yellows and to a less degree to mosaic (Walker and others, 1957). A resistant form of the Charleston Wakefield cabbage, known as Y. R. Charleston Wakefield, has been developed and released to the seed trade (Larson and others, 1956).

Potato. Potatoes are subject to a number of diseases where the growing of resistant types is an important factor in control. Varieties with varying degrees of resistance to late blight include Kennebec, Pungo, and Cherokee. The varieties Menominee, Saranac, and Sequoia show resistance to *Verticillium* wilt. Other diseases for which resistance has been developed are scab and the bacterial disease, ring rot. Thomas and Zaumeyer (1953) state that, of the new potato varieties released since 1932, resistant varieties account for approximately 50 per cent.

Tomato. These have a history similar to potatoes in that a number of varieties have been developed during the last forty years with variable degrees of resistance to diseases. The latter include early blight, *Fusarium* wilt, *Verticillium* wilt, curly top, spotted wilt, and gray leaf spot. The finding in Peru of a wild, small-fruited species known as the *Red Currant* has made possible the development of wilt-resistant tomatoes. It has been crossed with a number of commercial types, the hybrid showing the new type of resistance (Thomas and Zaumeyer, 1953).

Resistance in Orchard Trees

Apple. Apple orchards under California conditions are generally grown from apple root, because roots are tolerant of wet soil and do well in deep loam. The root is susceptible to the crown gall disease, but seldom seriously.

"French apple roots are practically resistant to the oak root fungus." The attack occurs most frequently on the scion variety, if near the soil surface, and extends both upward and downward. Fire blight (pear blight) on apple is less injurious in California than in many other districts. Attacks of the root-knot nematode (*Meloidogyne maroni*) are also seldom of a serious nature. A satisfactory rootstock, resistant to wooly apple aphid, has not been found (Day, 1947). Commercial varieties of apple are now being developed with partial resistance to fire blight under eastern conditions (Stevenson and Jones, 1953).

Peach. "Commercial varieties mostly of the clingstone type are tolerant of peach mosaic." (Stevenson and Jones, 1953).

Pear. Day (1947) lists the variety Old Home as a (pear) blight resistant, French seedling for use as a rootstock for various commercial varieties of pear. Old Home seedlings are not, however, resistant to blight; propagation must be by vegetative processes, for example, root cuttings or layering. Old Home may be used for the entire rootstock and scaffold branches or it may be grafted on quince root. The desired scion is then worked. Old Home thus gives blight protection from the top worked scion through the crown and root. The variety Hardy may also be substituted for Old Home between the quince root and the top. Stevenson and Jones (1953) list the variety Richard Peters as immune to fire blight and the varieties Orient, Head, and Pineapple as highly blight-resistant.

INSECT-RESISTANT PLANTS

The value of insect-resistance as a means of avoiding loss has been found successful in a number of instances. Entomologists are now working with plant-breeders in the development of more commercial varieties showing varying degrees of resistance, or even immunity. For the current year, about 4 per cent of the funds for the United States Entomology Research Branch are devoted to this subject. "Cooperative research is under way on corn borer and corn earworm resistance in corn, Hessian fly and wheat stem sawfly resistance on wheat, sugar-cane borer resistance in sugar cane, and spotted alfalfa aphid and pea aphid resistance in alfalfa." Corn varieties are available that reduce cornborer losses by 70 per cent. At least one variety of alfalfa is known that is not seriously affected by spotted alfalfa aphid infestations, which completely destroy susceptible varieties (Knipling, 1956).

Wheat

Varieties with varying degrees of resistance to the Hessian fly (*Phytophaga destructor*) are being released to the important wheat-growing areas. Big Club 43 and the variety Paso 48 are adapted to parts of California.

Pawnee, a satisfactory commercial variety beyond its fly-resistant quality, is the most widely grown variety in the United States. Ponca, a hard, red winter wheat is recommended for parts of Kansas and Oklahoma. Varieties of soft, red winter wheats are now being developed and will soon be available for distribution (Cartwright and Jones, 1953).

The Rescue variety of hard, red spring wheat, bred in Canada, is resistant to the wheat-stem sawfly (*Cephus cinctus*). Rescue is now grown generally in Montana and North Dakota (Packard and Martin, 1952).

Corn

Resistance to attack by the corn earworm (*Heliothis zea*) is now being shown by a number of hybrids being grown commercially. Several hybrid varieties are being cultivated in the Southeast, including Dixie 18, a yellow dent corn, and Dixie 11, a white hybrid, as partial protection against the earworm and the rice weevil, *Sitophilus oryza* (Blanchard and Douglas, 1953). The European corn borer (*Pyrausta nubilalis*) is also being attacked through the development of resistant types of corn (Bradley, 1952).

The chinch bug (*Blisus leucopterus*) is a serious enemy of the small grains, of corn and the sorghums. Early planting and the use of the more resistant varieties of corn and sorghum are recommended (Wakeland, 1952).

Alfalfa

Alfalfa suffers from attacks both by the common pea aphid (*Macrosiphum pisi*) and the spotted alfalfa aphid (*Therioaphis maculata*). The former is widely distributed; the latter has recently been found in the Southwest and spreading rapidly eastward. The resistance of the Ladak variety to the pea aphid has been recognized for several years. Stanford (1956) in a report of co-operative work between the California Agricultural Experiment Station and the Agricultural Service, Department of Agriculture, states that the alfalfa variety, Lahontan, has decided resistance to the spotted alfalfa aphid. This variety had been developed for its resistance to the stem nematode and to bacterial wilt. Two other alfalfa varieties have been developed for growing in California—one known as *Africa*, for use in the desert areas and the extreme southern San Joaquin Valley, and a second known as *Caliverde*, for most of the remainder of the state. The most resistant plants of the variety Lahontan are being crossed with Africa and Caliverde plants to retain resistance to the alfalfa aphid and, at the same time, give better winter growth than occurs with the Lahontan variety alone. Further work in the development of resistance from the Buffalo variety of alfalfa is in progress at the Kansas Agricultural Experiment Station (Harvey and Hackerott, 1956).

Cotton

Cotton is subject to attack by many types of insects, but none more injurious than the boll weevil (*Anthonomus grandis*). Wannamaker (1957) is attempting by plant-breeding to make the plant less attractive and "thus increase our ability to cope with the boll weevil problem . . . by cultivative and insecticidal measures of control."

REFERENCES

Abbott, E. V., "1953 Yearbook," Washington, D.C., U.S. Dept. Agr., 1953.

Barnes, W. C., and Epps, W. W., *Plant Disease Reporter*, **40**, 1093 (1956).

Blanchard, R. A., and Douglas, W. A., *U. S. Dept. Agr. Farmer's Bull.*, **1651** (1953).

Bradley, W. G., "1952 Yearbook," Washington, D.C., U.S. Dept. Agr., 1952.

Cartwright, W. B., and Jones, E. T., U. S. Dept. Agr. Farmer's Bull., **1627** (1953).

Clayton, E. E., "1953 Yearbook," Washington, D.C., U.S. Dept. Agr., 1953.

Coons, G. H., *ibid.*

Day, L. H., *Calif. Agr. Exp. Sta. Bull.*, **700** (1947).

Grogan, R. G., and Others, *Calif. Agr. Exp. Sta. Circular*, **448** (1955).

Hanson, E. W., and Kreitlow, K. W., "1953 Yearbook," Washington, D.C., U.S. Dept. Agr., 1953.

Harvey, T. L., and Hackerott, H. L., *J. Econ. Entom.*, **49**, 289 (1956).

Holton, C. S., and Tapke, V. F., "1953 Yearbook," Washington, D.C., U.S. Dept. Agr. 1953.

Jones, F. R., and Smith, O. F., *ibid.*

Knipling, E. F., *Agr. Chem.*, **11** (11), 52 (1956).

Larson, R. H., and Others, *Phytopathology*, **46**, 623 (1956).

Leukel, R. W., and Tapke, V. F., *U.S. Dept. Agr. Farmer's Bull.*, **2069** (1954).

———, *ibid.*, **2089** (1955).

Martin, J. H., and Salmon, S. C., "1953 Yearbook," Washington, D.C., U.S. Dept. Agr., 1953.

Middleton, J. F., and Others, *ibid.*

Packard, C. M., and Martin, J. H., "1952 Yearbook," Washington, D.C., U.S. Dept. Agr., 1953.

Parris, G. K., *Fla. Agr. Exp. Sta. Bull.*, **491** (1952).

Reed, L. B., and Doolittle, S. P., *U.S. Dept. Agr. Home & Garden Bull.*, **46** (1955).

Robert, A. A., "1953 Yearbook," Washington, D.C., U.S. Dept. Agr., 1953.

Schroeder, W. T., *ibid.*

Sisler, W. W., and Timian, R. G., *Plant Disease Reporter*, **40**, 1106 (1956).

Smith, A. L., "1953 Yearbook," Washington, D.C., U.S. Dept. Agr., 1953.

Smith, I. M., and Stafford, E. M., *Calif. Agr. Exp. Sta. Circular,* **445** (1956).

Smith, R. E., *ibid.*, **120**, (1941).

Stanford, E. H., *Calif. Agriculture*, **10** (7), 3 (1956).

———, and Others, *Calif. Agr. Exp. Sta. Circular,* **442** (1954).

Stevenson, F. J., and Jones, H. A., "1953 Yearbook," Washington, D.C., U.S. Dept. Agr., 1953.

Sylvester, E. S., and Severin, H. H. P., *Calif. Agr. Exp. Sta. Leaflet,* **46** (1955).

Thomas, H. R., and Zaumeyer, W. J., "1953 Yearbook," Washington, D.C., U.S. Dept. Agr., 1953.

Wakeland, C., "1952 Yearbook," Washington, D.C., U.S. Dept. Agr., 1952.

Walker, J. C., "1953 Yearbook," Washington, D.C., U.S. Dept. Agr., 1953.

———, and Others, *Phytopathology*, **47,** 269 (1957).

Wannamaker, W. K., *J. Econ. Entom.*, **50,** 418 (1957).

Wingard, S. A., "1953 Yearbook," Washington, D.C., U.S. Dept. Agr., 1953.

Zaumeyer, W. J., and Thomas, H. R., *ibid*.

Part II
Chemical Control of Insects, Plant Diseases, Weeds, and Rodents

5. INORGANIC AND ORGANIC COMPOUNDS AS PESTICIDES

Dependence upon natural and biological control of insects and the development of resistant plants being insufficient to protect us from economic losses in many fields, we find it necessary to resort to the use of chemicals. Such use may be but a temporary stopgap while other measures are being developed, or it may be accepted as customary. Whether temporary or permanent, however, it brings problems of chemical residues on foods and livestock feeds, host-plant injury, and developing insect resistance. The need of abundant high-quality food is so great, nevertheless, that the problems associated with chemical usage must be met, and the demand for pesticides is increasing rather than diminishing.

This trend is shown in the following outline by Knipling (1956) of the approximate divisions of research funds for the Entomology Research Branch of the Department of Agriculture for the current fiscal year.

Research Area	Per cent of Total Effort
Chemical Control	69
Biological control	8
Biology, ecology, etc.	7
Insect classification and identification	6
Insect resistance in plants	4
Insect pollination and bee management	4
Cultural and other control methods	2

Chemical control includes studies of attractants and repellents, co-operation with industry in the development of new insecticides, and much attention given to the problems of chemical residues on treated plants and that of insect resistance to insecticides. Biological control, including both the field of parasites and predators and the various insect pathogens, bacteria, fungi, and viruses, is receiving an increased amount of attention. Included also are studies on the structure of the chemical compound as related to toxicity. The latter covers the work on systemic insecticides that protect the young plant without disturbing beneficial insects. The latter field is further elaborated upon by Ripper (1956) in the theory of "balanced arthropod populations." He states that a successful demonstration of the use of the systemic schraden has been made in South Africa, and that 90 per

71

cent of the British hop acreage has been treated with this insecticide for the last six years with very good results. This treatment is for the hop aphid and the hop red spider mite.

PESTICIDE STATISTICS

The production of pesticides during 1956 increased more than during any previous year. The total pesticide inventory in October, 1956, was 95.3 million pounds, a very large increase over the previous year. DDT continued to lead in production, both for domestic and export materials. Calcium arsenate showed a decided increase, reflecting the belief that the boll weevil is developing resistance to the chlorinated hydrocarbon insecticides. Benzene hexachloride, on the gamma basis, made a decided gain in production, and there were moderate gains in aldrin, chlordane, dieldrin, endrin, heptachlor, and toxaphene. Production of lead arsenate dropped decidedly, as did that of cryolite.

Copper sulfate consumption shows the increased competition of organic fungicides. The yearly average consumption of 34 million pounds for the previous three years dropped in 1956 to 28 million pounds. Among the herbicides, the hormone sprays 2,4-D and 2,4,5-T continued strong, while sodium chlorate showed a decided gain in production (Shepard, 1957).

Canadian sales of pesticides for the year ending June 30, 1957, totaled almost 20 million dollars. Agricultural dusts and sprays amounted to 7 million dollars, while herbicides were a close second with almost 6.5 million dollars (Staff, Dominion Bureau Statistics, 1958).

TABLE 1

Foreign Trade in Pesticides—1958

Commodity	Receiving Countries	Value (in dollars)
DDT, technical	48	4,944,781
DDT, formulations containing 20 to 74%	42	1,713,060
DDT, formulations containing 75% or more	51	11,980,503
Benzene hexachloride	27	1,472,471
2,4-D and 2,4,5-T (herbicides)	47	2,896,001
Herbicides	56	5,854,514
Agricultural sulfur	25	253,298
Organic phosphorus	66	4,163,085
"Polychlor" insecticides	82	17,477,853
Agricultural insecticides	73	10,147,791
Fungicides	66	7,437,344
Fumigants	49	1,066,928
Household and industrial pesticides	85	4,958,217
Disinfectants	65	2,985,702

* Adapted from H. H. Shepard and C. A. Graham, *NAC News* (1959) of the Nat. Agr. Chem. Assoc.

Crop Protection Through the Use of Pesticides

The percentage of crops treated with insecticides and the corresponding return in market value varies greatly. Orchard fruits, especially apples and peaches, require thorough protection against both insects and diseases. Estimates of annual losses from uncontrolled insect attack range from 85 to 90 per cent, or even a total commercial loss (Decker, 1956). The estimate of crop losses from various sources are not additive, but occur concurrently. Cherries, grapes, and strawberries may show losses almost as great as those of applies and peaches. Pears also have suffered severely in the past, especially from pear blight. In fact, large pear-growing areas in the West have been compelled to abandon commercial pear-growing because of this disease. Improved methods of cultural operations and chemical control have greatly reduced losses.

As indicated in Chapter 4, sugar-beet culture in the western areas suffered from the disease known as *curly top* until resistant varieties were developed and better methods for the control of the carrier insect were developed. Commercial vegetable-crop production has also suffered severely both from insect attack and diseases. These losses, both in the commercial field and the home garden, have been reduced by the use of organic compounds.

Wheat, oats, barley, and corn are often grown without appreciable loss from insects, except that in recent years the European corn borer has caused increasingly large losses in corn despite the use of insecticides. In years past, the small grains, wheat, oats, and barley have suffered from various diseases. Severe outbreaks are now prevented by growing resistant varieties and the use of seed fungicides.

INORGANIC COMPOUNDS

Insecticides used prior to the advent of DDT were almost exclusively inorganic chemicals. The exceptions were the plant derivatives, nicotine, pyrethrins, and rotenone, together with petroleum, creosote, and thiocyanates. Refinements in dosage and application were the principal subjects of investigation. Since the materials used, compounds of arsenic, fluorine, sulfur, and partly refined petroleum oil, are in varying degree inherently dangerous to plants, the margin of safety between pest control and plant tolerance is small.

For the first time, crop residues of arsenic and fluorine on food crops received careful consideration of their relation to public health. Insect resistance to standard methods of chemical control was beginning to be recognized.

The fluorine compounds, cryolite and sodium fluorosilicate, once used as substitutes for arsenicals, were restricted in use because of poor adherence and the residue which was left on the fruit at harvest time.

Despite the criticism of the inorganic compounds, they continue to be used in many fields and are regaining ground in others. Calcium arsenate, once in disfavor, is being used in larger amounts in the southern cotton belt for insect control as insect resistance to a number of organic insecticides grows. Lead arsenate is now being used in a number of districts as a control for codling moth on apples and pears in place of organic compounds, the latter having been found more injurious to beneficial insects. Under Nova Scotia conditions of apple-growing, cryolite is listed by Glen (1954) as less injurious to natural enemies than are parathion, DDT, and sulfur. It is also classed as of moderate toxicity to the honey bee.

Sulfur (elemental) as an insecticide, although supplanted in part by organic compounds, including those containing sulfur, is still in common use. Ground and wettable sulfur is used in large quantities in California against the citrus thrips and the citricola scale. It is also used generally in the control of certain plant-feeding mites. Sulfur is known to be toxic to a number of predaceous mites, but is one of the safest of the pesticides in relation to bees. For cotton insects, it is used as a diluent and carrier for a number of insecticides, including DDT, BHC, and toxaphene.

Fungicides

Copper and sulfur, both in the elemental form and as compounds, have been the principal dependence of the plant pathologists in the control of plant diseases. Both are now being displaced for certain types of plant diseases by organic compounds.

Bordeaux mixture and basic copper compounds maintain their position as dormant applications for deciduous orchard trees. Organic compounds, however, are rapidly leading as foliage applicants, because for many purposes, they are less hazardous, give better control, and cause less shading of the leaf than does bordeaux mixture.

New values in the toxicity to fungus spores of various metals, including copper, silver, mercury, and zinc, have been shown by McCallan (1956) and Miller and McCallan (1957). Silver has been found to be decidedly the most active of any of the toxicants tested, with mercury a rather close second.

Sulfur as a fungicide is used both in the elemental form and in inorganic and organic compounds. The usual commercial form is a ground dust, 90 per cent of which will pass a 325-mesh screen, and of a 97 to 99 per-cent purity. The smaller the particle the greater the exposed surface, with a corresponding increase in activity. Since the sulfur vapor given off by the particle is effective over only a small fraction of an inch, a uniform distribution is necessary. The fungicidal action of sulfur is limited by the same climatic conditions as is the insecticidal; that is, effective amounts of volatilized sulfur are not released except by an exposure of a few hours at a temperature of 68°F or above. Injury to susceptible host plants may result at exposure of 90°F and above (de Ong, 1956). Lime-sulfur solution as a control of apple scab and other orchard diseases has been largely replaced by organic compounds of mercury and other substances.

The largest field of use for sulfur as a fungicide is in the control of powdery mildew (*Uncinula necator*) of the European type of grape, as grown in the southwestern area of the United States. Sulfur has also been the standard control agent for powdery mildew on apple, caused most commonly by the fungus *Podosphaera leucotricha*. However, because of the tendency to dwarf the foliage, reduce yields, and cause scalding of the fruit and foliage, it is being supplanted by organic compounds such as Karathane and Mildex (Kirby, 1957).

Brown rot caused by the fungus *Monilinia fructicola* is a serious disease of peaches, plums, and cherries, attacking both in the orchard and on packed fruit in transit. A number of applications of either dusting or spraying sulfur may be necessary to hold the disease in check in the orchard, with a final dusting at the grader.

Mercury, in the form of organic compounds, is being used to an increasing extent as the first application in the control of apple scab. It is as seed fungicides, however, that these compounds are coming into extensive use, for example, as a protection against bunt in wheat.

Soil Sterilants and Defoliants

Sodium chlorate and borates are used as temporary soil sterilants for seasonal use. Mixtures of the two give the rapid action of the chlorates and the longer action of the borates. The mixture reduces the danger of flammability from the chlorate when used alone. The chlorates are also used as defoliants.

Sodium arsenite and arsenic trioxide are used as more nearly permanent soil sterilants. They persist in the soil longer than chlorates, but are dangerous to use along highways and on grazing land (Crafts and others, 1955).

ORGANIC COMPOUNDS

The advent of DDT, dithiocarbamates, 2,4-D, and warfarin have advanced pest control along every line. Important as these contributions are, their greatest value probably lies in the stimulus they have given both to research and the demand for pesticides.

The development and wide use of organic pesticides not only protects our food supply but has advanced the control of the insect-borne diseases, malaria and typhus fever, throughout the world. Crop disasters caused by locust invasions and diseases of grain and potatoes are checked or reduced in degree. Worm-free and disease-free foods are produced and marketed in greater amounts than ever before (Miller, 1957). It is only by the careful use of pesticides that high-quality fruit, vegetables, and other crops can be grown in sufficient quantities to maintain our high standards of diet.

Insecticides

DDT first came into use by the military as a protection against lice, the carrier of typhus fever. When released for commercial sale, its value was quickly established against the house fly and the mosquito. Both insects have developed resistance of varying degree in many districts. However, there are many areas in this country, and importantly in foreign lands, where it is the chief dependence in protecting against insect-borne diseases.

In orchard work, DDT has shown the best control of codling moth of any insecticide—but only at the price of destroying a number of beneficial insects and mites. This has led to increased populations of harmful insects and mites which were previously of minor importance—a condition which has necessitated supplementary sprays or combination sprays that will control the principal pest insects.

The history of DDT is similar to that of many of the chlorinated hydrocarbons and the earlier forms of phosphate compounds. Certain types of insects may develop resistance to an insecticide, but broader application may show its value in a newly developed field. Examples are that of dieldrin as a repellent for chinch bugs, chlordane as a protective against termites and roaches, and endrin for grasshoppers.

The systemic type of insecticide, such as demeton (Systox) and OMPA (schraden, Pestox III), represents a distinct advance in toxicology. They do not kill quickly when absorbed by the sprayed foliage; rather, the toxic action extends over several days, plant mites being usually more susceptible than aphids. Even soaking cotton seed in a solution of OMPA has protected the plant against insects for six weeks. With livestock, the systemic insecticides Dow ET-57 and Bayer 21/199 are showing promise as a protection against the cattle grub, *Hypoderma* (Harris and Others, 1959; Drummond, 1959).

Fungicides and Bactericides

The dithiocarbamates are a very important group of fungicides which were discovered in 1934. Included are ferbam (Fermate), maneb (Manzate), zineb (Dithane Z-78), and ziram (Zerlate).

Ferbam is used principally as an orchard application for apple scab, apple blotch, and cedar rust. Maneb is principally a vegetable fungicide and, to a limited extent, an orchard control agent. Zineb and ziram are the chief control agents for a number of vegetable diseases, including early and late blight of tomatoes and potatoes, rust, anthracnose, and downy mildew. Ziram is being used to an increasing extent in orchard control work.

Captan is a widely used compound on orchard trees, vegetables, flowers, and for grape diseases, except powdery mildew. Seed fungicides include a number of organic mercurials, such as Ceresan, and the nonmercurials chloranil and dichlone (Phygon).

Vancomycin, an antibicaterial agent produced by *Streptomyces orientalis*, is especially active against gram-positive bacteria. It is primarily bactericidal rather than bacteristatic. Vancomycin is translocated both to the apical portion and to the roots of the plant, and accumulates both in the lower leaves and the roots. It is readily absorbed both through the roots and the seeds and carried to the upper portions of the plant (Mehta and Others, 1959).

Herbicides

The hormone-type compounds, 2,4-D, 2,4,5-T, and related compounds are the most widely used of any of the weed-killers. They are especially effective in killing broad-leaved weeds in small grain. Grassy weeds, not being susceptible to the hormone compounds, are controlled by applications of Dalapon or IPC.

General-purpose weed-killers include certain of the dinitros (dinitro-o-cresol), the petroleum fractions with high aromatic content, and pentachlorophenol.

Rodenticides

Warfarin is one of the newer types of rodent poisons which kill by checking the normal clotting of the blood. It requires a number of feedings (multiple dosage) to be fatal. It is mixed with a cereal base and distributed as a bait. Its principal use is against the Norway rat and the mouse. Compound 1080 (sodium fluoroacetate) is used for rodents around buildings, ships, and in the field. The latter is a very toxic material and should be used only by professionals.

A number of the insecticides and fungicides for use on food crops and livestock feed may, under certain conditions, show persistent residues which might be detrimental to public health.* To avoid such possibility, and to give direction for proper usage, a number of safeguards, including careful toxological study, have been established before a compound may be marketed.

---

* A celebrated example was the heated controversy over cranberry contamination in late 1959.

PESTICIDE REGULATIONS

The consumers interest in the nutritional value and the safety of the food is protected not only by the care of the farmer but also the manufacturer, federal and state Departments of Agriculture, Federal Food and Drug Administration, Public Health Service—and the physician. The legal authority under which the federal departments operate is Public Law 518, popularly known as the Miller Amendment of the Federal Food and Drug Act, and the Federal Insecticide, Fungicide, and Rodenticide Act of 1947. Intrastate shipments are controlled under state registration.

Under the Miller Amendment, the Food and Drug Administration is given the authority to establish, on a scientific basis, the amounts of chemical residue from the application of pesticides which is tolerated on marketable raw (unprocessed) fruits, vegetables, and livestock products, and for fodder for dairy cattle and cattle for market. Crops found exceeding these tolerances are subject to seizure and taken off the market. Pesticides are not subject to sale until they have been registered by the Department of Agriculture for specific purposes; they must also have approval of the Federal Food and Drug Administration.

Residual tolerances for specific crops are released by the Food and Drug Administration as soon as they are determined, following careful studies of potential hazard to the public health. The tolerances as established are published in the *Federal Resgister** at Washington.

Such findings may be modified as additional data pertaining to the use of any pesticide are determined. Residues not greater than the permitted amount should result from following the directions for use, for time limit between the final application and harvest, and dosages printed on the label as registered by the Department of Agriculture for specific crops. Deviation from such instructions, or use of a pesticide for which no tolerance is established, is at the grower's risk.

The original amount of residue from a recommended dosage of a pesticide may be much in excess of the legal tolerance. Such residue is reduced, however, by a number of factors during the required interval of time between the final application and harvest. These factors include the effect of wind and rain, and physical and chemical decomposition of a compound by light, heat, moisture, and vapor pressure. The type of formulation is also important, since dusts and wettable powders disappear more quickly than emulsions. Decker (1957) found that, under controlled conditions, a study of the vapor pressure as related to the dissipation of insecticide residues showed the following order of disappearance: lindane, aldrin, heptachlor, chlordane, dieldrin, toxaphene, methoxychlor, and DDT.

* A summary of published tolerances up to April 30, 1957, grouped according to crop, is found in *NAC News* **15(4)**, (May, 1957), published by the National Agricultural Chemicals Association.

The tolerance for various pesticides permitted on raw fruits and vegetables varies according to the toxicity of the compound. A few, such as petroleum oils, pyrethrins, and the copper compounds, require no tolerance because of their harmlessness to man. Others, such as mercury-containing compounds, have "zero" tolerances, either because a safe level in the diet of warm-blooded animals has not been determined; or the chemical has alarming physiological effects; or it is toxic but as normally used will not be found on raw agricultural commodities; or all residue is normally removed through washing or weathering prior to introduction of the commodity in interstate commerce. The tolerance for DDT and for lead arsenate is 7 ppm, that for methoxychlor, 14 ppm, while that for the fungicide captan is 20 ppm on apples and certain other fruits. For the more toxic insecticides, such as aldrin and chlordane the tolerance may be as low as a fraction of 1 ppm.

The amounts of tolerance are determined by toxicologists in the Food and Drug Administration working with test animals under various methods of application and dosage. Experimental work with a product may extend over a period of two or three years.

Determination of Residues

The use of pesticides on agricultural crops being limited by the established tolerances in parts per million of the various compounds, there must be accurate and acceptable methods of sampling the crop and determining the amounts of residue present. Sampling should be planned carefully to give a typical representation of conditions over the entire treated area. It should either show the outside limits of the residue that may occur or represent the average arithmetic mean. Uniformity of sampling is very necessary so that the few samples which can be analyzed are typical (Harris, 1956; Lykken and Others, 1957).

The first step in the analytical process is the "elimination of interfering substances present in the solutions obtained from the processing operations." This and the determination of the amount of residue present require skilled analysts "using the techniques and procedures that are sufficiently reliable and sufficiently sensitive to assure recognition and acceptance under the Miller Pesticides Amendment and thus lead eventually to successful commercial application of a new and useful pesticide chemical." (Gunther, 1957)

Secondary Effects from the Use of Pesticides

Interest in the control of orchard insects, fungi, and bacteria have in the past been largely centered on toxicity to the pest, without too much injury to the host. The general adoption of organic pesticides, with various combinations of insecticides and fungicides, in the spray program, and more careful evaluation of results, have led to greater emphasis on fruit flavor, appearance, yield, and keeping-qualities; tree vigor and the effect on insect and mite populations also receive consideration. Garman (1954), in work on apples in Connecticut, found an impaired quality of fruit from injured trees. This might have resulted from injury to bark or leaves. On the other hand, fruit finish after two years work was found to be outstanding due to use of a lead arsenate-captan combination. Scald occurred whenever sulfur was used. Inclusion of the fungicide glyodin was superior to sulfur-ferbam combinations. Lead arsenate tended to reduce acidity and minerals. Garman (1956) reports favor of the combination of methoxychlor-TDE-captan and malathion in 1954, and methoxychlor-captan in 1955. Powdery mildew increased in both years, presumably because of the extensive use of captan and glyodin without sulfur. The latter difficulty has been met by Daines (1957), who recommends the addition of sulfur to captan or glyodin sprays, followed by Karathane in the late cover sprays.

It is also noted that increased yields follow the use of many of the newer types of fungicides. This is presumed to be due to the foliage being retained in better condition than where sulfur-copper combinations were used. Longer retention of the foliage would result in larger fruit buds, with corresponding crop increases. Glyodin has been found to suppress mite populations, while captan appears to increase mite attack. Combination sprays of fungicides for orchards is stressed rather than the use of single compounds.

Boswell (1955) notes the adverse effect of BHC applications on the flavor and odor of peaches. An early light spray of lindane may not affect the flavor of fresh fruit, but the flavor of canned fruit may be affected by late, heavy applications. All isomers of BHC apparently contributed to poor fruit flavor, that from the alpha being the least noticeable. Similar results were noted in the spraying of vegetables.

Attractants. Baits containing a toxic material and an attractant have for many years received much attention. One of the earliest was formaldehyde added to milk as a fly poison. Metaldehyde combined with calcium arsenate and added to either bran or dried apple peeling is an old formula, but is still preferred as a control for snails and slugs. Arsenical compounds were commonly used for the earlier forms of baits, but, only with the development of quick-acting organic phosphate compounds, such as malathion and parathion, has the greatest efficiency been obtained. In the Hawaiian campaign against the Oriental fly (*Dacus dorsalis*) and the Mediterranean fruit fly (*Ceratitis capitata*), it was found that the slow-acting poisons, dieldrin, aldrin, DDT, chlordane, and nicotine bentonite, did not kill quickly enough for the dead flies to be collected and counted. The most effective bait-spray was one containing parathion as the toxicant and a protein hydrolyzate as the attractant (Steiner, 1952).

In the southern-Florida Mediterranean-fruit-fly campaign, an acid hydrolyzate of corn protein was used as the attractant and malathion as the toxicant. The latter was substituted for parathion because of its low toxicity to man. The common formula was as follows:

25 per cent Malathion Wettable Powder	2 pounds
Protein Hydrolyzate (1 to 2 pints)	1¼ to 2½ pounds
Water to make	1 gallon

This formula was applied by airplane at the rate of a gallon per acre. In addition to the hydrolyzate, oil of angelica seed was used as an attractant in survey work (Lockmillar and Thomas, 1957).

Dry fly-baits with malathion, parathion, or other phosphate compound as the toxicant are used commonly in barns as a control for the housefly. Sugar or corn meal mixed with molasses is the usual attractant.

Other common uses of attractants feature geranol-eugenol for the Japanese beetle, and various compounds in the gypsy-moth campaign in the northeastern states.

Repellents. Insect repellents include not only those used to protect humans and livestock from biting flies and mosquitoes, but also from migrating insects, such as chinch bugs, and as protectants for seed grain and in reforestation. Young orchard trees are protected against the attack of mice and rabbits by applications of nicotine and Arasan (thiram). Among the earliest practices was application to the person of one of the essential oils —oil of citronella, lavender, rosemary, or pennyroyal. These are effective for only a few hours. The present trend is toward the development of organic compounds that will give protection for from one to several days.

One of the first synthetic organic compounds for use on cattle was Crag Fly Repellent. It is added to a toxic fly spray to give repellency. This combination of a repellent and a toxic compound has been followed commonly, although repellents are being developed which will be self-sufficient when used alone. A cattle spray to be used with pyrethrins and a synergist such as piperonyl butoxide is R-11. The latter is effective as a repellent against horn flies and stable flies, as well as mosquitoes and roaches (Goodhue, 1956). The compound R-326 is an active repellent for use on dairy and beef cattle, and as a premise spray (Goodhue and Stansbury, 1953; Goodhue, 1956). The compound, Tabutrex, is another repellent registered as both for flies and roaches.

Cutkomp and Harvey (1958) have shown the gains in weight of beef cattle from protection against the horn fly and the stable fly, by the use of various repellent-insecticide combinations applied by a treadle sprayer. The net profit from the 90-day summer-period treatments after deducting costs was $3.36 per head for 1954, $10.92 per head for 1955 and none in 1956. The formulas used were principally pyrethrins with different synergists in petroleum distillate, and MGK repellents R-11 and R-356.

A field study was made in Oregon of repellents against the mosquitoes *Aedes dorsalis* and *A. communis*, and the deer fly (*Chrysops discalis*). Diethyl-toluamide was the most effective of twelve repellents tested as a skin applicant. It was about twice as effective as the standard mixture containing dimethyl phthalate (40 per cent), dimethyl carbate (30 per cent), and ethyl hexanediol (30 per cent). The protection time ranged from 336 to 404 minutes. The effect of the repellents against *C. discalis* was similar to that of the standard mixture. As clothing treatments, the sixteen mixtures and four of the seven individual repellents were very effective after twenty-six days of aging. Effectiveness was lost after two rinses (Gilbert, 1957).

Protection against wood ticks, *Dermacentor andersoni* and *D. variabilis*, is possible to a large extent by impregnating socks, shirts, and trousers with a 5 per-cent solution or emulsion of dimethyl phthalate or ethyl hexanediol (Staff, U. S. Dept. Agr., Entom. Res. Branch, 1955).

Repellents for the lone-star tick (*Amblyomma americanum*) giving the longest protection were mixtures of ethyl hexanediol (30 per cent), butyl acetanilide (30 per cent), and benzyl benzoate (30 per cent) applied as water emulsions. The mixtures were applied to army fatigue uniforms of herringbone twill at the rate of 3.6 grams per square foot. This treatment gave an average repellency of 95 per-cent for the first 5 weeks (Gouck and Gilbert, 1955).

Chemical protection of seeds is now being used in reforestation and range-seeding as a protection against losses from birds and rodents. Anthraquinone is used as a bird repellent, and Arasan (thiram), both as a bird and rodent repellent. Another forestry use of repellents is the spraying of pulp wood with a 12 per-cent gamma BHC as a protection against losses from boring beetles (Shenefelt and Others, 1958).

Repellents for use against termite attacks on lumber in damp locations include pressure treatment with creosote, zinc meta-arsenite, and pentachlorophenol. The latter compound may also be applied by brush to all surfaces of timbers laid against concrete or buried in the soil, but such application is less durable than impregnation. Pentachlorophenol is oil soluble, and sodium pentachlorophenate is water soluble. These chemicals also prevent wood decay. Chlordane and BHC (gamma benzene hexachloride) at concentrations of 1 to 10,000 to 1 to 20,000 are used as soil poisons, giving protection against termites for 10 years or more in sandy soils. Hetrick (1957) states that experiments in operation only seven years with aldrin, dieldrin, and heptachlor indicate a much longer period of protection at very low dosages.

REFERENCES

Boswell, V. R., *J. Econ. Entom.*, **48**, 495 (1955).
Crafts, A. S., and Buck, C. C., *Calif. Agr. Exp. Sta. Bull.*, **739** (1955).

Cutkomp, L. K., and Harvey, A. L., *J. Econ. Entom.*, **51**, 172 (1958).

Daines, R. H., *Agr. Chem.*, **12** (4), 32 (1957).

Decker, G. C., *Bull. Entom. Soc. America*, **2** (1), 2 (1956).

————, *Agr. Chem.*, **12** (2), 39 (1957).

de Ong, E. R., "Chemistry and Uses of Pesticides," 2d ed., New York, Reinhold Publishing Corp., 1956.

Drummond, R. O., *J. Econ. Entom.*, **52**, 512 (1959).

Garman, P., *ibid.*, **47**, 731 (1954).

————, *ibid.*, **49**, 521 (1956).

Gilbert, I. H., *ibid.*, **50**, 46 (1957).

Glen, R. J., *ibid.*, **47**, 398 (1954).

Goodhue, L. D., and Stansbury, R. E., *ibid.*, **46**, 982 (1953).

————, *Agr. Chem.*, **11** (7), 32 (1956).

Gouck, H. K., and Gilbert, I. H., *J. Econ. Entom.*, **48**, 499 (1955).

Gunther, F. A., *J. Agr. Food Chem.*, **5**, 498 (1957).

Harris, E. D., and Others, *J. Econ. Entom.*, **52**, 425 (1959).

Harris, T. H., *J. Agr. Food Chem.*, **4**, 413 (1956).

Hetrick, L. A., *J. Econ. Entom.*, **50**, 316 (1957).

Kirby, R. S., *Agr. Chem.*, **12** (5), 41 (1957).

Knipling, E. F., *ibid.*, **11** (10), 52 (1956).

Lockmiller, N. R., and Thomas, M. J., *ibid.*, **12** (3), 34, (1957).

Lykken, L., and Others, *J. Agr. Food Chem.*, **5**, 501 (1957).

McCallan, S. E. A., Plant Protection Conference, England (1956).

Mehta, P. P., and Others, *Phytopathology*, **49**, 177 (1959).

Miller, D. L., *National Business Woman*, **36** (6), 16 (1957).

Miller, L. P., and McCallan, S. E. A., *J. Agr. Food Chem.*, **5**, 116 (1957).

Ripper, W. E., *Agr. Chem.*, **11** (11), 47 (1956).

Shepard, H. H., *U. S. Dept. Agr. Pesticide Situation Rpt., 1956–1957.*

————, and Graham, C. A., *Nat. Agr. Chem. Assoc. News*, 1959.

Staff, *U. S. Dept. Agr. Entom. Research Bur. Leaflet*, **387** (1955).

Staff, Canadian Dominion Bur. Statistics, "1958 Report."

Steiner, L. F., *J. Econ. Entom.*, **45**, 838 (1952).

Shenefelt, R. D., and Others, *Agr. Chem.*, **13** (1), 38 (1957).

6. FIELD CROP INSECTS, DISEASES, AND WEEDS

Until the introduction of the European corn borer, the grain-farmer had but little need for insecticides. However, the gradual spread of infestation by this insect, accompanied by heavy increases in the borer population, has led to a decided demand for chemical control. In the earlier stages of the invasion, dependence was placed on deep plowing, proper disposal of the old cornstalks, and the introduction of parasites and predators from Europe. These measures, although helpful, have not prevented heavy losses. The combined chemical, cultural, and biological control measures have reduced the losses in corn production, but have not prevented further distribution of the insect.

The early introduction of the Hessian fly and the development of the chinch bug into a major pest have resulted in serious losses. Much attention has been given to the adjustment of planting dates and the development of resistant varieties, but these methods have given only partial relief. The use of repellent barriers, such as narrow strips of dieldrin, between fields of small grains and the later-maturing field corn is now proving helpful in protecting the latter.

The small grains, wheat, oats, and barley are subject to heavy losses annually from smut. Waves of rust infestation, under favorable climatic conditions, sweep our principal grain-producing states and move into Canada, causing heavy reductions in yield. Such losses are being reduced by the use of resistant varieties and the use of seed fungicides. The combination of these two methods has placed grain-farming on a more stable basis.

Weed control by chemicals is another major contribution to grain-farming. Millions of acres are now sprayed annually with herbicides.

Cotton and tobacco have experienced heavy losses from insects, disease, and weed invasion. Promising new compounds are being developed which will no doubt extend the possibility of reduced pest damage.

The spread of the imported fire ant (*Solenopsis saevissima* v. *richteri*) in the southeastern States has led to much experimentation in the use of insecticides and their proper dosage. Much discussion has resulted as to possible danger to wildlife, and broad lines of research are being developed to determine the most satisfactory form of control. Current findings favor applications of 2 pounds of heptachlor or dieldrin or 4 pounds of chlordane per acre, which, when broadcast as granules, give good control for from 3 to 5 years. Lower dosages of these insecticides gave good control for a year, but were ineffective thereafter (Blake and Others, 1959).

CORN

Insects Attacking Corn

The European corn borer (*Pyrausta nubilalis*) was first discovered in this country in 1917 near Boston. It had apparently entered from Europe on broomcorn some years before. Since that time, it has spread over the eastern states, the midwest, and is reported as far south as Alabama. There are two strains of the insect, one that is single-brooded and another that is double-brooded, in the central and northern states; three broods are common in the Gulf States. The insect is primarily a pest of corn, both field and sweet corn. It also attacks broomcorn, soybean, millet, oats, pepper, and sorghum, and a great host of other wild and cultivated plants.

The young larvae tunnel into the corn stalk and feed also upon the ears, midrib of the leaf, tassel buds, husks, and leaf sheaths. Entry is usually made between the leaf sheath and the stalk or the stem of the ear. Other disease organisms may find entrance through the entry holes and still further weaken the plant. The injury to the corn crop is now measured by hundreds of millions of dollars annually (Bradley, 1952).

The winter is passed in the borer, or worm, stage inside the cornstalk, cob, or weed-stalk. Late in the spring, a hole is cut to the surface of the hiding place to provide an opening for the adult moth. The larva then pupates and about two weeks later the moth emerges to begin ovipositing. The moth flies about actively depositing the eggs in masses, principally on the corn plant. Several hundred eggs are deposited by each female moth. The adult moth lives but 10 to 24 days but, because of irregularity of emergence, they may be found throughout the summer (Bradley, 1952).

Cultural-control measures consist of disposing of cornstalks in such a way that the borers hiding within them may be killed. Plowing under to a depth of about six inches is effective if the surface is left clean of vegetation that will provide hiding places. The borers usually crawl to the surface, where they are exposed to the attack of birds, and insect parasites and predators. Infested corn should be cut close to the ground to make into silage, or be shredded and fed or used for bedding. Infested cornstalks that are fed directly are a source of danger unless the uneaten parts are collected and destroyed. Such measures are of little value, however, unless they are followed generally in a community (Bradley, 1952).

Natural control measures for the European corn borer include the introduction and establishment of a number of parasites from France, Italy, Korea, and Japan. Of this number only two, *Lydella stabulans grisescens* and *Macrocentrus gifuensis*, are of appreciable value in field control. A fungus, *Beauveria bassiana*, obtained from a consignment of corn-borer larvae from Manchuria and cultured and distributed as spores in the field, has not proven to be a practicable control (Clausen, 1956).

The development of borer-resistant corn, both inbred and hybrid, has received much attention from plant-breeders and resulted in strains of corn that will endure heavy attacks of borers with least damage. Great numbers of lines of corn drawn from South America, Mexico, and from varieties of corn grown in Europe under borer conditions are used in the work (Bradley, 1952).

Applications of DDT* as a spray and as a granulated dust in concentrations of 1.5 pounds of active material, 0.5 pounds of EPN, and 1.5 pounds of heptachlor per acre gave satisfactory control of the first brood of European corn borer in 1953. Granule formulations of heptachlor and DDT at 1.5 pounds and EPN at 0.5 pounds per acre reduced the second brood in 1954. Malathion in concentrations of 2 pounds per acre was ineffective. It was concluded that granulated formulations of insecticides are as effective as emulsion sprays for the control of the European corn borer (Cox and Others, 1956, 1957). Similar results were obtained with the granulated insecticides DDT, endrin, dieldrin, heptachlor, and aldrin in the control of the first brood of the European corn borer (Gould and Wilson, 1957).

Two applications of DDT have been found by Cox and others, 1958 to give better control of the borer than one application. The best indicator for the proper time of applying the insecticide was when 75 per cent of the plants showed evidence of insect-feeding in the leaf whorls.

The initial Thiodan applications as a borer control gave a higher residue on the emulsion-treated corn than on the granular-treated corn. After one week's exposure to the end of the experiment, the differences were but slight. Small residues of both formulations persisted for more than nine weeks (Lindquist and Others, 1959).

Corn fodder treated with DDT or other insecticides with long-lasting residues should not be fed to dairy cattle or cattle being fed for the market.

The sugar-cane borer (*Diatraea saccharalis*) is the most important insect enemy of the sugar cane in the United States. Efforts to control this pest by the use of parasites have thus far been unsuccessful. Applications of cryolite full strength at the rate of 10 pounds per acre has been used successfully in the past. A dust of 40 per-cent ryania is now being used com-

* Dosages for pesticides are usually stated in terms of the active ingredient unless otherwise specified. Read the label carefully.

monly. The latter material has also been found helpful in protecting corn against the sugar-cane borer (Arbuthnot, 1958).

The lesser cornstalk borer (*Elasmopalpus lignosellus*) is a pest of corn, beans, and grain and others of the grass family in the southern United States and South America. Besides attacking cultivated crops, there are many weed hosts, including water grass, Johnson grass, and volunteer grain. The principal damage is caused by the larva boring into the plant stem in the seedling stage. Several plants may thus be injured by the same insect.

Cultural control consists in destroying all living plants some weeks before planting. Flood irrigation over level surfaces will also kill many of the larvae.

The best chemical control has resulted from applying narrow bands of dieldrin or endrin, at dosages of 4 to 8 ounces per acre, along seed furrows or over the seedling plants (Reynolds and Others, 1959).

The corn earworm (*Heliothis zea*) is a very destructive enemy of ear corn and is distributed throughout the country wherever the crop is grown. It attacks sweet corn principally, but is also found on field corn to a lesser extent. The degree of injury is regulated largely by the number of generations annually. In the more southern states, the life cycle of egg to adult is completed in a month, there being perhaps seven generations a year. In the Corn Belt, the insect has three or four generations a year. The first generation attacks the bud or central shoot and then the unfolding tassel, but the principal injury is to the fresh silk; from there the larva feeds its way down into the ear itself. Feeding may be confined largely to the tip of the ear or may extend to half the length of the ear. When feeding is completed, the larvae drop to the ground, burrow down a few inches and pupate. During the summertime, the adult moth emerges from the pupa in about two weeks. The moths are strong flyers and may either deposit their eggs on newly emerged silk, or fly to other fields, such as cotton, or drift northward to later-developing corn. The winter is passed in the pupa stage, buried in the ground. About 400 eggs are laid by each female.

Damaged ears of sweet corn are trimmed before marketing or being taken to the cannery. Trimmed corn brings a lower price, and the extra labor increases the production cost.

Natural Control

Cannibalism among the ear worms is one of the principal means of reducing their number. Two worms coming in contact with each other fight until one is injured beyond recovery. The survivor may then eat its enemy. Entry to the ear being usually through the tip, large numbers of the worms are killed at this point. Field corn, with long protected tips, encourages this tendency of larvae to enter at one point, thus bringing them into closer contact with each other.

The exposed eggs and newly hatched larvae are subject to attack by a parasitic wasp, *Trichogramma minutum*, a predaceous bug, *Orius insidiosus*, and many birds. Rainstorms and early frosts take a heavy toll, and a large number of the hibernating pupae die in the soil from cold and excess moisture. Disease also kills large numbers, especially in prolonged wet weather (Blanchard, 1953).

Chemical Control for Sweet Corn

The corn earworm (and the second-brood corn borer where present) is controlled with a DDT emulsion to which a light mineral oil is added. The latter should be a refined, white mineral oil of 45- to 90-seconds Saybolt viscosity. Three applications should be made: the first, the day after the silks appear; the second, three days later; and the third, another three days later. The spray or dust should be applied thoroughly to the silks.

The spray formulas for one acre or for a small plot are as follows: Add one gallon of 25 per-cent DDT emulsifiable concentrate to 1 gallon of the light mineral oil; add water to make 25 gallons. This is sufficient for one acre. One-third pint of 25 per-cent DDT emulsifiable concentrate is added to one-third pint of the light mineral oil; add water to make a gallon. This is sufficient for a plot 17 by 100 feet (Staff, 1957).

Dust formulas (MacGillivray and Minges, 1956) are as follows: Five per-cent DDT dust is applied with a stencil or paint brush to each ear. Requires 30–35 pounds per acre.

Ground-dusters may be used for light-to-moderate infestations. Use 5 per-cent DDT dusts or granules at 35 to 40 pounds per acre. Make three to four applications at three- to four-day intervals. For heavier infestations, apply 10 per-cent DDT dusts by power-dusters or airplane.

DDT is a poisonous material and should be handled and stored with care. Follow directions carefully. Avoid having residues of DDT on the corn grains of more than 3.5 ppm.

Neither corn fodder nor husks should be fed to dairy cattle or animals being fed for the market.

For garden applications, use any type of hand-duster or sprayer. Tractor-mounted or high-clearance sprayers or dusters are used for commercial acreages. Machines should be equipped with a boom, with nozzles adjusted to each row. Pressures should range from 50 to 150 psi, depending on the number and types of nozzles, gallons applied per acre, and the speed of the sprayer. The usual type of row-crop dusters are not suitable for applying granules without adjustment. Adjust single-outlet applicators to deliver directly over the row. For multi-outlet applicators, close all outlets except those directly over the row (Luckmann and Others, 1957).

Under Alabama conditions, Eden (1958) found that DDT applied daily as a 2-pound emulsion for 7 days, and then at 2-day intervals, was superior to Phosdrin at 0.25-pound and Chlorthion at 1.0-pound concentrations. Sevin gave results similar to DDT, but injured the foliage.

A survey of field corn at harvest in Louisiana showed that kernel damage averaged more than 8 per cent, due largely to the rice weevil (*Sitophilus oryza*). This loss increased during storage of 10 months to 22 per cent. The predisposing cause of the loss was bird damage to the husk. An application of one pound of endrin in one gallon of white mineral oil to the individual ears on July 6 and August 3 gave good protection against the weevil (Floyd and Powell, 1958).

Miscellaneous Insects

Corn Rootworm. This is the larva of a small green-and-black spotted beetle, sometimes called the *cucumber beetle*. There are three common species: southern corn rootworm (*Diabrotica undecimpunctata howardi*), northern form (*Diabrotica longicornis*), and the western corn rootworm (*Diabrotica virgifera*). All have similar feeding habits. The beetles become active when the temperature reaches about 70°F, and feed on grasses and alfalfa. Eggs are laid around the roots of host plants in the early spring, a second generation coming in midsummer. Each female may lay as many as 500 eggs. The larvae hatching from these eggs feed on the sprouting seed and tunnel into the roots. As the stalks grow larger, the larvae bore into the crown of the young plant and destroy the growing bud. Side-shoots may develop, but seldom produce good corn. Later in the season, the larvae kill or weaken many of the plant roots, causing the plant to lodge, weakening it, and making it difficult to harvest (Staff, 1955).

The rootworm is controlled in corn by applications of aldrin or heptachlor at the rate of ½ to 1 pound per acre, or with chlordane at the rate of 1 to 1½ pounds per acre. Broadcast the recommended amount of insecticide as a spray, or dust over the soil surface, before planting. Follow this immediately by working the insecticide thoroughly into the soil by disking. The dusts may be purchased already diluted. The emulsified concentrate of the insecticide may be diluted with water in any amount that the sprayer will conveniently use in treating an acre. A mixture of insecticide and fertilizer may be applied either before, or at the time of, planting. If applied at planting time, use the minimum amount that will give the recommended dosage of insecticide. The mixture should be applied as a side-dressing with a fertilizer attachment (Staff, 1955).

Experiments in Wisconsin by Apple (1957), to determine the minimum amounts of insecticide to use in the control of corn rootworm, showed that heptachlor was no better than aldrin at dosages of 1 pound per acre for broadcast applications, and ½ pound per acre in starter-fertilizer. But, by reducing the application rates one-half, heptachlor gave similar results to those obtained at higher dosage; the results with aldrin were less effective.

Seed-Corn Maggot. The larva of a small, gray fly, *Hylemya cilicrura*, attacks the planted seed of a number of crops, including corn, beans, peas, barley, and potatoes, as well as attacking the young plants. The injury may be especially severe in cold weather when germination is slow. Replanting when the ground is warmer may be all that is necessary. Seed may be protected by an application of lindane—either the wettable powder or the emulsion—in a 75 per-cent concentration, at the rate of 1⅓ ounces per 100 pounds of seed. One of the organic seed fungicides should be added. Howitt (1958) found that *H. antiqua* was resistant to the chlorinated hydrocarbons and many of the organic phosphate compounds, but was controlled by a furrow treatment of 3 pounds per acre of Trithion and ethion and 2 pounds per acre of Guthion and Bayer 21/199.

Chinch Bug (*Blissus leucopterus*). This bug feeds on grasses, small grains, corn, sorghum, Sudan grass, and even lawn grasses. The newly hatched bugs are bright red and wingless, but develop wings as they mature. The mature insect is about one-eighth inch long. Heavy rains kill many of the tiny red nymphs, but not the larger forms. A succession of hot humid days may result in many of the older nymphs and adults being killed by disease.

The chinch bug develops rapidly in small grains and, as these mature and dry up, the bugs migrate out of the fields on foot into adjoining fields of corn, sorghum, and Sudan and other grasses. Serious injury may occur to infested fields.

Infestations of small grains is occasionally severe enough to warrant control measures. The greatest injury, however, is usually to growing crops and, for their protection, barriers of dieldrin are used. These are made at concentrations of 0.5 pound per acre, applied as sprays either by ground machines or by air. The application should be made at the beginnning of the migration and applied at least two rods into the small grain and an equal distance into the corn, or as far as the bugs have migrated, and with wider bands at each end. The spray is applied directly to the soil. A heavy rain coming on a newly applied barrier may be disadavantageous, and it will be necessary to repeat the application. If the bugs are well-established in the cornfield and hiding in the loose soil, then a rain may help to carry the dieldrin down to them. For medium infestations, a barrier will be effective from 10 to 17 days in fair weather, long enough to last through the migration (Gannon and Decker, 1955; Hein, 1957).

Resistance

Resistance of corn to insect attack has been developed to a certain extent against the corn earworm by the extension of the husk 2 or 3 inches beyond the tip of the ear. Other characters of insect resistance in corn are also being developed in the breeding of hybrids and inbreds. Various strains of corn are also being developed which show resistance to chinch bugs, grasshoppers, and the corn leaf aphid. It has also been found that lines resistant to the corn leaf aphid are quite resistant to the European corn borer (Packard and Martin, 1952).

Diseases of Corn

Smut (Boil Smut). This is a disease caused by the fungus *Ustilago maydis*. Galls or tumorlike swellings are formed on the ears, tassels, and stalk. The galls range in size from that of a bead to a number of inches in diameter. They are at first covered with a whitish membrane which breaks open and shows a mass of black spores. Smut attacks both sweet corn and field corn. The disease is widely distributed, but the prevalence is limited. Ullstrup (1953) estimates the range of injury from smut in the Corn Belt to be from a trace to 6 per cent. The incidence of the disease and its effect on the corn crop in Indiana has been surveyed by Gaskin and Ullstrup (1958) with the following results: The per-cent loss of weight of ears on smutted plants ranged from 12.0 for small galls above the ear to 90.2 for ear galls. "The average total incidence of smut of all gall classes was 0.82 per cent, with a range from 0.0 to 7.0 per cent in different fields.... An estimated loss of 0.41 per cent in a 230-million bushel crop, which is an approximation of the most recent 10-year average of corn production in Indiana, would amount to about 943 thousand bushels."

The planting of resistant hybrids is recommended as the most practical preventive in field corn. Infestations in gardens should be destroyed before being allowed to scatter the spores.

Dry Rot. Also known as *Diplodia ear rot,* this is a destructive disease of corn. The entire ear may be affected, especially in cases of early infection. The ear appears shrunken and husk adheres tightly to the ear. The disease is caused by the fungus *Diplodia zeae.* Ear mold, or pink rot, is another destructive disease of corn found more in the drier parts of the Corn Belt and in the western states. It is caused by different species of the fungi *Fusarium* and *Gibberella.* The choice of inbred lines with close husk covers is the best preventive (Ullstrup, 1953).

Weeds of Corn

A commonly used weed killer in corn is 2,4-D, both as a pre-emergence and a post-emergence application. There is some danger from both methods, so local agricultural officers should be consulted and the directions on the label followed closely.

Broad-Leaved Weeds. Controlled by 2,4-D, these include wild mustard, wild radish, lamb's-quarters, cocklebur, cheese weed (common mallow), burr clover, pepper grass, ragweed, and sweet clover. Many other semisensitive species occur but vary in different parts of the country.

Grasses. *Grassy weeds* and *bluegrass* are quite resistant to 2,4-D, except as pre-emergence applications.

Control. The earlier recommendations (1949–1951) for the use of 2,4-D were principally for post-emergence sprays, using dosages of about 0.25 pound per acre of the ester formulation and about 0.5 pound of the amine type. Such use should be on heavy soils only. The time of application is to be gauged by the emergence of the majority of weeds. Later applications should be made with the nozzle discharging near the ground to avoid contact with the corn plant.

Spurrier and Others (1957), studying Illinois conditions, stress the value of pre-emergence sprays of 2,4-D as a control for weeds in corn. "This treatment should not be used on light or sandy soils." Application is made before the weeds and grasses emerge so as to prevent them from choking the corn before it gets started. Such spray is more effective when applied under proper moisture condition for favorable growth. The dosage should not be more than 2 pounds of 2,4-D acid per acre. It may be applied any time after seeding until the corn comes through the ground, but not after the leaves unfold. The ester type alone is suggested for pre-emergence sprays.

For grassy annual weeds (foxtail and cheat), Randox is recommended as a pre-emergence spray at the broadcast rate of 4 pounds of acid equivalent (4 quarts) in at least 20 gallons of water. For both grasses and broad-leaved weeds, use 3 pounds of Randox acid and 1 pound of the ester form of 2,4-D in a similar amount of water. The Randox formula may be sprayed directly over the moist planted row in 12-inch bands, using 5 gallons of water per acre. Avoid early cultivation of corn following pre-emergence treatment. Do not apply Randox on sandy soils. A dinitro (dinitro-o-sec. butyl phenol) weed killer may also be used as a pre-emergence spray at a dosage of 8 to 10 pounds of active ingredient per acre, applied before the corn comes through the ground.

As a post-emergence spray for corn, sprays of 2,4-D are effective only against broad-leaved weeds. Spurrier and Others (1957) suggest these only if normal cultivation will not control weeds. If 2,4-D is applied, there will be least danger if the nozzles are set close to the ground so as to apply the spray to the soil and the base of the plant. It should not be applied after the tassels start to form. Stalk brittleness may result from 2,4-D applications made following high daytime temperatures (85° to 90°F); this will result in stalk breakage in high winds. Dosages for corn up to 4 feet high are 0.25 pound of the ester form or 0.5 pound of the amine form per acre. Higher rates may be used as the corn grows taller if the nozzles are further extended, and the spray kept off the plant as much as possible.

SORGHUM (GRAIN); SORGO (SWEET SORGHUM)

The insect pests of sorghum are much the same as for corn, but vary in the degree of injury which they cause. Some of the more injurious forms are the chinch bug, corn earworm, and the corn leaf aphid. Insects considered less injurious to the sorghums are the southwestern corn borer, the European corn borer, and grasshoppers. The use of resistant forms has been the most common method of reducing losses from insect attack. The Atlas variety of sorgo is recognized for its resistance to chinch bugs, as are also the kafir varieties Blackhull and Western Blackhull. Honey sorgo is a new variety used for sirup and forage (Packard and Martin, 1952).

The corn earworm has been found by Burkhardt (1957) to be a major pest of grain sorghum in Kansas. Infestation in some fields ran as high as 100 per cent, with some heads harboring sixteen larvae. This causes a reduction in germination and a loss of weight. Phosdrin at dosage ranges of 0.375 to 0.5 pound per acre gave the quickest and highest degree of control. DDT at concentrations of 1.5 to 2.5 pounds per acre gave good control, but left an objectionable residue, except for grain being used for seed. A boom-type ground-sprayer gave the best results.

The sugarcane borer (*Diatraea saccharalis*) attacks sorghum in the Gulf States similarly to the way the European borer attacks field corn in the North. Full-strength cryolite has been used for a number of years as a control. Weekly applications are made while the first-generation borers are hatching from the egg. The second generation is controlled by four airplane applications of cryolite. The use of cryolite has been largely supplanted by similar applications of the plant-extract ryania (Packard, 1952).

A chinch bug flight invasion of sorghum was checked by applications of toxaphene, Thiodan, and dieldrin. Other insecticides tested were less effective. Toxaphene was used at the rate of 3 pounds per acre on July 3 and again on July 15. The control of chinch bugs on July 12 was 86 per cent and, on July 25, 87 per cent. A single application of Thiodan at 0.5 pound per acre on July 15 showed a control of 82.5 per cent on July 25. A single application of dieldrin at 0.25 pound per acre on July 15 showed a control of 88 per cent on July 25. The application was by boom at the lower part of the plants where the bugs congregated, with a dosage of 4 gallons per acre (Randolph and Newton, 1959).

Diseases of Sorghum.

Sorghum and Sudan grass are subject to a number of fungus leaf diseases. They include rough spot, anthracnose, leaf blight, zonate leaf spot, gray leaf spot, target spot, sooty stripe, and rust. These are controlled largely by the use of resistant varieties (Leukel and Martin, 1953).

Sorghum smuts are of three different types, corresponding to those found on sweet sorghum, grain sorghum, and Sudan grass.

Covered kernel smut, caused by the fungus *Sphacelotheca sorghi,* shows no stunting effect, and is seen only with the appearance of the head. The smut galls are at first covered with a gray or brown membrane. When this breaks, the mass of black spores are seen. During threshing, the smut galls are broken open and the spores attach themselves to sound seed. The spores germinate with the seed at planting time and grow inside the plant.

Loose kernel smut is caused by the fungus *S. cruenta.* This disease is less common, being found principally in the southern Great Plains. All groups of the sorghums are attacked, but some varieties are resistant. Infected plants are stunted and often show several side branches. The spores attach themselves to seeds, germinate the the same temperature, and invade the young seedlings.

Control of the covered kernel and loose kernel smut is the same—either growing resistant varieties or treating the seed with one of various fungicides before planting. Those varieties having persistent glumes should be treated with a volatile fungicide, such as Panogen or Ceresan M (Leukel and Tapke, 1954).

Sorghum-seed treatments for the control of covered kernel smut (*Sphacelotheca sorghi*) were made by Webster and Leukel (1959) on glume-free seed of Combine-60 kafir and on glumed seed of Rancher sorgo. No marked reduction in germination was noted from any of the fungicides used. Percentage of infection in the untreated area averaged 54.4 on the Combine-60 kafir. Dosage for the nonmercurials was 2 ounces per bushel of seed, while that for the mercurials was 0.75 ounce. "Phygon, Spergon and five mercurials eliminated smut infection completely. The other treatments with one exception reduced infection to less than 3 per cent. Vancide, a nonmercurial liquid, allowed 11.9 per cent infection."

Rancher sorgo seed was treated in the same way, and with the same dosages. Percentage of infection in the untreated area averaged 37. Phygon, Spergon, and the seven mercurials eliminated the smut infection. Three other nonmercurials (Arasan 15, Arasan S.F.M., and copper carbonate) reduced infection to 6 per cent. The percentage of infection among the other compounds ranged from 9 to 40.

The fungicides tested included Arasan, Orthocide, Panoram, Phygon, Spergon, Arasan S.F.M., Delsan, Vancide, copper carbonate, Ortho Seed Guard, Panoram D-31, Agrox, Ceresan M, Puraseed, Panogen, Chipcote, Setrete, and Ceresan 100 (Webster and Leukel, 1959).

Head smut is caused by the fungus *S. reiliana*. It is not commonly found in the United States, and has caused but little loss. The entire head is affected. When the head is broken open, the smut spores are scattered by the wind and rain. Control is through sanitation and seed treatment with the organic mercurial seed fungicides (Leukel and Tapke, 1954).

Sorghum grassy weeds may be controlled by a broadcast of Randox as a pre-emergence spray at the rate of 4 pounds of acid equivalent (4 quarts) in 20 or more gallons of water per acre. Instead of being broadcast, the dilute spray may be placed in a 10-inch band over the planted row, using 5 gallons of the 20 per acre solution. The same directions apply as for treating corn. Do not use Randox on sandy soil. The operator should wear goggles and gloves for protection (Spurrier and Others, 1957).

The use of 2,4-D in sorghum, if necessary, should be only as an emergency measure. It may be applied as a post-emergence spray at not over 0.25 of a pound of the ester form, or 0.5 pound of the amine form per acre. Sorghum tolerance for 2,4-D is greatest between the 4- to 12-inch stage of growth (Spurrier and Others, 1957).

SMALL GRAINS: WHEAT, OATS, BARLEY

Insects Attacking Small Grains

Greenbugs (*Toxoptera graminum*) are one of the most serious enemies of wheat, especially in the wheat belt of Kansas, Oklahoma, and Texas. To a less extent, it is injurious to oats and barley. The insect oversummers on a number of summer and fall varieties of grass (Dahms and Others, 1954). It emerges in the spring and attacks the growing grain crops, feeding on these until near maturity. The sap is sucked, and an injurious salivary fluid that stunts the plant is injected. Young plants are killed with even a light infestation. Larger plants succumb to heavy attacks and are either killed or fail to tiller (put forth shoots). Damage to the crops is similar whether the attack comes in February, March, or April (Dahms and Woods, 1957).

Increases in the greenbug population were found to occur where there was a high nitrogen content of the soil and increased plant vigor. Wheat following alfalfa was more tolerant of greenbugs, as shown by larger populations of the latter, than wheat growing in soil taken from wheat land

(Daniels and Porter, 1956). This was confirmed by tests with fertilizers. "Although greenbug populations per row-foot were highest where the most nitrogen was applied, there were less greenbugs per gram of foliage on the same treatment." Less greenbug damage and fewer greenbugs per gram of plant are associated with plant size and vigor (Daniels, 1957).

Resistance to the greenbug has been studied at length at the Kansas Experiment Station, but as yet nothing much more promising than the commonly known Pawnee variety has been developed (Painter and Peters, 1956).

Chemical control of the greenbug was unsatisfactory until the development of parathion for field use. This practice was quickly established and, in 1950, an estimated 650,000 to 1,100,000 acres were sprayed in Oklahoma alone. The emulsion formulation was commonly used, with dosages ranging from 0.2 to 0.3 pound of actual parathion per acre (Ashdown and Others, 1952). Dahms and Others (1957) conducted experiments which showed Metacide to be the most satisfactory control for the greenbug, with favorable results also from demeton and parathion. A tolerance of 8 ppm has been established for malathion as a preharvest and postharvest application on barley, oats, and wheat.

A native parasite, *Aphidius testaceipes*, is efficient in controlling the aphid in late spring and summer, but usually only after severe damage has been caused (Clausen, 1956).

The injury caused by the feeding of the apple grain aphid (*Rhopalosiphum fitchii*) was compared by Kantack and Dahms (1957) with that resulting from the greenbug. Injury symptoms resulted more quickly, susceptibility to freezing was greater, and tillering was checked to a greater degree in the plants infested with the greenbug.

The eriophyid mite, *Aceria tulipae*, is stated by Kantack and Knutson (1958) to be a serious pest of wheat because it is the vector (carrier) of wheat-struck mosaic virus. Spray applications in the spring of various insecticides did not give satisfactory control. Seed treatment with systemic toxicants at dosages not above 0.125 pound per bushel in various inert carriers gave control ranging from 75 to 97 per cent. The best results were obtained with American Cyanimid 12008 and 12009.

Hessian Fly (*Phytophaga destructor*). Protection against attacks by this insect is obtained largely through the development of resistant varieties. Nonresistant varieties are planted at a late date to minimize the danger of infestation. The wheat variety, Pawnee, was released to the Nebraska farmers in 1942, and to Kansas and Oklahoma farmers in 1943, as being partially resistant to Hessian fly. This degree of resistance, coupled with the rather low humidity of central Kansas, favored by a number of dry years, resulted in a decided reduction in the Hessian-fly population. In a few years, this variety became the leading wheat. The strain has good marketing qualities and is resistant to certain of the diseases attacking wheat. Other varieties are being developed for the more humid conditions of eastern Kansas. The soft, white wheat varieties, Big Club 43 and Poso 44, have been developed as Hessian-fly resistant for the use in the Montezuma Hills district of California (Painter, 1954; Packard and Martin, 1952). Protection by the use of resistant varieties is a continuous struggle because differences in susceptibility vary in different parts of the country, and new races of the Hessian fly occur (Gallun, 1955).

Diseases of Wheat

Smut. Wheat in this country is subject to attack by three common smuts: bunt, or stinking smut, caused by the fungi *Tilletia caries* and *T. foetida*; loose smut, caused by the fungus *Ustilago tritici*; and flag smut, caused by the fungus *Urocystis tritici*.

Losses from stinking smut include both reduction in yield and degrading because of the odor. Infected wheat heads containd smutted kernels or smut balls instead of the grain. In threshing, the smut balls are broken, and the spores cover other grains or are blown to the field. The latter, however, remain infective only in the Pacific Northwest, where the soil remains dry until seeding time in the fall. The spores attached to the seed-grain germinate under conditions similar to those required in the case of seed-wheat.

Smut control depends upon (1) the use of smut-free seed, or at least seed that has been carefully cleaned; (2) the choice and use of varieties that are known to give a high degree of resistance for the particular district; and (3) seed treatment with a satisfactory type of organic seed fungicide (Leukel and Tapke, 1954).

Three types of seed fungicides are commonly used in treating wheat seed as a preventive of bunt—mercury derivatives, hexachlorobenzene derivatives, and pentachloronitrobenzene. All materials tested gave good control of seed-borne smut, but only HCB and PCNB formulations controlled the soil-borne smut. The latter two gave simultaneous control of both types (Purdy, 1956a). Two compounds alone inhibited spore germination of common bunt (*Tilletia caries*) by vapor action, Panogen 15 and Anticarie. The mercury compounds, Ceresan and Agrox, were ineffective in this test. Panogen 15, alone, controlled bunt by vapor action on dry seed (Purdy and Holton, 1956).

In a study of the effect of seed fungicides on germinating wheat seed, Hsi (1956) states that both stand reduction and seedling injury should be included. It was found in some cases, that seedling injury gave a more critical measure of phytotoxicity than did stand reduction. The findings corroborate other findings to the effect that mercury injury to wheat seed is influenced by difference in varieties, type and dosage of fungicide, and duration of storage after treatment.

Rust. "Wheat is subject to stem rust, *Puccinia graminis tritici*, leaf rust, *P. rubigovera*, and stripe rust, *P. glumarum*." The latter form however, is of minor importance. Each species is made up of many different races which may attack certain varieties of a grain crop but not others. Both stem and leaf rust have caused serious losses of wheat and still are quite injurious—especially in favorable climatic conditions—despite the development of resistant types of grain (Martin and Salmon, 1953).

Wheat stem rust develops in the form of pustules on stem and leaves; when these open, the wind carries the spores to other plants. During favorable weather, spores develop within a week; hence, spread of the disease may be extremely rapid. Many races of stem rust have been discovered, but only a few are important. These races vary in their ability to attack certain varieties of wheat. The susceptibility of a wheat variety depends upon the presence of a race or races of rust that are capable of attacking the variety. This condition may change from year to year. In the southern states, the rust lives on volunteer grain and grasses through the summer and infects fall-sown grain. Spores are also blown down from the grain fields in the North, and aid in carrying the infection through the winter or on the fall-sown grain. Under favorable weather conditions, the rust developing on grain in the southern states may be blown northward, infecting crops in Oklahoma and Kansas (Martin and Salmon, 1953).

As mentioned earlier, another form of rust infection on wheat is from the alternate host, the common barberry (*Berberis vulgaris*), an introduction from Europe, and certain native species of barberries. Rust infection may begin, adjoining such contaminated bushes, before that drifting in from southern states.

The control of rust depends very largely upon the development of resistant varieties and the elimination of barberry bushes wherever found. Airplane applications of sulfur have at times been beneficial, but since disease outbreaks are largely dependent upon weather conditions, it is seldom practical to attempt chemical control (Martin and Salmon, 1953).*

* The failure of rust-resistant commercial varieties of cereals to exhibit satsfactory protection against attacks of leaf and stem rust of wheat and other grains, has led to the study of chemical protection. The results are given in a series of four papers. (1) A series of chemical compounds have been studied by Keil and Others (1958a) as control agents of leaf rust of rye, *Puccinia rubigo vera* (DC) Wint. f. sp. *secalis* (Ericks.) Carleton. Many compounds were found with protective properties, while other acted as eradicants. (2) Peturson and Others (1958) show by field trials that stem rust of wheat, *Puccinia graminia* Pers var. *tritici* Ericks & E. Henn, and leaf rust of wheat *Puccinia rubigo-vera* (DC) Wint. f. sp. *tritici* (Ericks) Carleton were satisfactorily controlled by four nickel salt amine complexes under field conditions. (3) Keil and Others (1959b) show the effect of various nickel salts alone and in combination with zineb (Dithane

Scab. Scab or *Fusarium* head blight of wheat and other grains and grasses is a serious disease only in the more humid parts of the country. The fungus penetrates into the kernel and breaks down the starch, protein, and fats into other products, some of which may be harmful. Scabbed wheat should not be used for human food or fed to hogs. Seed treatment of clean grain with organic mercurial fungicides is recommended (Dickson, 1953).

Diseases of Oats

Covered smut of oats, caused by the fungus *Ustilago kolleri*, and loose smut of oats, caused by the fungus *U. avenae*, are largely controlled by growing resistant varieties. These diseases and the seedling blight of oats, caused by the fungus *Helminthosporium victoriae*, are also controlled by treatment with the volatile forms of the organic mercurial fungicides, Panogen and Ceresan M. The seed grain is stored for one or more days after treating with Panogen before planting, while for the latter compound, a storage period of one week or more is necessary (Arny and Leben, 1954).

Diseases of Barley

Covered smut of barley, caused by the fungus *Ustilago hordei*, and nigra loose smut caused by *U. nigra*, result in serious losses throughout this country. They are controlled by the use of resistant varieties, crop rotation, and seed treatment. For the latter disease, a number of organic mercurial fungicides are available, including Ceresan M, Panogen, Agrox, Mema, and Merculine. These compounds are very poisonous and should be handled with gloves in an open room away from both food and feeds.

Nuda smut of barley resembles nigra loose smut, but develops differently in the grain, thus requiring different methods of treatment. The germinating spore penetrates into the developing barley seeds and becomes so deeply embedded that surface treatment with chemicals is of no value.

Control is achieved by the use of certified smut-free seed or of seed from resistant varieties. Another control involves treating the seed barley by the hot-water method. Loosely woven burlap sacks are half-filled with grain and soaked for 5 hours in water near a temperature of 70°F. Sacks should be rolled occasionally to avoid caking.

The sacks are removed and drained for about a minute and placed in a

---

Z-78) at 0.5 to 2 pounds per 100 gallons, in the control of rye leaf rust in the greenhouse. (4) Forsyth and Peturson (1959), following co-operative laboratory experiments with the Rohm and Haas Company, show the results of field tests at Winnipeg, Manitoba. It was found by greenhouse tests that both leaf and stem rusts of wheat can be controlled by rather low concentrations of nickel compounds through both eradicative and protective action. The nickel salt amine complex bis [N-(2-hydroxyethyl) dodecylmethylbenzyl amine] nickel (II) chloride (known as RH-1) and nickel chloride hexahydrate are both eradicants, but the latter is more easily removed by simulated rain.

water bath heated to 120°F, being held for a minute. Then they are placed in water heated to *exactly 126°F for exactly 11 minutes*. This temperature is maintained by adding hot water or steam as needed. The water is stirred to keep the temperature uniform, and the sacks rolled to give uniform penetration.

Following the eleven-minute treatment, the seed grain is placed in cold water to check the action of the heat. The seed may also be raked out into a thin layer to promote rapid cooling. It is then thoroughly dried to be ready for sowing. Some germination injury results from the treatment, so it should be confined only to enough seed for smut-free sowing of the next year's crop (Leukel and Tapke, 1955).

There are a number of other less important diseases of barley, but these can usually be controlled by the use of resistant varieties or seed-treating with organic fungicides.

Weeds of Small Grains

Small grains may be treated with the amine form of 2,4-D just as they begin to tiller—or even when completed—but never after the boot is formed. For this reason, fall- or winter-sown grains are not treated until the following spring, often in April. For annual weeds such as wild mustard and radish, use 0.25 to 0.5 pound of 2,4-D per acre. The smaller amount is for the ester formation; the amine form is prepared as the larger amount. Cocklebur, ragweed, pigweed, smartweed, and pepper grass are susceptible at these dosages. Legumes seeded with grain vary in their susceptibility to 2,4-D. The amine formulation should be used, and the dosage reduced to 0.25 pound per acre (Slife and Others, 1950; Spurrier and Others, 1957). Perennial weeds such as bindweed (wild morning glory) and Canada thistle may be controlled by dosages of 0.5 to 1 pound of the acid type per acre on infested points. This will be somewhat injurious both to legumes and grain.

Weeds of Rice. The use of 2,4-D for weed control has become a common practice and, in some of the older rice-growing districts, it is a necessity for successful rice-growing. The dosage ranges from less than a pound to 1½ pounds per acre in any amount of water convenient for application by aircraft. The checks should be well-filled with water and the plants thoroughly established before spraying. Because of the danger of drift to susceptible crops, a number of states have legal restrictions on the use of 2,4-D or related compounds in the vicinity of cotton, vineyards, or tomatoes. In California, permits from an agricultural officer are required before such compounds can be purchased. The state regulations require, in addition, that nozzle orifices for aircraft shall not be less than 0.125 inch in diameter, and pressure must not be greater than 45 psi for aircraft.

ALFALFA, CLOVER, AND GRASSES

Insects Attacking Alfalfa

Spotted Alfalfa Aphid (*Therioaphis maculata*). This aphid has, within recent years, developed into a serious alfalfa pest in the southwestern states, and is spreading eastward. It is a small, grayish insect with four to six black spots on the back. It is smaller than the green-pea aphid, jumps readily, and gives off heavy amounts of honeydew. It attacks first on the lower part of the plant, feeding on the underside of the leaf and on the stem. The growth of the alfalfa is stunted, and the foliage is covered with honeydew in which a black fungus grows. The hay becomes unpalatable and, with heavy attacks, baling becomes difficult. Seedling plants are quite susceptible to attack, and the stand is weakened or killed. Control consists of chemical treatment, releases of parasites and predators (see Chapter 2), and use of resistant varieties. The spotted alfalfa aphid is principally an enemy of alfalfa, but also attacks burr clover (*Medicago hispida*), sour clover (*Melilotus indica*), black medic (*Medicago lupulina*), and berseem (*Trifolium alexandrium*). Other species of clover are largely free of attack (Reynolds and Anderson, 1955).

Demeton (Systox), a systemic and contact insecticide, gives prolonged control of the spotted aphid lasting over several days, with a minimum of injury to beneficial insects. The dosage used is 2 ounces of the active material per acre. It is formulated as an emulsion concentrate, using a half-pint per acre diluted in a suitable amount of water according to equipment used. Trithion at a dosage of 4 ounces of the active ingredient was more harmful to beneficial insects than demeton, but much less dangerous than parathion a 3 and 4 ounces of active material per acre, and malathion at 9.7 ounces per acre. The latter two compounds and phosdrin gave control for less than a week. The milder action of demeton should reduce any tendency to the development of resistance or the build-up of secondary outbreaks of insects (Stern and Others, 1958; Stern and Reynolds, 1957).

The serious injury which the alfalfa aphid, *Therioaphis maculata*, causes to seedling alfalfa and the difficulties of repeated spray or dusts has led to work with systemic insecticides as a seed treatment. Roth (1959) has shown the value of Di-syston, 0,0-diethyl S-2-(ethylthio) ethyl phosphorodithioate, for such purpose. The difficulty of coating the small alfalfa seed, with its smooth surface, was overcome by applying the insecticide as an emulsion concentrate, mixing thoroughly, and adding pyrophyllite, as necessary, to dry the seed and leave it free from lumps.

Di-syston, at a dosage of 2 pounds of active material per 100 pounds of seed, gave a high degree of protection for up to 52 days, and was superior to lindane, Thimet, Diazinon, and Trithion.

Resistance to injury from the attack of the spotted alfalfa aphid is especially high in the Lahonton variety of alfalfa. This is found both in the seedling and mature plant (Howe, 1957). It was found by Harvey and Hackerott (1956) that alfalfa seedlings resistant to attack by the spotted alfalfa aphid could also be found among susceptible varieties.

Pea Aphid (*Macrosiphum pisi*). This insect attacks all peas, whether grown in the garden, field, or as sweet peas. It also feeds on clover and alfalfa. Control is the same as for the spotted alfalfa aphid.

Alfalfa Weevil (*Hypera postica*). This weevil has been a pest in the western states for many years and is now spreading into the eastern states. It overwinters in the adult stage and, in early spring, begins ovipositing when the young alfalfa plants are about 1 to 2 inches tall. Both the larvae and the adult beetles feed on the leaves and the growing tips. The leaves are skeletonized, then dry and turn a grayish color. Control is by crop management and by the use of insecticides.

Alfalfa that is grown for hay may be protected by harvesting the first crop when most of it is in the bud stage. The crop must be cut close and cleaned and removed from the field promptly. The larvae are deprived of food and shelter and, being exposed to the sun, many of them are killed.

The overwintering adults in the western states may be killed in alfalfa, grown for seed, by application of dieldrin or heptachlor. The dosage is 4 ounces per acre of active ingredient diluted with water to a convenient amount, owing to the equipment used. Heptachlor may also be applied as a dust. If the early spring treatment has been omitted, then an application of methoxychlor, parathion, or other recommended insecticide should be made if the larvae become abundant during the season.

Grasshoppers present in damaging numbers in alfalfa may be controlled in the young stage by an application of aldrin as an emulsion concentrate, at the rate of 2 ounces of the active ingredient per acre. It should not be applied within 10 days of harvesting or pasturing. On seed-alfalfa, aldrin, heptachlor, chlordane, or dieldrin may be used as recommended.

Alfalfa Caterpillar (*Colias philodice eurytheme*). This was at one time a serious pest of alfalfa in the West, but has been checked by insect parasites and predators. (See Chapter 3 on the use of diseases as a control measure.) Methoxychlor is the only insecticide recommended for use in hay crops as a control where natural checks are inadequate.

Meadow SpittleBug (*Philaenus leucophthalmus*). The spittlebug is a pest of alfalfa and clover in the Northeast and North Central States. It feeds on the crowns and folded leaves, sucking out the plant juices. The host plant is stunted and the yield of forage reduced. The young, surrounded by the mass of spittle, are thus protected from enemies. Control is by application in early spring of one of the following insecticides: endrin, 2 ounces, or methoxychlor, 1 pound per acre. There are available as emulsion concentrates, to be diluted with water in convenient amounts according to equipment (Staff, 1959).

Spider Mite. Control of this pest on seed-alfalfa is often a serious problem in the southwestern states. Its feeding causes a heavy shedding of bloom. Under California conditions, applications of sulfur dusts at dosages ranging from 15 to 40 pounds per acre, according to severity of attack, will control the Atlantic mite (*Tetranychus atlanticus*) and depress other mite species. Sulfur may cause petal burn of flowers when applied at high summer temperatures. Lygus bugs, *Lygus* may also be controlled by an application of toxaphene as an emulsion concentrate. The dosage is 3 pounds of the actual material per acre.

Clover Root Borer (*Hylastinus obscurus*). BHC and lindane are successfully used as a control for this insect, but with reports of impairment of flavor to potatoes when grown in the same soil following the use of either material. Gyrisco and others (1959) confirmed the finding of "off-flavor" to potatoes when grown in the same soil the following year after an application of lindane at a dosage of 1 pound per acre. No effect on the flavor of potatoes was noted when grown the third year following the last application. However, red kidney beans, variety California Light Red, when grown under the same conditions, showed no effect in flavor.

Miscellaneous. Under Wisconsin conditions, Medler and Brooks (1957) found that the principal injurious insects of seed alfalfa were grasshoppers, leafhoppers, and plant bugs. Chemical control consisted of mixtures of DDT plus one of several other insecticides, including aldrin, chlordane, dieldrin, and toxaphene. Yields of seed were low, presumably on account of a lack of pollinating insects.

The placement of beehives in relation to red-clover seed production has been studied by Walstrom (1958) in Iowa. It was his finding that the best results in pollinating occurred with the location of the beehives within a 400-foot range. Lower seed production resulted from wider spacing of the hives. This agrees with findings of alfalfa-seed production in California. In the latter area, it is customary to allow two or more hives per acre, to be distributed in crossroads across the field, rather than grouping all the hives at one point.

Insecticides used in alfalfa which show little or no toxicity to the honeybee include Kelthane, Dipterex, Hercules AC-528, Chlorbenside, Methyl chlorobenzilate, and Holcomb C-326 (Anderson and Atkins, 1958). Pea-aphid control experiments in Washington by Johansen and others (1957) showed little or no effect on honeybees due to applications of demeton or of schraden to the alfalfa while in bloom.

Alfalfa and Clover Diseases

Alfalfa is subject to virus-, bacterial-, and fungus-caused diseases which are frequently aggravated by frost injury. Alfalfa dwarf is a virus disease common in California. It is carried from plant to plant by several species of leafhoppers and spittlebugs. Infected plants lose vigor for several months—the stems are short and the leaves darker than normal. Susceptible plants usually die within a few months after infection. The variety California Common has been developed into a new strain known as California Common 49, which is quite resistant to the disease.

A bacterial wilt, caused by *Corynebacterium insidiosum,* is widely distributed in this country, but most serious in the central northern areas having much rain or irrigation and frequent winter injury. The disease does not become serious until the third crop year. Four resistant varieties have been developed. Ranger and Vernal are sufficiently hardy for northern use. The variety Buffalo was developed in Kansas, and Calverdi is a product of the California Agricultural Experiment Station (Jones and Smith, 1953).

The clovers are subject to a great number of diseases caused by fungi, bacteria, and the viruses. The most important of these are the root and crown complex caused by a group of soil-inhabiting fungi. *Sclerotinia* crown and stem rot is caused by *Sclerotinia trifoliorum,* a widely distributed disease in regions having mild winters. It attacks alfalfa and all the commercially grown clovers, in addition to many other clover varieties. The fungus growth spreads from the leaves downward to the stems and roots. Infection remains viable in the soil for many years, and control is difficult. Clean cultivation, deep plowing, and long rotation are helpful (Hanson and Kreitlow, 1953).

Southern anthracnose, caused by the fungus *Colletotrichum trifolii,* is a serious disease of red clover in the southern clover belt. It is most active at moderately high summer temperatures. The disease may cause severe reduction of both hay and seed, and even destroy the stand. A resistant variety, Kenland, is now available (Hanson and Kreitlow, 1953).

Weeds of Alfalfa and Clover

Legumes are very sensitive to 2,4-D and related compounds. The amine form is safer and should be used in preference to the ester formulation. Spurrier and others (1957) state that, under Illinois conditions, 2,4-D or MCP acid may be applied to alfalfa, red, and other varieties of clover in the spring while the crop is still in the early dormant stage, at the rate of 0.125 to 0.25 pound in 5 to 20 gallons of water per acre. This application may also be made immediately after hay harvest. Sweet clover is not to be sprayed with 2,4-D. This treatment will affect broad-leaved weeds only and not grasses.

General contact sprays of dinitros, diesel oil, and specially treated weed oils are used under California conditions as controls for grassy and broad-leaved weeds in established legume stands. The amounts and time of application are varied according to the crop and type of weed.

Seedling Sprays. Small broad-leaved weeds (2 to 4 leaves) may be controlled by the application of 4 to 6 quarts of dinitro selective in 15 to 20 gallons of water (air application) or 60 to 80 gallons of water (ground equipment). Alfalfa seedlings may be injured at air temperatures of 85°F and above (Stanford and others, 1954).

Established Stands. Twenty to 45 gallons of diesel oil, plus 1 quart of general dinitro, in 40 to 70 gallons of water are used for seedling grasses and small broad-leaved weeds. The diesel oil should be that used for fuel rather than that for automotive purposes, the latter being more refined. Yellow-star thistle may be controlled by applications of 2 quarts of dinitro general in 100 gallons of water, between the first and second cuttings. For winter-growing grasses, I.P.C. should be applied from October 15 through November and irrigated in. It may also be applied in late February under California conditions. The dosage used is 3 to 5 pounds of active material in 60 to 100 gallons of water. Excessive water leaches it beyond the root zone, and it becomes ineffective (Stanford and others, 1954).

Permanent Pastures. Many of the broad-leaved weeds in pastures, such as dandelion, burdock, and mullein, may be controlled by applications of 2,4-D acid at 0.5 to 1.5 pounds per acre in 15 to 100 gallons of water. Local agricultural officers should be consulted for exact dosages to be used.

Dandelion may also be killed in lawns of mixed clover and grass by applying a solution of 2,4-D with a small paint brush directly to the plant. Application must be made in full sunshine and preferably under good growing conditions.

COTTON

Insects Attacking Cotton

The wide distribution and succulent nature of cotton has led to attack by a host of insects and diseases. The insecticides used for many years were calcium arsenate and, when needed, nicotine. These have been largely supplanted by organic compounds. The number of applications and the dosage should be held at the lowest point practicable with good pest control. This reduces the danger to beneficial insects and also reduces the possibility of developing resistance to the insecticide.

Boll Weevil (*Anthonomus grandis*). This weevil is one of the most serious pests of the Cotton Belt. It is only due to heavy losses to overwintering adults and to other natural control agencies that it is possible to produce cotton profitably. The injury caused is the result of feeding of the larvae in the squares (unopened flowers) and in the boll. Control methods include the development of varieties resistant to insect attack, introduction and distribution of parasites, sound cultural practices, chemical defoliation, and the use of insecticides. Since it is often customary to apply two or more insecticides as mixtures for the common insects and mites of a district, the use of toxicants will be discussed later (Gaines, 1952).

Bollworm (*Heliothis zea*). The moth hibernates in the soil in the pupal stage, emerging in the spring during a period of a month or more. The first-generation moths oviposit on clover, peas, and young corn. The second generation attacks corn ears, if available; the third and later generation attacks cotton, where that crop is grown. The eggs are laid on the tender tips of the growing cotton plant—squares, bolls and stems. A weekly inspection of the cotton will show the presence of the young worms, which are most easily killed at this stage. The eggs are heavily attacked by predaceous insects, and the larvae by parasites. To avoid injuring the beneficial insects, insecticides should be applied as early in the season as practicable with good control (Ewing, 1952).

Pink Bollworm (*Pectinophora gossypiella*). This insect is found commonly in all the principal cotton-producing countries of the world, according to reports, except Mexico and the United States. In the two latter countries, it has been found occasionally for a number of years, but, by determined efforts, has been limited by quarantine measures to restricted areas. It also occurs in wild cotton in southern Florida but is reduced in number by careful inspection and destroying of wild plants (Curl and White, 1952).

The small brown moths ($\frac{4}{5}$ inch from tip to tip of the wing) develop from the overwintering larvae and begin ovipositing on the squares and young bolls, into which the newly hatched larvae bore. The mature larvae are about a half-inch long and have a pinkish appearance. They complete their growth in 8 to 12 days, cut their way out of the boll, and drop to the ground, where they pupate. Seven or eight generations occur in regions of long growing seasons (Curl and White, 1952).

The preferred food of the larvae is the kernel of the seed. After devouring its contents, the larva cuts its way through the lint to another seed and may eat all the seeds of a lock or cell. Injury to the boll varies with the number of larvae present. In light infestations, the boll may be only partly destroyed and be worth picking—although with damaged lint. In severe infestations, the bolls are shed and drop to the ground. Oil production is reduced by the seed injury (Curl and White, 1952).

Federal quarantine, supplemented by that of the states, regulates the movement of cotton and its products that might harbor and spread infestation. Seed cotton is shipped only to adjoining regulated areas or certain gins. Cotton seed and lint in infested areas is treated under supervision of an inspector in such a way as to kill all pink bollworms. In certain districts, all cotton plants must be destroyed by a definite date and the fields kept free of all seedlings until the normal planting time (Curl and White, 1952).

Chemical Control. DDT, used according to the 1958 recommendations, continues to be the principal insecticide for the boll weevil, bollworm, and pink bollworm. The exceptions involve areas where resistance to DDT is definitely established. For these districts, the insecticides used are certain of the organic phosphates, methyl parathion, malathion, and Guthion, and increasing amounts of calcium arsenate. The phosphates are also recommended for control of fleahoppers, leafworms, aphids, and mites (Gaines, 1958). Toxaphene and sulfur combinations have proven valuable in many instances in the control of the boll weevil and mites. The chemicals favored in the control of the fire ant (*Solenopsis geminata*) are heptachlor and dieldrin.

Cotton insect control in the lower Rio Grande Valley, Texas, showed the highest gain of seed cotton with methyl parathion, 2.5 per cent, plus DDT, 5 per cent, for the season of 1953. The following year the greatest gain was with dieldrin, 2 per cent, plus methyl parathion, 1 per cent, plus DDT, 5 per cent (McGarr, 1957). Insecticide tests (Pfrimmer, 1958) against the boll weevil and the bollworm, showed excellent control at dosages from 0.25 to 0.6 pound of Guthion per acre. Calcium arsenate dust at 13.85 pounds of active material per acre, methyl parathion at 0.5 and 0.67 pound, EPN at 0.5 and 0.8 pound, and malathion at 2.05 and 3.81 pounds were slightly less effective.

Field tests in Texas with Sevin in dosages of 1.5 to 2.5 pounds per acre at 4- to 7-day intervals gave control of the pink bollworm and boll weevil comparable to that obtained with standard insecticides. In the laboratory, it was also found effective against the cabbage looper *(Trichoplusia ni)* and the cotton aphid (*Aphis gossypii*) (Bottger and others, 1958).

Mount and Arant (1957) determined the effects of BHC with high (40 per-cent) and low (15.1 per-cent) gamma isomer content and of lindane upon the cotton aphid. The dusts were made up at 3 per-cent concentration. All formulations of BHC and lindane were highly effective in killing aphids. No significant differences were found between the various dusts.

Experiments in Texas by Cowan and Others (1958) have shown that Sevin dusts of 1.6 to 2 pounds per acre were more effective against the bollworm than sprays of 1.0 and 1.5 pounds, or than toxaphene at 4 pounds plus DDT at 2 pounds applied as a spray. Applications were made at intervals of 5 to 7 days. Thiodan sprays and dusts of 0.7 pound per acre were as effective as the toxaphene-DDT spray for the bollworm. The desert spider mite (*Tetranychus desertorum*) was controlled by parathion, Chipman R-6199 (Tetram), Guthion, and Diazinon at 0.25 pound, and Hercules AC-528 (Delnav) at 0.5 pound, per acre.

Brazzel and Others (1959) found Guthion to be an effective ovicide of the pink bollworm. For the larval stage, Guthion and DDT were superior to the other insecticides tested.

Beneficial Insects and the Effect of Insecticides. The effect of certain insecticides upon the beneficial insects and spiders found upon the cotton plant has been determined by Gaines (1954). The formulas used were in the following concentrations: (1) dieldrin 1.5, plus DDT 5, plus sulfur 40 per cent; (2) toxaphene 20, plus sulfur 40 per cent; (3) BHC (gamma 3 per cent) plus DDT 5, plus sulfur 40 per cent; (4) BHC (gamma 3 per cent), plus DDT 5, plus sulfur 40 per cent, and calcium arsenate. Amounts applied per acre ranged from 8 to 15 pounds. All applications were made by airplane during the early morning. One treatment was made July 7 followed by a second on July 28. Ten applications 4 or 5 days apart were required from July 28 to September 3. All injurious pests were controlled with each treatment.

The beneficial-insect population was greatly reduced by the application on July 7, but built-up by that of July 28. "After the second to fourth application had been made in the regular boll weevil poisoning program, beneficial insects and spider populations were practically eliminated." (Gaines, 1954) Similar results were found by Glick and Others (1954) in that dust applications of insecticides through June and up to July 20 were much safer for beneficial insects than those applied through August. Toxaphene-sulfur dust gave the lowest population of pest insects and the highest population of beneficial insects.

Systemic Insecticides. It was found by Parencia and Others (1957) that a number of systemic compounds would protect seedling cotton against thrips (*Frankiniella*), the cotton aphid (up to 4 and 5 weeks), and to a less extent the serpentine leaf miner (*Liromyza pusilla*) and the cotton flea hopper *(Psallus seriatus)*. The compound Thimet was found to give the best results in control, without interference to germination. Reynolds and Others, (1957) confirmed Parencia's findings in treating various seeds with Thimet and Bayer 19639 as a protection against several types of insects. Both materials were also found helpful in protection against spider mites.

Hopkins and Others (1959) were able to make significant reductions in the population of cotton aphids by side applications of 10, 20, and 30 pounds of Thimet and Bayer 19639. The effect lasted 15 months. Significant reductions in the aphid populations also resulted for one growing season from seed or furrow treatment with 1 to 3 pounds per acre at planting time. This application also aided in the control of greenbugs on the following oat crop.

Resistant Cotton Insects. The reported development of resistance by various insects to the chlorinated hydrocarbons, toxaphene, and to certain organic phosphate compounds has become a matter of general concern. As yet, the areas showing resistance are largely limited in size, except certain sections in Louisiana where the boll weevil is apparently increasingly difficult to control. Gaines (1957) recommends a number of cultural operations as contributing to weevil control. These include the destruction of cotton plants as early as possible before the first killing frost, early planting, and use of recommended varieties together with fertilization. Following such practices in the control of the boll weevil will reduce the trend to developing resistant insects and, at the same time, permit the parasites and predators to attack other cotton pests.

The susceptibility of the boll weevil to toxaphene has been shown by Mistric and others, (1958) to be related to previous field usage of chlorinated hydrocarbon insecticides for weevil control. "Weevils from fields subjected to intensive insecticidal treatment were much less susceptible than those from nearby fields where little insecticide had been used." Guthion, malathion, methyl parathion, and calcium arsenate were superior to toxaphene in insect control and cotton yield in a field where the weevil population had previously experienced toxaphene.

The effect of mixtures of insecticides on boll weevils of varying susceptibility to the individual insecticides, has been studied in the laboratory by Roussel and others (1959). Insecticide mixtures gave additive effect only to weevils susceptible to chlorinated hydrocarbon insecticides. Weevils resistant to these insecticides, however, showed synergistic action to the mixture of toxaphene and DDT. The mixtures of endrin and DDT and lindane and DDT showed additive effects only.

Diseases of Cotton

An estimate of the 1957 reduction in yield of cotton caused by disease has been compiled by Smith and Others (1958). The summary was prepared by co-operators in the cotton-growing states for the Cotton Disease Council. The report showed a loss of 12 per cent. The total loss in bales was 1,586,276. Diseases listed included *Fusarium* wilt, *Verticillium* wilt, bacterial blight, root rot, seedling diseases, *Ascochyta* blight, boll rots, and Root Knot.

Fusarium wilt is caused by the fungi *Fusarium oxysporum* and *F. vasinfectum*. The disease is associated with the meadow or root-rot nematode (*Pratylenchus pratensis*), the root-knot nematode (genus *Meloidogyne*), and other forms of nematodes. The fungus enters at the feeding points of the nematodes and spreads throughout the woody portions of the plant, clogging the water-carrying vascular ducts. Losses caused by the combined attack of nematodes and wilt disease have ranged as high as 75 to 90 per cent of the crop, before the development of resistant varieties. The wilt fungus is carried inside the cotton seed and, once introduced, is spread by spores to the entire field. The fungus lives in the soil indefinitely once it is introduced, and no known economic method of eradication is available. Control measures consist of the use of resistant varieties adapted to the particular locality and the use of balanced fertilizers. The soil fumigants ethylene dibromide and D-D, (the trade name of dichloropropane and dichloropropene) are the best protectants against nematodes (Smith, 1953).

Verticilluim wilt is caused by a soil-borne fungus. It is an important cotton disease in the lower Mississippi Valley and the Southwest. Many of the cotton varieties of upland, Egyptian, Pima, sea island, plus some South American varieties, have a high degree of resistance. Varieties that show the highest degree of resistance for the particular district should be chosen for planting (Presley, 1953).

Cotton root rot, as caused by the fungus *(Phymatotrichum omnivorum)*, attacks the roots of a great variety of trees, vegetables, and grasses. Distribution of the disease is principally by growth of the mycelial strands of the fungus from root to root of the host plants, or by free growth through the soil. Nonsusceptible crops grown in the infected fields for from 2 to 4 years afford considerable protection. Tap-rooted weeds should be avoided during the rotation. The incorporation of large amounts of organic material, either manures or legume cover crops, is helpful in reducing loss (Blank, 1953).

Anthracnose boll rot is associated with with the common seedling blight and damping-off diseases in the humid areas of the cotton-growing states. The distribution of the fungus on cotton seedlings may be similar to the area affected with anthracnose boll rot. Seed is contaminated at the cotton gin by contact with leaves and other trash, and when such seed is planted, the spores attack the young seedlings. Seed treatment with Ceresan and related forms and Dow 9-B protects the seedlings. Dosages range from 1½ ounces to a bushel of fuzzy seed to 3 ounces for 100 pounds of re-ginned seed (Neal, 1953).

Bacterial blight is caused by the bacterium *Xanthomonas malvacearum*. It attacks all above-ground parts of the cotton plant. It may be found in all cotton growing areas, but is especially severe in the southwestern parts of the United States. It causes angular water-soaked areas on the leaves and, on the balls, water-soaked lesions that are dark-colored when dry. Seedlings of upland varieties are blighted, and the mature plants are defoliated and the bolls rotted. The bacteria overwinter on the surface of the seed, within the seed coat, and on the diseased stalks and boll. Rain and wind spread the bacteria from plant to plant, but dry, hot weather checks the disease (Blank, 1953).

Control measures include chemical treatment of the seed with disinfectants and acid-delinting of the seed. Rotation of crops is recommended, with plowing under of infected material and irrigating if necessary to promote decomposition. The use of resistant varieties is consdered the most practical way of protection (Blank, 1953).

Weeds of Cotton

The cotton plant is extremely sensitive to the hormone type of weedkiller, such as 2,4-D andMCP. Even slight drift from aircraft applications of such compounds has been known to injure cotton miles away from the treated field. Legal restrictions on the use of this type of herbicide are now established in many of the cotton-growing districts. Flame-throwers are used extensively against some types of weeds. A number of pre-emergence types of weedkiller are being developed and offer much promise for this type of control.

TOBACCO

Insects Attacking Tobacco

Aphids. These—especially the green peach aphid—infest tobacco both in the plant bed and in the field. Parathion, as a 1 per-cent dust, is used for both places. The dosage for the plant bed is 1 pound per 100 square yards. This should not be applied within 5 days of transplanting. The field dosage is 8 to 30 pounds per acre, owing to the size of the plant, or corresponding amounts of emulsion concentrate. Cutting should not begin within 15 days of the last application. Malathion may be substituted for parathion, using a 4 per-cent dust or emulsion concentrate. The application of malathion should not be made within 3 days of transplanting (Staff, 1959).

Budworm (*Heliothis virescens and H. zea*). The larvae of these two moths attacks the growing tips of the tobacco plant and, being hidden beneath the unfolding leaves, are difficult to reach. Two methods of applying insecticides to the top of the plant are used: (1) by hand equipment for dusting or spraying, or (2) by power sprayers making frequent treatments as preventive measures. Another method is the use of baits made of lead arsenate or of DDT combined with corn meal, at the rate of 1 to 75 pounds. The bait is applied as a pinch to the growing tip. Good results have also been obtained with endrin dust of 1 or 2 per-cent concentration or DDT dust, 10 per-cent, applied with a plunger duster to the tip of the plant. Hand sprays of similar concentration may also be used (Guthrie and Others 1957).

Hornworm (*Protoparce sexta*). Control for this insect is similar to that for budworms. In addition, TDE is used as a 10 per-cent dust. (For predators, see page 29).

Cutworms (*Feltia, Euxoa messoria, Amathas c-nigrum*). These are larvae of heavy-bodied, dull-colored moths. They usually hide in the soil during the day and feed at night. The stem of the young plant is cut, and the leaves near the ground fed upon. Natural control of severe weather, parasites, predators, and birds hold them in check; otherwise, they would be much more injurious.

Control in the plant bed amounts to application of a dust of 10 per-cent DDT or 1 to 2 per-cent endrin at the rate of 1 pound per hundred square yards. These materials may also be applied as sprays, diluted as directed, using 3 to 5 gallons for the same area.

Field applications require applications of DDT or endrin dusts at the same concentration at the rate of 10 to 15 pounds per acre.

Baits for use in the plant bed or field are prepared as follows:

Wheat bran, 50 pounds
Aldrin, 25 per-cent wettable powder, 4 ounces
Water to moisten

Chlordane, 1 pound of 50 per-cent wettable powder; or dieldrin, 4 ounces of 25 per-cent wettable powder; or heptachlor, 8 ounces of 25 per-cent wettable powder may be substituted for the aldrin. The water is added very slowly and mixed carefully. The bait is spread in the late afternoon, at the rate of 4 pounds (dry weight) per hundred square yards. Gloves made of natural rubber are used in mixing and distributing the bait (Chamberlin and Allen, 1957).

Flea Beetles. These are foliage-feeders, both in the plant bed and in the field. A 5 or 10 per-cent dust of DDT is used in the plant bed, at the rate of 0.75 to 1.5 pounds per hundred square yards. The material may also be applied as a spray, using 2 pounds of a 50 per-cent emulsion concentrate per hundred gallons and and applying 3 to 6 gallons per hundred square yards. In the field a 5 to 10 per-cent dust of DDT, or one of endrin at 1 to 2 per-cent, is used at the rate of 6 to 25 pounds per acre (Staff, "Handbook No. 120," Washington, D.C., U.S. Dept. Agr., 1959).

Diseases of Tobacco

Wildfire, a leaf-spot disease, is caused by a bacterium, *Pseudomonas tabaci.* A similar type of bacterial disease is known as *blackfire.* Serious losses occur both in the seed bed and the field. Control in the former is usually helpful in protecting the field crop. The standard method of treatment in the seedbed has been a drench of Bordeaux (3 pounds of copper sulfate and 4 pounds of hydrated lime to 50 gallons of water), applied with a sprinkling can at the rate of 25 gallons per hundred square yards. A stronger formula is that of 4 to 6 to 50, applied as a spray. Copper A or Tennessee Tribasic (fixed or basic commercial forms) may be substituted for the Bordeaux. Treatment should begin as soon as the plants are out of the ground and repeated every week or ten days as necessary (Clayton, 1953).

Applications of streptomycin spray, at a concentration of 200 ppm, and dusts at 1,000 to 4,000 ppm, gave better control of wildfire than did Bordeaux or terramycin spray. Three or four applications are made, at 7-day intervals, of 5 and 10 gallons per hundred square yards (Shaw and Thorne, 1956).

Black-shank disease is caused by the fungus *Phytophthora parasitica,* var. *nicotianae.* It is spread by moving water, soil, and plants. Drainage ponds may be contaminated by the spores and should not be used for setting out plants. The infection may also be carried by cultivating tools. Once the disease is established, it may remain alive for years. In the early stage of infection, the main roots are rotted and black. As the disease progresses, all the roots are killed, and the base of the stalk dies. The use of resistant varieties and crop rotation are the principal defenses (Clayton, 1953).

Blue mold is caused by a fungus, *Peronospora tabacina.* This is primarily a plant-bed disease. The spores live over in the soil; hence, infection usually starts in the old beds. The spores are produced abundantly and carried by the wind for many miles. The severity of the attack is governed by weather conditions, and for that reason, the need of chemical treatment is uncertain. Once the disease is established under favorable conditions, however, it is difficult to check. Affected plants may be delayed in growth from 2 to 4 weeks and then recover, thus giving opportunity for transplanting and perhaps normal growth. The recommended dosages for control are Dithane Z-78 and Zineb at 3 pounds per hundred gallons of spray (Clayton, 1953).

Weeds of Tobacco

The tobacco plant, like cotton, is sensitive to the action of the hormone compounds, such as 2,4-D and MCP. Flame-weeders are being used in the districts where the recently discovered witchweed (*Striga lutea*) is present. Fumigation with methyl bromide or chloropicrin in the seedbed will protect against weeds and insects.

REFERENCES

Anderson, Jr., L. D., and Atkins, Jr., E. L., *J. Econ. Entom.,* **51,** 103 (1958).
Apple, J. W., *ibid.,* **50,** 28 (1957).
Arbuthnot, K. D., *ibid.,* **51,** 562 (1958).
Arny, D. C., and Leben, C., *Phytopathology,* **44,** 380 (1954).
Ashdown, D., and Others, *J. Econ. Entom.,* **45,** 82 (1952).
Blake, Jr., G. H., and Others, *ibid.,* **52,** 1 (1959).
Blanchard, R. A., and Others, *U. S. Dept. Agr. Farmer's Bull.,* **1139,** (1953).
Blank, L. M., "1953 Yearbook," Washington, D. C., U.S. Dept. Agr., 1953.
Bottger, G. T., and Others, *J. Econ. Entom.,* **51,** 236 (1958).
Bradley, L. M., "1952 Yearbook," Washington, D.C., U.S. Dept. Agr., 1952.
Brazzel, J. R., and Gaines, J. C., *J. Econ. Entom.,* **52,** 301 (1959).
Burkhardt, C. C., *J. Econ Entom.,* **50,** 539 (1957).
Chamberlin, F. S., and Others, *U.S. Dept. Agr. Leaflet,* **417** (1957).
Clausen, C. P., *U.S. Dept. Agr. Technical Bull.,* **1139** (1956).
Clayton, E. E., "1953 Yearbook," Washington, D. C., U.S. Dept. Agr., 1953.
Cowan, C. B., and Others, *J. Econ. Entom.,* **51,** 645 (1958).
Cox, H. C., and Others, *J. Econ. Entom.,* **49,** 113 (1956).
———, *ibid.,* **50,** 52 (1957).
———, *ibid.,* **51,** 133 (1958).
Curl, L. F., and Others, "1952 Yearbook," Washington, D.C., U.S. Dept. Agr., 1952.
Dahms, R. G., and Others, *J. Econ. Entom.,* **47,** 1151 (1954).
———, *ibid.,* **50,** 443 (1957).
Daniels, N. E., and Others, *ibid.,* **49,** 600 (1956).
———, *ibid.,* **50,** 793 (1957).
Dickson, J. G., "1953 Yearbook," Washington, D.C., U.S. Dept. Agr., 1953.
Eden, W. G., *J. Econ. Entom.,* **51,** 822 (1958).
Ewing, K. P., "1952 Yearbook," Washington, D.C., U.S. Dept. Agr., 1952.
Floyd, E. H., and Powell, J. D., *J. Econ. Entom.,* **51,** 23 (1958).
Forsyth, F. R., and Peturson, *Phytopathology,* **49,** 1 (1959).
Gaines, R. C., "1952 Yearbook," Washington, D.C., U.S. Dept. Agr., 1952.
———, *J. Econ. Entom.,* **47,** 543 (1954).
———, *Agr. Chem.,* 12 (4), **41** (1957).
———, *ibid.,* 13 (1), **30** (1958).
Gallun, R. L., *J. Econ. Entom.,* **48,** 608 (1955).
Gannon, N., and Decker, G. C., *ibid.,* **48,** 242 (1955).
Gaskin, T. A., and Others, *U.S. Dept. Agr. Plant Disease Reporter* **42,** 374 (1958).
Glick, P. A., and Others, *J. Econ. Entom.,* **47,** 681 (1954).
Gould, C. J., and Wilson, M. C., *ibid.,* **50,** 510 (1957).
Guthrie, F. E., and Others, *ibid.,* **50,** 328 (1957).
Gyrisco, G. C., and Others, *ibid.,* **52,** 473 (1959).
Hanson, E. W., and Kreitlow, K. W., "1953 Yearbook," Washington, D.C., U.S. Dept. Agr., 1953.
Harvey, T. L., and Hackerott, H. L., *J. Econ. Entom.,* **49,** 289 (1956).
Hein, M. A., *U.S. Dept. Agr. Farmer's Bull.,* **1126** (1957).

Hopkins, A. R., *J. Econ. Entom.*, **52,** 304 (1959).
Howe, W. L., *J. Econ. Entom.*, **50,** 320 (1957).
Howitt, J. *ibid.*, **51,** 883 (1958).
Hsi, C. H., *U.S. Dept. Agr. Plant Disease Reporter,* **40,** 1065 (1956).
Johansen, C. A., *J. Econ. Entom.*, **50, 721** (1957).
Jones, F. R., and Smith, O. F., "1953 Yearbook," Washington, D.C., U.S. Dept. Agr., 1953.
Kantack, E. J., and Dahms, R. G., *J. Econ. Entom.*, **50,** 166 (1957).
Kantack, E. J., and Knuston, H., *ibid.*, **51,** 68 (1958).
Keil, H. L., and Others, *Phytopathology*, **48,** 652 (1958a); **48,** 690 (1958b).
Koehler, C. S., and Others, *ibid.*, **50,** 346 (1957).
Leukel, R. W., and Martin, J. H., "1953 Yearbook," Washington, D.C., U.S. Dept. Agr., 1953.
Leukel, R. W., and Tapke, V. F., *ibid.*
———, *U.S. Dept. Agr. Farmer's Bull.,* **2069** (1954).
———, *ibid.,* **2089** (1955).
Lindquist, D. A., and Others, *J. Econ. Entom.*, **52,** 102 (1959).
Luckmann, W. H., and Others, *Ill. Agr. Exp. Sta. Circular,* **773** (1957).
MacGillivray, J. A., and Minges, P. A., *Calif. Agr. Exp. Sta. Circular,* **457** (1956).
Martin, J. H., and Others, "1953 Yearbook," Washington, D.C., U.S. Dept. Agr., 1953.
McGarr, R. L., *J. Econ. Entom.*, **50,** 632 (1957).
McGraw, J. R., *Phytopathology,* **42,** 343, (1952).
Medler, J. T., and Brooks, *J. Econ. Entom.*, **50,** 336 (1957).
Mistric, W. J. and Others, *ibid.*, **51,** 719 (1958).
Morgan, Jr., O. D., *U.S. Dept. Agr. Plant Disease Reporter,* **40,** 908 (1956).
Mount, R. H., and Arant, F. S., *J. Econ. Entom.*, **50,** 251 (1957).
Neal, D. C., "1953 Yearbook," Washington D.C., U.S. Dept. Agr., 1953.
Packard, C. M., "1952 Yearbook," Washington, D.C., U.S. Dept. Agr., 1952.
———, and Martin, J. H., *ibid.*
Painter, R. H., *J. Econ. Entom.*, **47,** 1036 (1954).
———, and Peters, D. C., *ibid,* **49,** 546 (1956).
Parencia, C. R., and Others, *ibid.*, **50,** 31 (1957).
Peturson, B., and Others, *Phytopathology,* **48,** 655 (1958).
Pfrimmer, T. R., *J. Econ. Entom.*, **51,** 41 (1958).
Poos, F. W., *U.S. Dept. Agr. Leaflet,* **341** (1955).
Presley, J. T., "1953 Yearbook," Washington, D.C., U.S. Dept. Agr., 1953.
Purdy, I. H., *U.S. Dept. Agr. Plant Disease Reporter,* **40,** 996 (1956a).
———, and Holton, C. S., *Phytopathology,* **46,** 385 (1956).
Randolph, N. M., and Weldon, Newton, *J. Econ. Entom.*, **52,** 759 (1956).
Reynolds, H. T., and Anderson, L. D., *ibid.*, **48,** 871 (1955).
Reynolds, H. T., and Others, *ibid.*, **50,** 527 (1957).
———, *ibid.*, **52,** 63 (1959).
Roth, V. D., *ibid.*, **52,** 654 (1959).
Rousell, J. S., and Others., *ibid.*, **52,** 403 (1959).
Staff, U.S. Dept. Agr., *Entom. Research Service Leaflet,* **391** (1955).
Slife, F. W., and Others, *Ill. Agr. Exp. Sta. Circular,* **658** (1950).
Smith, A. L., "1953 Yearbook," Washington, D.C., U.S. Dept. Agr., 1953.
———, and Others, *U.S. Dept. Agr. Plant Disease Reporter,* **42,** 169 (1958).
Spurrier, E. C., and Others, *Ill. Agr. Exp. Sta. Circular,* **771** (1957).
Staff, U.S. Dept. Agr., *Entom Research Service Leaflet,* **391** (1955).

————, *ibid.,* **368** (1956).

————, *ibid.,* **411** (1957).

————, "Handbook No. 120," Washington, D.C., U.S. Dept. Agr. 1959.

Stanford. E. H., and Others, *Calif. Agr. Exp. Sta. Circular,* **442** (1954).

Stern, V. M., and Reynolds, H. T., *J. Econ. Entom.,* **50,** 816 (1957).

Stern, V. M., and Others, *Calif. Agr.,* **12** (1), 4 (1958).

Ullstrup, A. J., "1953 Yearbook," Washington, D.C., U.S. Dept. Agr., 1953.

Walstrom, R. J., *J. Econ. Entom.,* **51,** 64 (1958).

Webster, O. J., and Leukel, R. W., *U.S. Dept. Agr. Plant Disease Reporter,* **43,** 348 (1959).

7. ORCHARD AND VINEYARD INSECTS, * DISEASES, AND WEEDS

The choice of pesticides and the number of seasonal applications in the case of orchard and vineyard should be made with due regard to established tolerances, effect on beneficial insects, and flavor and appearance of the fruit crop. In some instances, it has been found that the use of dinitros, mineral oil, and sulfur, and certain of the organic compounds, has led to increased populations of insects and mites that were once of minor importance. Comparison of combination-spray programs of insecticides and fungicides has shown significant difference in flavor, yield, and finish of the fruit. The variety of new pesticides being developed gives increasing opportunity for critical selection (see Chapters 2 and 5).

Weed control will not be discussed for each type of orchard tree, since all are more or less susceptible to the hormone type of herbicides, and vineyards are especially susceptible. Spot work is practiced, but only with decided care. The common use of cover crops, usually legumes or broad-leaved weeds, also interferes with weed control. An exception in common practice is the use of low-grade petroleum oils sprayed over the young weed growth in place of tillage as a weed control—as practiced in California citrus groves. During the first year, when weed growth is heavy, a power-sprayer is required, using a total average of 250 gallons of cheap fuel oil per acre. Two to four applications are usually required just to cover the leaf surfaces without runoff. Smaller amounts are used each succeeding year, the average total for the season being about 25 to 75 gallons of oil per acre in the third year. With this system water penetration increases, plow sole disappears, and erosion is reduced.

APPLE

Insects

Aphids. Aphids are one of the more injurious insects attacking the apple. They include the apple aphid (green), apple grain aphid, rosy apple

---

* Before applying insecticides to fruiting trees or vines, consult an agricultural officer as to the pesticide tolerances for certain fruits. See list page 142.

aphid, and the wooly apple aphid. Their life history varies in different parts of the country, but in most instances they spend all or a large part of their life on the apple tree. The first three are foliage-, twig-, and fruit-feeders. Infested apples are stunted in growth and often twisted in shape. The wooly aphid is a bark-feeder, throwing out bunches of fiberlike wool and causing warty-like excrescences. It feeds both on the upper part of the tree and on the roots.

Control of the species, which deposits an overwintering egg on the tree, is by dormant applications of 1½ pints of 20 per-cent emulsion concentrate of dinitro-o-cresol per hundred gallons. Where the European red mite (*Panonychus* [*Metatetranychus*] *ulmi*) and the clover (almond) mite (*Bryobia praetiosa*) are present the dinitro may be reduced to 1 pint and added to 3 per-cent mineral-oil emulsion. This also checks the San José scale (*Aspidiotus perniciosus*) and assists in checking the Forbes scale (*A. forbesi*).

Spring and summer applications of insecticides are frequently necessary since dormant sprays may only delay the severity of attacks and because of infestation from alternate hosts.

For summer infestations, phosphate compounds such as parathion, malathion, or demeton are used, according to the manufacturer's directions. Parathion should not be used within 14 days of the harvest and should not be used on the McIntosh apple or related varieties. (See directions elsewhere for other time intervals between sprays.) Nicotine sulfate is also recommended at a dosage of ¾ to 1 pint of a 40 per-cent concentration per hundred gallons, plus 1 pound of hydrated lime to ensure the full release of the nicotine (Staff, U.S. Dept. Agr., 1959; Staff, Calif. Agr. Exp. Sta., 1959).

The prolonged value of the systemic insecticides, demeton, Meta-systox, and Isolan, as a control of the apple aphid (*Aphis pomi*) has been shown by Glass and Chapman (1955).

The systemic compounds Thimet and demeton are reported by Madsen and Bailey (1959) as giving excellent control of the rosy apple aphid (*Anuraphis roseus*), in 1957, under California conditions. Of the non-systemic compounds, Diazinon alone was effective, but ethion, Thiodan, and Guthion were not satisfactory. In the 1958 experiments against both the rosy and the apple aphid, the systemic compounds Di syston, American Cyanamid 18706, and dimethoate gave excellent control. Sevin was partially effective, and Guthion unsatisfactory.

The wooly apple aphid (*Eriosoma lanigerum*) is a serious pest of the apple in many commercial apple districts. The principal injury that this insect causes on most varieties is the weakening of tree vigor and a heavy deposit of honeydew in which a smut fungus grows. However, in the

Watsonville district of California, this aphid, in addition to the usual injury it causes, enters the core of the Yellow Newton Pippin apple, and, if in numbers, it interferes with the use of the apple for canning. To control the wooly aphid on the apple, it is necessary not only to use an insecticide capable of killing a high proportion of the insects in the aerial portion of the tree but also to check the movements of aphids from the roots.

Diazinon and Thimet used with both 4- and 6-week intervals between applications checked the dispersal of the aphids with but few exceptions. Trithion showed heavier aphid movement, even when applied at 4-week intervals. The malathion plot showed rather heavy build-ups, indicating a weak residual action. The August spray of this material gave the best protection against core infestation. Materials such as Thimet and Diazinon, which give a high initial kill, also prevent upward movements and give the longest protection (Madsen and Hoyt, 1957).

Scale Insects. The more important species are those of the genus *Aspidiotus*, the Forbes, Putnam, and San José scales. Of lesser importance are the oystershell scale (*Lepidosaphes ulmi*) and the scurfy scale (*Chionaspis furfura*). For the control of the *Aspidiotus* scales, the same type of dormant mineral-oil sprays at 3 per-cent dosage as mentioned under aphids should be used. A dosage of 3 to 4 per-cent dormant oil is recommended for the oystershell and the scurfy scales.

A foliage application of parathion may be necessary if the dormant-oil spray does not control the scale insects. Minimum time before harvest is 14 days. For the Forbes, Putnam, and San José scales, this material is applied at a dosage of ½ to 1 pound of a 15 per-cent wettable powder when the newly hatched scale insects (crawlers) are present in numbers on the foliage and fruit. A dosage of 2 pounds of the same form of parathion per hundred gallons of spray is used for the oystershell and scurfy scales as the eggs are hatching. This is applied about the time of the first cover spray for codling moth. DDT, at a dosage of 2 pounds of a 50 per-cent wettable powder per hundred gallons may be substituted for the parathion. Minimum time for DDT before harvest is 30 days.

Codling Moth (*Carpocapsa pomonella*). It was for the control of this insect that arsenical insecticides were first used in the apple orchards of this country. It was also for the standardization of the arsenical, Paris green, that our first insecticide laws were enacted (de Ong, 1956).

The codling moth was primarily a pest of apples and pears, but has extended its range to include the English (Persian) walnut, with occasional attacks on the stone fruits. Since the latter part of the twentieth century, some form of arsenical, and particularly lead arsenate, has been the standard control chemical. Increasing resistance to this method of control and the accumulation of dangerous amounts of arsenicals in the soils from the persistent use of lead arsenate, led to the general adoption of DDT for codling moth control soon after its commercial availability in 1945. Field trials in New York apple orchards, from 1948 through 1953, of DDT at a dosage of 2 pounds of 50 per-cent wettable powder per hundred gallons of spray mixture gave excellent control. "Lead arsenate gave relatively poor control in most tests." Methoxychlor was slightly less effective, and DDD even less so. The organic phosphates, including parathion, EPN, and malathion, "in a full season program were inferior to DDT for the prevention of late season entries." The conclusion was that "DDT remains the best control agent for codling moth in New York ... as long as resistance does not develop" (Glass, 1954). Serious resistance, however, was reported by Cutright (1954) and Glass and Fiori (1955). The spread of resistance through Indiana, Illinois, and Kentucky is shown by Hamilton (1956) and recognized as a general condition by Porter (1957). Minimum days from last spray of DDT to harvest, 30 or, if of more than five applications, 40 days.

Other problems developed by the general use of DDT in codling moth control include the development from minor to major importance of certain insects—particularly spider mites—either because of a lack of susceptibility or of toxicity to parasites and predators. This factor has become so commonly accepted that it is now recognized that some form of miticide, such as an organic phosphate, is usually necessary to control spider mites. The red-banded leaf roller (*Argyrotaenia velutinana*) and the plum curculio (*Conotrachelus nenuphar*) have in some districts developed to such importance as to require shifting one or two cover sprays to lead arsenate instead of DDT. TDE (DDD), which has been commonly used in the northeastern district as a control of the red-banded leaf roller, is now reported by Glass (1957) as being less effective, indicating that resistance is developing.

Pickett (1955) recommends that the apple-growers of Nova Scotia use spray programs that are less dangerous to parasites and predators, thus reducing the cost of control with but a slight increase of injured fruit. He recommends the use of glyodin, captan, Bordeaux mixture, and mercury eradicants as fungicides; and nicotine, lead arsenate, and ryania as insecticides. This would almost eliminate sulfur, dormant oils, dinitro-o-cresol, chlorinated hydrocarbons, and the organophosphates as orchard sprays. Ryania at dosages of 5 or 6 pounds of the pure compound per hundred gallons of spray has been found to give satisfactory control of the codling moth and yet permit large populations of predaceous mites to develop (Clancy and McAllister, 1956; Hamilton and Cleveland, 1957). Favorable results have also been found by Garman (1956) in combining ryania with fungicides in the development of fine-flavored apples.

Guthion, a phosphate compound, is giving control of both the codling moth and the red-banded leaf roller, and also protects against the plum curculio, the green apple aphid, and the European red mite and the two-spotted mite. Dosage used per hundred gallons is 1½ pounds of a 25 percent wettable powder. It should be handled with the same degree of caution as parathion (Asquith, 1958). A minimum of 15 days from last spray to harvest is required.

Japanese Beetle. An outbreak of adult Japanese beetles (*Popillia japonica*) on apple trees and other crops in North Carolina led to a study of the toxicity of various insecticides for this stage of the insect. Twenty-eight organic compounds were used in a comparative study of residual action for up to 35 days. The insecticides were applied as emulsion concentrates to glass surfaces. The deposit was calculated in micrograms of insecticide per square centimeter, 10.9 μg/cm being equivalent to 1 pound per acre of surface. The deposit rate was then reduced by one-half, until no mortality occurred. Compounds showing superior residual action were also determined for their LD-50 values. Guthion and Sevin were the most effective, both in toxicity and length of residual life. Phosdrin showed the most rapid action. Sevin and Guthion, although slower than methoxychlor, gave positive kills, and at much lower dosage rates (Gast, 1959).

European Red, Two-spotted, and Other, Mites. Phosphate sprays may be used to control mites where resistance has not developed. Otherwise, for summer control, add to the DDT cover sprays one of the following, at the dosage given on the label: Kelthane, Chlorobenzilate (except for the Delicious and Jonathan varieties in some districts), and Sulphenone. Do not apply Kelthane within 7, or Chlorobenzilate within 14, days of harvest.

Diseases

Scab. Scab, caused by the fungus *Venturia inaequalis*, is the most serious of the many diseases of the apple. It attacks the foliage and the fruit of the bearing tree, and the foliage of the nursery tree. It is prevalent throughout the apple-growing regions of the world, except in the warm, dry areas. The disease is especially severe in the northeastern United States and the adjoining region of Canada, and much less severe in the Pacific areas.

The scab fungus develops on the dead leaves after they fall, the degree of growth depending upon the amount of living scab fungus present on the leaves before falling. Spores developed on the dead leaves mature and are discharged into the air during the rainy weather of the early spring. These spores set up infection on exposed portions of the new growth. The period from the opening of the cluster buds, until the leaves are fully extended, is the most critical. Infection very frequently begins on the sepals of the blossom buds and spreads to the young fruit; hence, control at this time is very essential. Apple varieties vary in their susceptibility to the fungus, so that control work should begin first on those known to be most easily damaged. The development of scab-resistant varieties is being attempted, but as yet is incomplete (Keitt, 1953).

Conners (1958) states that "in all apple growing districts of this country [Canada], except British Columbia, a salable crop cannot be grown without a fungicide spray program and even in British Columbia the trees in most districts are regularly sprayed for scab." He estimates that apple scab in Nova Scotia, through direct loss and spraying expense, costs the growers $733,000 yearly.

Scab control has been dependent upon Bordeaux mixture to a large extent, but fruit-russeting frequently follows its use. Lime-sulfur solution and wettable sulfur are also effective, but sometimes cause injury; hence, attention is now given to organic fungicides. Eradicant, as well as protectant, sprays are being used. An application of one of the dinitro compounds at the rate of a half-gallon of the concentrate per hundred gallons of water is made directly to the ground surface by a boom attachment. It is made in the early spring, before the apple buds open enough to expose susceptible tissue. Mercury compounds are being used as the first eradicant application, but cannot be used in the cover sprays later because of the danger of residues. Wettable sulfur and organic compounds such as carbamates are now being favored (Keitt, 1953).

Daines (1957) states that, in New Jersey orchards, the use of organic fungicides has not only improved disease control but has also in many instances resulted in better fruit finish, yields, tree vigor, and insecticidal values. Varietal response to a number of fungicides is given.

Because of uncertain weather conditions in early spring, when the control of apple scab is so vital, it is sometimes necessary to spray trees in full bloom. Rich (1957) has investigated the possibility of injury to the open bloom. It was his finding that "captan, dichlone, ferbam, glyodin and sulfur do not seriously reduce pollen germination or fruit set when applied to apple trees in bloom."

The fungicide Cyprex has been found to give a high degree of protection against apple scab. The dosages used ranged from ¾ to 1½ pounds per hundred gallons, with from 3 to 5 applications. Fruit infections ranged from 0 to 1 per cent for all treatments. The 2-pound dosage protected the foliage for about 30 days. It is considered that ¾ pound would give satisfactory protection with, probably, no objectionable residue (Powell and Others, 1958).

Powdery Mildew. This disease of the apple is usually caused by the fungus *Podosphaera leucotricha*. The disease is now distributed throughout the principal apple-growing districts of the world. It was only during the early part of the twentieth century, however, that it became an important disease in commercial orchards in this country. The mildew fungus overwinters in two ways—as a thick-walled spore and also as fine filaments within lateral and terminal leaf and flower buds. Leaves developing the following spring from the infected buds are covered with mildew. Spores from the infected points are carried by the wind to other leaves, and germinate at temperatures ranging from 50° F to 68° F when near the dew point. The fungus develops best on the growing tips of the twigs; hence, it is checked in early summer as active twig growth ceases. Bordeaux and other copper compounds were first used in control but caused too much injury. Sulfur fungicides tend to dwarf the foliage and, in high temperatures, may cause severe damage. The organic fungicides ferbam, captan, and glyodin then came into general use for apple scab and other diseases, but did not control the mildew. This permitted the latter to establish itself widely. Suggestions for control include sulfur for the early part of the season, followed by Karathane or Mildex for later use (Kirby, 1957).

Bitter Rot. This is caused by the fungus *Glomerella cingulata* and is primarily a disease of the fruit, although it also attacks twigs and branches, where it may persist for several years. A few infected fruits shrivel, clinging to the twig over winter, and in the spring produce spores for infecting the new crop. Fruit infections begin to appear in mid-June and continue to develop through the summer.

Control of the disease depends first upon the removal of the cankered areas, dead twigs, and the "mummies." Bordeaux mixture has been the standard fungicide for use against the disease, but because of foliage injury, it is being supplanted by the organic compounds ferbam and captan. The dosage used is 2 pounds per hundred gallons of water. The organic compound Dichlone is also effective at a dosage of ¾ to 1 pound per hundred gallons, but may cause leaf-spotting at high temperatures (Dunegan, 1956).

Cedar-Apple Rust. This disease is caused by the fungus *Gymnosporangium juniperi virginianae*. Besides this species, there are two other forms of rust which attack the apple. Hawthorn rust, caused by the fungus *G. globosum*, attacks the apple leaf only. Quince rust, caused by the fungus *G. clavipes*, attacks the fruit of certain apple varieties. Commercial varieties of apple vary in their susceptibility to the various types of rust.

The cedar rust fungus lives for almost two years on the cedar tree, but completes its cycle on the apple tree. Infection of cedar leaves begins between spring and early summer from lesions on apple leaves. Galls, known as "cedar apples," develop and complete their growth the following spring. These galls produce spores which are carried to the apple, and infestation is again repeated.

Control was first directed to the removal of the offending cedar tree, but since this was impractical with large stands of cedars, attention was turned to the use of fungicides. Several applications of Bordeaux mixture annually were first recommended, but this was expensive and often resulted in injury to leaves and fruit. Lime-sulfur solution was then tried and, because it also controlled scab, came into general use. The organic fungicide ferbam (Fermate) is now commonly used because it requires fewer applications. It is used at a dosage of 1 to $1\frac{1}{2}$ pounds per hundred gallons of water (Palmiter, 1953).

Hamilton and Szkolnik (1957) evaluated a number of the newer fungicides against cedar-apple rust and found Omadines and Thioneb gave promising results similar to those from ferbam.

Root Diseases. French apple roots are partially resistant to the oak-root fungus (*Armillaria mellea*). The fungus does not attack the root directly, but attacks the scion if the bud union is below the surface of the ground. The fungus then extends both upward and downward into the root system. The apple root is also subject to attack by the crown gall disease, caused by the bacterium *Phytomonas tumefaciens*. This, however, is more a disease of the nursery than of the established tree (Day, 1947).

ALMOND

Insects

Scale Insects. See Apple.

Peach Twig Borer. See Peach.

Peach Tree Borer, Western (*Sanninoidea exitiosa graefi*). This insect feeds underneath the bark, both below and above the crown of the tree. Crystals of the fumigant paradichlorobenzene are applied during early fall, in a ring around the tree about 2 inches from the trunk. This is covered closely with soil and packed down with a shovel. Dosage for trees one to three years old is $\frac{1}{4}$ to $\frac{1}{2}$ ounce; for four- to five-year-old trees, $\frac{3}{4}$ ounce; for older trees, 1 to 2 ounces. Mounded soil around young trees should be removed after 3 or 4 weeks (Staff, Calif. Agr. Exp. Sta., 1959).

Almond Mites. The brown almond mite (*Bryobia praetiosa*) is controlled in the "popcorn" stage of the opening buds by applying $1\frac{1}{2}$ pints of Genite-923 emulsion; or $1\frac{1}{2}$ to 2 pounds of 50 per-cent ovex (Ovotran) wettable powder with the early spray for the peach twig borer (*Anarsia lineatella*). For spring and summer control of mites, use ½ pint of 20 per-cent TEPP emulsion per hundred gallons or as directed on the container. Do not use TEPP within 3 days of harvest.

Diseases

Oak-root Fungus. This disease is caused by the fungus *Armillaria mellea*. The root-stocks upon which the almond are grown, and also those of the stone fruits, are subject to attack. The usual treatment is soil fumigation with carbon disulfide prior to planting. Spot treatment may be necessary following the first application because eradication is difficult. All stumps and as many of the roots as possible should be removed. Warm porous soil is essential for treatment; coarse, gravelly soil is difficult to treat successfully.

Apply a light irrigation that will wet the soil to a depth of 6 inches. Then make holes 5 or 6 inches deep, 18 inches apart, and in a diamond formation. Pour 2 fluid ounces of carbon disulfide into each hole and close immediately with the heel. (Mechanical and hand applicators are also available.) All living plants and insects are killed by the application, so keep a few feet from vegetation of any form. The gas may persist in the soil for 6 to 8 weeks, after which the area may be planted.

Carbon disulfide should be kept away from fires or electric switches because the vapor is very explosive.

APRICOT

Insects

Scale Insects. See Apple.

Peach Twig Borer. See Peach.

Orange Tortrix (*Argyrotaenia citrana*). This is a major pest of the apricot in the coastal counties of California. For control, apply TDE (DDD), 2 pounds of 50 per-cent wettable powder per hundred gallons of water at the time of petal fall.

Codling moth and orange tortrix under California conditions may require a second application of TDE about the middle of May. It should not be applied within 30 days of harvest. To avoid TDE residues, parathion, 2 pounds of a 25 per-cent wettable powder, or malathion, 4 pounds of 25 per-cent wettable powder, may be substituted. Minimum time between application and harvest: parathion 14, and malathion 7, days.

Tent Caterpillar (Malacosoma). Larvae overwinter within the egg shell and begin feeding early in the spring. As they mature, they assemble late in the day in colonies, or within "tents" which they spin for their protection. The caterpillars soon defoliate large areas of the tree.

They are usually controlled by the same applications as those for the orange tortrix.

Peach Tree Borer. See Almond for use of paradichlorobenzene; see Peach for use of DDT, Guthion, and parathion.

Diseases

Brown Rot. Brown rot on apricot is caused by the fungus *Monilinia laxa*. It attacks the blossoms and extends down into the twigs, where it remains dormant through the summer, starting growth after the rains begin. Severe infections are controlled by application of 2 or 2½ pounds of mono-calcium arsenite per hundred gallons of water, during the dormant season and before the bud scales open. The mixture should not be combined with oil or zinc sulfate. Do not prune trees or apply oil sprays within 3 weeks of the application of the arsenical.

Applications for control are made as necessary in the red-bud stage. Later, Bordeaux mixture or fixed coppers as directed, or 2 pounds of 50 per-cent captan wettable powder, ¾ pound of 50 per-cent dichlone, or 2 pounds of the carbamate maneb per hundred gallons of water are used.

Oak-Root Fungus Disease. See Almond.

CHERRY

Insects

Scale Insects and Black Cherry Aphid (*Myzus cerasi*). See Apple.

Cherry Fruit Fly (*Rhagoletis cingulata*). Two to 3 applications of a combination of lead arsenate, 2½ to 3 pounds, and 2½ to 3 pounds of hydrated lime per hundred gallons of water should be made. Treatments are begun when the first adult flys are trapped, and at 10- to 14-day intervals following. This formula is for use only on processing fruit after removing residue. Reduce dosage to 1 pound per hundred gallons of spray for English Morello variety. Minimum days between application and harvest: lead arsenate, 14, malathion, 3, methoxychlor, 7, and parathion, 14. Other insecticides used instead of lead arsenate are malathion—2 pounds of 25 per-cent wettable powder at 10-day intervals; methoxychlor—2 pounds of 50 per-cent wettable powder; parathion—1 to 2 pounds of a 15 per-cent wettable powder; or rotenone—2 to 3 pounds of 4 to 4.5 per-cent powder. All dosages are used in 100 gallons of water (Staff, U.S. Dept. Agr., 1959). In a comparative laboratory study of the effect of insecticides on the cherry fruit fly, Frick (1957) found that under conditions existing in the state of Washington, the insecticides Diazinon and Perthane were the most promising for orchard use.

Pear-Slug (*Caliroa cerasi*). Parathion, ¾ pound of 25 per-cent wettable powder, or malathion, 1½ pounds of 25 per-cent wettable powder per hundred gallons of water should be used for this disease. Dusts of parathion, 2 per cent, 30 to 40 pounds per acre, or nicotine, 4 per cent,

25 to 30 pounds per acre may also be used. Minimum days between application and harvest: parthion, 14, malathion, 3, nicotine, 3.

Pear Thrips (*Taeniothrips inconsequens*). Apply DDT, 2 pounds of 50 per-cent wettable powder per hundred gallons of water as bloom buds show white, and just after bloom.

Plum Curculio (*Conotrachelus nenuphar*). Two to 3 sprays of EPN at 1 to 1½ pounds of 25 per-cent wettable powder per hundred gallons, beginning at petal fall, should be applied. Methoxychlor, 2 pounds of 50 per-cent wettable powder; parathion, 2 pounds of 15 per-cent wettable powder, or lead arsenate, 2 to 3 pounds, plus 2 to 3 pounds of hydrated lime, may also be applied. Smith (1957) reports favorable results in curculio control, especially on cherry, with a combination spray of wettable sulfur, 5 pounds, hydrated lime, 2 pounds, and lead arsenate, 2 pounds. Minimum days between application and harvest: EPN, 21, methoxychlor, 14, parathion, 14, and lead arsenate, 30. In laboratory tests, it was found that the "residues of each of the materials caused reduced feeding and oviposition."

Soil applications of aldrin, dieldrin, or heptachlor, as wettable powders at the rates of 2 to 4 pounds in 500 gallons of water per acre, controlled the plum curculio in cherry orchards for a number of years. The applications were made with a power-sprayer with a boom attachment. The treatment was more efficient in cleanly cultivated orchards than in heavy sod (Stelzer and Fluke, 1958).

Diseases

Leaf Spot. This disease, caused by the fungus *Coccomyces hiemalis* is serious to the cherry in the eastern United States, and less severe in California. At the beginning of attack, it appears on the leaves as small spots of dying tissue; these enlarge and may cover the entire leaf surface. Severe defoliation often results. The disease also attacks the fruit and its stem.

Control consists in disking or plowing under the old leaves during the winter, or spraying the old leaves on the ground with sodium salt of dinitro-o-cresol. The choice of foliage fungicides varies with the variety and with local success. They include sulfur, Bordeaux mixture, fixed coppers, and one of the carbamates, such as ferbam or maneb.

Oak-Root Fungus Disease. See Almond.

CITRUS

Insects

Aphids (Various Species). Control is usually obtained by one of several formulas used in the control of scale insects—a light- or medium-grade of petroleum oil*, 1 to 1¾ gallons as emulsive, or 2 gallons of emulsion, plus ½ pound of parathion, 25 per-cent wettable powder, per hundred. Malathion is, in some formulas, substituted for parathion at the dosage of 1 pound of 25 per-cent wettable powder per hundred gallons of water. If the latter is used as an emulsion concentrate, it should be with the minimum of emulsifier now available for use on citrus.

Where aphids alone are to be controlled, nicotine dust at 4 per-cent concentration is used at 50 to 60 pounds per acre. The spray formula is 12 ounces of 40 per-cent nicotine sulfate plus 8 ounces of casein spreader per hundred gallons of water. Rotenone extract may also be used at the rate of 1 pint per hundred of 2.5 per-cent concentration, or combined with petroleum according to manufacturer's recommendation. Malathion is used for aphids alone at the rate of 1½ pounds of 25 per-cent wettable powder per hundred. Minimum days between sprays and harvest: parathion, 14, malathion, 7.

Mealybugs (Various Species). Dependence is largely placed on control by parasites and predators, a survey of which is given by Bartlett and Lloyd (1958) (see Chapter 2). Where necessary to use insecticides, parathion at a dosage of 1½ pounds of 25 per-cent wettable powder per hundred, or parathion, 1 pound, and malathion, 1½ pounds, of 25 per-cent wettable powder is recommended. Days between sprays and harvest: see Aphids.

Mites. The citrus red mite (*Panonychus* (*Metatranychus*) *citri*) is one of the more important enemies of citrus trees. Jeppson and others (1957) found that populations were highest on lemon trees during the period of greatest growth. The low humidities and higher temperatures of interior points, however, were especially unfavorable to mite development.

Control is by use of 1¾ gallons per hundred of light-medium or medium grade petroleum oil as directed by local agricultural officers. The citrus mite has developed varying degrees of resistance to the commercial types of phosphate compounds (Jeppson and others, 1958).

In a study of various California oils of the light-medium and medium grade, Riehl and others (1958) found that the killing action of these oils against the citrus red mite "is associated with the highest boiling portion of the oil." Riehl also found (1956) that, by proper timing of sprays for

---

* Light-medium oil, 52–61% distilled at 636° F, unsulfonated residue 92%. Medium oil, 41–49% distilled at 636° F, unsulfonated residue 92%. Emulsive oils contain sufficient dissolved emulsifier to form an emulsion by adding water. Oil emulsions contain a certain amount of water besides the emulsifier. Sprays should not be applied during bloom because of danger to bees and other beneficial insects. (*Courtesy* 1958 Spray Program for California Citrus Fruit, Citrus Experiment Station, University of California.)

certain varieties and districts, annual applications of the usual type of emulsive petroleum oils could be made with little or no interference to growth, yield, or quality of fruit. Cressman (1955) confirms these findings and states that Valencia oranges were sprayed with special light, light-medium, and medium oils without affecting the amounts of solids or the maturity ratios.

It has been shown by Riehl and Wedding (1959a) that no consistent inhibition of photosynthesis of Eureka lemon or Bearss lime leaves occurred from applications of California light-medium or medium grade spray oils at the deposit level of 150 μg/sq cm of leaf surface. (This amount of oil deposit is known to be sufficient for the control of California red scale and citrus red mite.) Higher deposits of oil caused a slight inhibition of photosynthesis. Recovery of photosynthesis occurred in less time in plants treated with naphthenic oils than those treated with paraffinic oils.

Comparative experiments were conducted on Eureka lemon and Bearss lime as to the effect of naphthenic (western type) and paraffinic (eastern type) oils of saturated, narrow-cut petroleum fractions of comparable molecular weight on the transpiration of citrus plants. Transpiration loss was expressed as milligrams of water transpired per square centimeter of leaf surface per hour. "On the day following application of concentrations of 1.75 percent oil in aqueous mixture, transpiration of the oil-sprayed plants was reduced more than half that of untreated plants for both the naphthenic and the paraffinic oils and for both varieties of citrus . . . . For narrow-cut fractions of comparable molecular weights of 306 and 308, recovery was faster in the plants sprayed with the naphthenic oil than with the paraffinic oil" (Riehl and Wedding, 1959b).

The advantages of oil sprays—scale control, lack of toxicity to man and other warm-blooded animals, and lack of toxic-residue hazards— permit them to be used as desired without danger to the tree or the crop.

In the southeastern states, Spencer and Selhime (1957) found that, when parathion was substituted for oil in scale insect control, the population of citrus mites increased. Oils could not be added to the sulfur-parathion combination because of incompatability.

Citrus Bud Mite (*Aceria sheldoni*). For control, petroleum as for the citrus red mite, or Chlorobenzilate, ½ pound of 25 per-cent wettable powder per hundred, is used.

Citrus Rust Mite (*Phyllocoptruta oleivora*). For control, wettable sulfur at 4 pounds per hundred, or dusting sulfur 60 to 80 pounds per acre, is used.

Scale Insects. The California red scale (*Aonidiella aurantii*) is one of the most serious enemies of citrus trees in many parts of the southwestern states. It attacks leaves, bearing-wood, and fruit. (For control, see the formulas for insecticides, including light-medium and medium petroleum oils alone, and in combination with parathion and malathion, as given under Aphids. For details of the choice of insecticide and time of application see local agricultural officers.) Consideration should be given to the value of parasites and predators in natural control. The Florida red scale (*Chrysomphalus aonidum*) is subject to a high degree of control by natural means (Muma, 1955). Various combinations of petroleum oil, parathion, sulfur, and a miticide have been developed for use against this insect and other pests (Spencer and Selhime, 1957). Minimum days between last application and harvest: petroleum oil and parathion, 30.

Purple Scale (*Lepidosaphes beckii*) and Yellow Scale (*Aonidiella citrina*). See California red scale, above.

Black Scale (*Saissetia oleae*). See red scale formulas for use of oil. Alternative formulas are oil sprays, as above, but with not less than 1¼ gallons, plus rotenone as recommended by manufacturers; or kerosene (horticultural grade) 1½ gallons plus DDT, 1½ pounds as wettable powder or emulsion concentrate, as directed; or petroleum oil plus parathion as above per hundred. Minimum days from last application to harvest: petroleum oil and parathion or DDT, 30.

Citricola Scale (*Coccus pseudomagnoliarum*). The control method long used for this scale includes lime-sulfur, 5 gallons, plus wettable sulfur, 4 pounds per hundred, or a sulfur dust of 100 pounds per acre. Timing should be according to local conditions. Later formulas include 2 per-cent DDT in the dusting sulfur; or 6 pounds of parathion, 25 per-cent wettable powder in 100 to 400 gallons of water.

Formulas, choice of insecticides, and timing should all be checked with local agricultural officers, as should interval between last application and harvest.

Citrus thrips (*Scirtothrips citri*). Control of this insect is necessary in many districts to prevent scarring of the fruit and to protect new growth. See Citricola scale for certain districts. Other formulas include 1 quart of nicotine sulfate, 40 per cent, plus 4 pounds of sugar in 100 to 200 gallons per acre; or sabadilla, 0.5 per-cent liquid preparation at a dosage of 1 to 1½ gallons, plus 10 pounds of sugar, in 100 to 300 gallons of water.

Diseases

Foot Rot (Brown Rot Gummosis). This disease is caused by the fungus *Phytophthora citrophthora*. The common symptom is the presence of diseased bark and the exudation of gum, usually near the soil line. The bark lesions may extend upward several inches, killing the bark and staining the wood dark. The dead bark shrinks and the margins split in dry weather. Injury to the crown roots may be so serious as to kill the tree. Wet soil and damp locations favor the growth of the fungus. The use of resistant varieties of citrus rootstock, such as sour orange and trifoliate orange, offers the best method of protection against the disease.

Infection of the root crown is treated by removing the soil to expose the crown and roots, and allowing them to dry. Covering the crown and a foot of the lower trunk every year with a thin water suspension of ready-mixed Bordeaux will aid in preventing further infection. One of the coal tars, *Avenarius carbolineum*, may also be used as a disinfectant (Klotz and Childs, 1953).

Psorosis. This is a group name for certain virus diseases with somewhat similar symptoms, notably those produced on young leaves. No methods of transmission are known except by bud grafts and accidental root-grafting in the field. Young leaf symptoms appear as small cleared areas in the new growth, being much lighter than the remainder of the leaf. These areas disappear as the leaves mature. Associated with the leaf symptoms are concavities of various size on the trunk, and larger limbs beneath the bark. Gum appears through the bark as it cracks. Prevention of this type of disease is through the use of buds from healthy trees.

There is no known cure for psorosis-affected trees, but their life can be prolonged by chemical treatment of affected areas and by bark scraping. The loose, discolored bark lesions are scraped and, on larger limbs, extended over a 4-inch surrounding margin of bark. Small limbs are cut off about a foot below the affected part. The treatment is repeated every second year.

Bark-scaling is induced by applying a 1 per-cent solution of dinitro-o-cyclohexyl phenol in kerosene. The manufacturer's directions should be followed closely. This treatment will prolong the productive life of trees with moderate infection (Wallace and Grant, 1953).

Tristeza. This disease of citrus is also caused by virus infection. In California it is known as "quick decline." The disease varies in degree. Some trees decline and die quickly, while others with mild symptoms may linger on for years. Infection is transmitted by bud-grafting and is also carried by citrus aphids.

Prevention of infection is achieved by bud-grafting from healthy trees and choice of rootstocks known to be tolerant for that particular area. Tolerant rootstocks are those whose sweet orange tops show no sign of the disease, even when exposed to infection by the *Triteza* virus.

PEACH

Insects

Aphid, Green Peach (*Myzus persicae*). For the overwintering egg, petroleum oil, 4 gallons per hundred, is used as the buds swell. Foliage applications include Guthion, 0.3 pound of active material; malathion, 0.5 pound of active material; parathion, 0.15 pound of active material; or nicotine sulfate, ¾ pint of 40 per-cent concentrate per hundred gallons. Minimum time in days from last application to harvest: Guthion, 15, parathion, 14, malathion, 7, and nicotine sulfate, 3.

Mites (Brown Almond and European Red). For the overwintering egg, petroleum oil, 3 gallons per hundred, is used in the dormant stage. For summer use, apply EPN, 0.25 to 0.5 pound of active material; malathion, 0.5 to 0.75 pound of active material; or TEPP, ⅔ pint of 20 per-cent emulsion concentrate per hundred gallons. Minimum time in days from last application to harvest: EPN, 21, malathion, 7, TEPP, 3.

Black Grass Bugs (*Genus Irbisia*). If it is necessary to control these, apply at petal fall DDT, 2 pounds of 50 per-cent wettable powder per hundred.

Japanese Beetle (*Popillia japonica*). For control, apply DDT, 1 pound of active material; methoxychlor, 1½ pounds of active material; parathion, 0.3 pound of active material, or rotenone, 2 ounces of active material per hundred gallons. Minimum days from last application to harvest: DDT, 7, methoxychlor, 14, parathion, 14, and rotenone, 1.

Peach Twig Borer (*Anarsia lineatella*). This enemy of the almond, peach, and apricot overwinters in the larval stage in little cells beneath the bark. As growth begins in the spring, the larva burrows down through the tips of the growing twig, killing them 3 or 4 inches back. A second brood emerges in early summer, and these larvae attack the fruit and other twigs. A third brood may be found on late peaches.

Control is by application of 2 pounds of DDT, 50 per-cent wettable powder per hundred gallons of water. The spray is used in the red bud stage of early spring. Basic lead arsenate, at a dosage of 3 or 4 pounds per hundred gallons of water, is also used instead of DDT.

Recent studies in California by Summers and others (1959) of the control of the twig borer on peaches and almonds, have shown the value of Sevin and Thiodan as control agents under the existing conditions of the test. Sevin as a 50 per-cent wettable powder, and Thiodan as a 25 per-cent wettable powder, tended to yield consistently lower twig borer counts in both twig and fruit than did DDT as a 50 per-cent wettable powder—each compound being used at 2 pounds of formulated material per hundred gallons. The differences in control were not, however, significant in every trial, and varied also from results due to use of basic lead arsenate, at 4 pounds, and parathion, at 25 per-cent wettable powder, in concentrations of 2 pounds per hundred gallons.

Stink Bugs. At petal fall, dieldrin, 0.25 pound of active material; Guthion, 0.3 pound of active material; or parathion, 0.3 pound of active material per hundred, should be applied. Minimum time from last application to harvest: dieldrin, 45, Guthion, 15, parathion, 14, days.

(Rings (1958) has catalogued each species of plant bug attacking the peach under Ohio conditions.)

Plum Curculio (Southern Areas). Apply parathion, 0.3 pound; Guthion, 0.3 pound; methoxychlor, 1.5 pound; or malathion, 0.5 to 0.75 pound of active ingredient per hundred gallons of water at petal fall, 10 days later, and 7 to 10 days after that. For lead arsenate, apply 1 month later and, for other materials, apply 4 to 5 weeks later and 2 weeks before harvest. In the North, apply 3 to 4 times, 7 to 10 days apart, beginning at shuck-off.

Lead arsenate (basic), 2 pounds, plus hydrated lime, 8 pounds; or dieldrin, 0.25 to 0.5 pound of active ingredient per hundred may be substituted for other materials in petal-fall, and first and second covers. Minimum time from last application to harvest: parathion, 14, Guthion, 15, methoxychlor, 21, malathion, 7, lead arsenate, 30, dieldrin, 45 days. Dieldrin is not to be used after the second cover. Parathion and Guthion are to be used only by trained operators (Staff, U.S. Dept. Agr., 1959a).

Peach Tree Borer (*Sanninoidea exitiosa*). (See Almond Insects, for directions on the use of paradichlorobenzene.)

A single application of parathion to the trunk and lower parts of the larger limbs of peach trees in New York, as a control of the peach tree borer, was as successful as three DDT sprays. Application just prior to the hatching of the earliest egg practically spanned the entire egg-laying period. Eggs present on the trunk received the direct spray, while those deposited later were exposed to the vapor arising from the residue (Smith and Wagenknecht, 1959). In districts having longer egg-laying seasons, two or more applications of a spray of parathion, 2 pounds of 15 per-cent concentration per hundred gallons, would probably be necessary.

Oriental Fruit Moth (*Grapholitha molesta*). In the Pacific Northwest, apply 2 to 3 sprays of DDT, 2 pounds of 50 per-cent wettable powder per hundred, the first spray at petal fall and the next in 12 to 14 days. If necessary, spray again in June, when moths appear in bait traps. In other areas, make 3 applications at 10-day intervals, beginning at shuck split. Minimum days from last application to harvest: DDT, 30.

Scale Insects (Various). Apply petroleum oil in 4 gallons of emulsion at the dormant season. If necessary, use malathion, 2 to 2½ pounds of 25 per-cent wettable powder, or parathion, 2 pounds of 15 per-cent wettable powder per hundred, at the end of the hatching season in early summer. Minimum days from last application to harvest: malathion, 3, parathion, 14.

Diseases

Oak-Root Fungus (Armillaria). See Almond.

Brown Rot. This disease on peach is caused by the fungus *Monilinia fructicola*. Under western conditions one application in the pink bud stage of 6 pounds of wettable sulfur; a fixed-copper fungicide plus adhesive; 2 pounds of 50 per-cent captan; ¾ pound of 50 per-cent dichlone; or one of the carbamates may be sufficient to control the disease. As a preventive of fruit rot, apply 10 pounds of wettable sulfur; 2 pounds of 50 per-cent captan; or 2 pounds of 70 per-cent maneb per hundred gallons; or 50 to 60 pounds of sulfur dust per acre. Two applications may be necessary, one about 4 weeks, the other 2 weeks, before harvest. Following heavy showers prior to harvest, apply 6 pounds of wettable powder or, in regions where lime-sulfur solution is tolerated by the peach, apply 2 gallons per hundred after the rain.

Under eastern conditions, blossom blight requires applications during the blooming season of 6 pounds of wettable sulfur; 1 gallon of lime-sulfur solution, or Phygon, 2 pounds per hundred, every 3 or 4 days. Two other sprays of sulfur are usually necessary before harvest.

Peach Blight (Shot Hole). This is caused by the fungus *Coryneum beijerinckii*. It attacks dormant leaf and blossom buds and twigs, but is seldom found on the fruit. Active growth of the fungus begins usually in the fall, after the tree is thoroughly wet and remains so for several hours. It is widely distributed over the world, but in the United States is serious only in the far-western states. Because of the dry summers and falls, growth is quiescent until the beginning of the heavy rainy season, and after the leaves have fallen. Since it is necessary to maintain a protective coating over the twigs during the heavy rains of winter, a 10–10–100 Bordeaux mixture applied between November 15 and December 15 is considered the best control measure.

Leaf Curl. This disease is caused by the fungus *Taphrina deformans*. The young leaves develop thickened distortions of a reddish color where severe defoliation follows, and if general this injures the fruit crop severely. The peach blight spray of Bordeaux mixture will do much to hold this disease under control. If this application has not been made, then, before the buds begin to swell, apply 3 pounds of ferbam; or 3 pounds of ziram, each in a 76 per-cent concentration to the hundred. Bordeaux mixture, 10–10–100, or a fixed copper may be substituted for the above compounds.

Because of occasional twig-killing of peaches on the Pacific Coast, from applications of Bordeaux mixture and fixed coppers as a fall control of leaf curl, a comparative study of various fungicides was made by English (1958). Ziram was found to be better than basic copper sulfate followed closely by ferbam plus an adhesive oil. Maneb and captan were decidedly inferior to the other compounds tested. Further tests will be made of the value of the organic compounds as a control of Coryneum blight.

PEAR

Insects

Aphids (Various). To the first codling moth spray, add parathion, 1 pound of 25 per-cent wettable powder; malathion, 2 pounds of 25 per-cent wettable; or Diazinon, 1 pound of 25 per-cent wettable per hundred. This will also aid in controlling the pear psylla (*Psylla pyricola*). Minimum days from last application to harvest: parathion, 14, malathion, 3, Diazinon, 14.

Pear Thrips. See Cherry.

Codling Moth. For this insect, apply DDT, 2 pounds of 50 per-cent wettable powder per hundred during the latter part of April and about 3 weeks later. A third spray should be made about the first of July on late varieties. Where populations are high, three applications may be necessary for the first brood, the first at petal fall and then at 25-day intervals. Parathion, 1 pound of 25 per-cent wettable powder, may be added to the DDT if the latter does not give satisfactory control. Madsen (1956) found that lead arsenate does not give commercial control of the codling moth. Ryania, methoxychlor, and Diazinon gave control comparable to DDT, while the last also controlled spider mites, leaf miners, and mealy bugs. Minimum days from last spray to harvest: DDT, 30, parathion, 14, lead arsenate, 40, and methoxychlor, 7.

Pear Slug. See Cherry.

Italian Pear Scale (*Epidiaspis piricola*). This is an important pest in the western district if moss and lichen are present. Control is achieved by a dormant application of 4 gallons of oil emulsion, or 3 gallons of emulsive oil, plus either 3 pounds of caustic soda or 10 to 15 pounds of hydrated lime.

Mites (Various). The phosphate compounds parathion and malathion may be used as directed for summer control where resistance has not developed. Chlorobenzilate, Sulphenone, or Trithion may be used as directed following the second codling-moth spray. The last material should not be used where resistance to phosphate compounds develops. Minimum days from last spray to harvest: Chlorobenzilate, 7, Sulphenone, 7, Trithion, 30, and parathion, 14.

Diseases

Pear Scab. This disease is caused by the fungus *Venturia pyrina*. Attacks occur on the flower parts, fruit, and leaves. Infections on the fruit stems may cause fruit drop. Scab spots enlarge as the fruit grows, causing varying degrees of distortion. Hot weather or fungicidal sprays may check growth of the spots. The fungus overwinters in infected twigs or on the infected leaves which drop in the fall. Moisture is necessary for the dissemination and germination of scab spores. From 5 to 48 hours of continued moisture is necessary for germination, depending upon the temperature. Growth is slow during the early period of infection; hence, scab spots do not become visible for from 2 to 3 weeks (Kienholz, 1953).

Scab control is achieved by an application of 2 gallons of lime-sulfur solution per hundred, or comparable sulfur compounds, as the manufacturer directs, when the opening buds show green tips. A second spray of the liquid lime-sulfur should be made at the cluster-bud stage; or 4 pounds of wettable sulfur; 1½ pounds of 76 per-cent ziram; 1½ pounds of 76 per-cent ferbam; or 1 quart of captan per hundred may be used. A third spray may be necessary at the calyx stage or petal-fall period, using similar dosages of ziram, or ferbam, or, on varieties not susceptible to sulfur, 4 pounds of wettable sulfur per hundred. During rainy seasons a further spray of ferbam or ziram is used at 2- or 3-week intervals.

Pear Blight. This is caused by the bacterium *Phytomonas amylovora*. Infection occurs during the main-blossom and late-blossom period, also attacking the succulent vegetative shoots. Infection is checked as rapid growth decreases during midsummer. It has been found that blossom infection is related to the concentration of sugar in the nectar, which has been found to vary from 3 to 55 per cent. The pear blight bacteria multiply only at sugar concentrations of 20 per cent to 30 per cent. Apparently the pollinating insects, active on warm days when the nectar concentration is high, distribute bacteria among the bloom; no increase seems to occur until high humidity or rain dilutes the nectar concentration. Epidemics of pear blight following rain—as frequently happens—confirm these findings (Scott, 1953).

The control of pear blight in western regions, where the disease has been severe, at first depended upon the expensive method of going over the orchards during the period of acute infection and pruning out the points of infection. Later it was found that applications of a Bordeaux mixture of a half-pound each of copper sulfate and hydrated lime per hundred gallons of water was as effective as stronger mixtures, without the injury resulting from the latter. Copper-lime dusts of 20 to 80 concentration are also used.

The antibiotic, streptomycin, is now being used in pear blight control as a dust containing 1,000 ppm of streptomycin in a pyrophyllite filler, at the rate of 40 pounds per acre; or it may be used at 60 ppm wettable powder per hundred gallons as a spray. Applications of this material as a dust or spray, or the Bordeaux mixture, are first made when 10 per cent of the bloom is out, and then at 5-day intervals during the blooming season. The Bordeaux mixture is not to be used on the varieties Anjou or Comice.

PLUM AND PRUNE

Insects

Aphids (Various). For these, use dormant applications of a dinitro compound, as manufacturer directs, or 3 gallons of dormant oil emulsion per hundred. Either formula will aid in controlling scale insects and the overwintering egg of mites. (For summer control, see Peach.)

Pear Thrips. See Cherry.

Plum Curculio. See Cherry. (Smith's (1957) experiments with lead arsenate, wettable sulfur, and hydrated lime did not show as high a degree of control on prunes as on cherry.)

Peach Tree Borer. See Almond.

Mites. Phosphate sprays used for other pests may check the summer attacks of mites.

Diseases

Brown Rot. Control of this disease in the popcorn stage of bloom is by sprays of 10–10–100 Bordeaux mixture; or fixed copper plus adhesive, as manufacturer directs. Dichlone, ¾ pound of 50 per-cent; captan, 2 pounds 50 per-cent; maneb, 2 pounds of 70 per-cent; or nabam, ½ gallon of 22 per-cent, mixed in the tank with iron or zinc and iron sulfates, may be used.

Summer control, if necessary, requires 30 to 35 pounds of sulfur dust per acre. This dust should not be applied at high summer temperatures.

Oak-Root Fungus. See Almond.

GRAPE

Insects

Aphids (*Aphis illinoisensis*). Nicotine sulfate, 40 per-cent, as 1 pint per hundred, plus soap or weak Bordeaux mixture is recommended.

Grape Berry Moth (*Paralobesia viteana*). A common spray program for this insect is DDT, 1½ pounds of 50 per-cent wettable powder per hundred. The first application is made at petal fall; the second, 10 to 12 days later, and the third 35 to 45 days later for the second brood. A sticker may be used, as directed by the manufacturer, for the first two sprays, but not for the third. Cox (1957) has found that, under Pennsylvania conditions, there is a tendency to build a higher residue than the 7 ppm now permitted for DDT. A spray program of two sprays of DDT and a third of parathion; EPN; or malathion gave similar control, with a lower DDT residue at harvest time. The dosages used were DDT, 1½ pounds of 50 per-cent wettable powder (sprays 1 and 2); or methoxychlor, 2 pounds of 50 per-cent wettable powder per hundred (spray 3). In other trials, the same dosage of DDT was used as above for the first two sprays, but parathion, 1½ pounds of 15 per-cent wettable powder per hundred was used for the third spray. Diazinon and Guthion were also found promising materials for the control of the berry moth. Minimum days from last spray to harvest: DDT, 40, EPN, 21, parathion and methoxychlor, 14.

Grape Leaf Folder (*Desmia funeralis*). For the control of this insect, apply DDT, 1½ pounds of 50 per-cent wettable powder per hundred, timed somewhat as for grape berry moth. Recommendations for control under California conditions are lead arsenate (standard), 4 pounds per hundred early in the season for the first brood only, to avoid excessive residue on the bunches. Wettable sulfur, 3 to 4 pounds per hundred, may be added to the lead arsenate application. If necessary to make later applications, substitute cryolite, 50 per-cent dust (with sulfur) at the rate of 20 pounds per acre. Minimum days from last spray to harvest: DDT, 40, cryolite, 14.

Grape Leafhopper (Erythroneura). This insect has been one of the most serious pests of California grapes, but is now under better control, due to use of organic insecticides and the work of parasites, especially on the second generation. For control, apply DDT, 1½ pounds of 50 per-cent wettable powder per hundred, as the petals fall, and as first cover spray, similar to the procedure for the grape berry moth. Under California conditions, a combination dust of DDT and sulfur is used, at the rate of 15 to 20 pounds per acre. Where the leafhopper has developed resistance to DDT, malathion, as a 4 per cent dust combined with sulfur, is applied at the rate of 15 to 20 pounds per acre in May and early June. Minimum days from last sprays to harvest: DDT, 40, malathion, 4.

Grape Mealybug (*Pseudococcus maritmus*). Apply EPN, 1½ pounds of 25 per-cent wettable powder, or parathion, 1 pound of 15 per-cent wettable powder per hundred. One or 2 applications 7 to 10 days apart should be made as overwintering mealybugs move from under the bark to base buds to grape clusters. Minimum days from last sprays to harvest: EPN, 21, parathion, 14.

Mites

Two-Spotted Spider (*Tetranychus telarius*). Control of the two-spotted mite is by applications of malathion, 2 pounds of wettable powder, when mites first appear and 7 to 10 days later. Parathion may be substituted for the malathion, using ½ to 1 pound of 15 per-cent wettable powder per hundred gallons. Minimum days from last sprays to harvest: malathion, 3, parathion, 14.

Pacific mite (*T. pacificus*), under California conditions, is controlled (preferably with sprays) either by TEPP, ½ pint of 20 per-cent emulsion concentrate at 5- to 7-day intervals, or Systox, 3 fluid ounces of 26 per-cent emulsion per hundred. Minimum days from last sprays to harvest: Systox (demeton), 21.

Powdery Mildew. This is caused by the fungus *Uncinula necator*. It is a very serious disease of the vinifera grapes on the Pacific Coast, where it attacks both the foliage and the fruit, destroying the entire crop if unchecked. In the East, the attack is confined largely to the foliage and cluster stems. Powdery mildew grows rapidly under the semiarid conditions of the West, where there is little rainfall and the humidity is moderately low. Sulfur dust of a purity of 95 to 98 per cent is the common control material in the western states, where thousands of tons are used annually. From 2 to 6 sulfur applications, using 5 to 10 pounds per acre, are made in the season. Application begins when the shoots are 5 to 8 inches long and may continue at intervals until the crop begins to ripen —and following any summer rain.

Under eastern conditions, Bordeaux mixture, 2–4–100; or a fixed copper; or ferbam spray is applied 2 or 3 weeks after bloom, and a second application is made two weeks later (Braun, 1953).

Black Rot. Caused by the fungus *Guignardia bidwelli*, this is a very destructive disease in the district east of the Rocky Mountains. Attacks extend to all green parts of the vine, including foliage and fruit. The spread of the disease is hastened by heavy rains. Control is by 3 or 4 applications of ferbam, 1½ pounds per hundred, or of Bordeaux mixture (4–4–100). The first application is recommended when the shoots are 18 to 24 inches long, with a second 1 or 2 weeks after bloom. Applications of copper sometimes cause injury to the vine (Braun, 1953).

Downy Mildew. Caused by the fungus *Plasmopora viticola*, this is a disease of the eastern grape-growing areas, especially of the cool northern district. Severe foliage infection resulting in partial or complete defoliation occurs in most varieties. Rotting of the fruit may also occur in the

American bunch varieties, but is less noticeable in the Concord and Delaware. Bordeaux mixture (4–4–100) is the usual control material, the first spray just before bloom, one immediately after, and another 7 to 10 days later (Braun, 1953).

Dead Arm. This disease, caused by the fungus *Cryptosporella viticola*, is widely distributed among grapes. Affected canes and arms show yellow, dwarfed, and ragged-edged leaves during midsummer. These conditions are caused by a canker on the arm or on the adjoining trunk which results in a rotting of the wood. Control measures for this disease in California include an application of sodium arsenite before the buds swell in the spring. Sodium arsenite, 3 quarts of a concentrated solution containing an equivalent of 4 pounds of arsenic trioxide per gallon per hundred gallons of water is used. The sodium arsenite spray should not be applied for 3 or more weeks before completion of vine pruning, and always before the swelling of the buds. The solution is very poisonous, so protective clothing should be worn (Staff, Calif. Agr. Exp. Sta., 1959).

BERRY

Insects

Strawberry Aphid (*Pentatrichopus fragaefolii*). This insect is not a serious pest in itself, but in the northwestern district, it is the carrier of the yellow disease and for this reason its control is important. Control measures include the use of certified planting stock and the destruction of diseased or weak plants. New plantings should be dusted every two weeks until after harvest. TEPP, 1 per-cent dust, at 8 to 10 pounds per acre for 6 applications, is used. For mature plantings, use 40 pounds of TEPP per acre for at least 3 applications (Breakey and Others, 1957). Other control materials include lindane, 1½ per-cent dust at 40 pounds per acre, or Systox, 1½ pints per hundred. This will also check the two-spotted mite. Application of Systox should be made at least 21 days before harvest; of lindane, 40; and of TEPP, 3.

Strawberry Root Weevils (Brachyrhinus). Three species of weevil attack the strawberry in the state of Washington. Soil treatment consists of chemical applications just before planting. Heptachlor powder in the amount of 7½ pounds (actual), distributed over the surface of each acre and immediately worked into the soil to a depth of 4 to 6 inches, is generally used. This dosage requires 75 pounds of a 10 per-cent heptachlor dust. Aldrin, at the same dosage, may be substituted for heptachlor. If chlordane is used, it requires 15 pounds of the actual material per acre (Breakey and Others, 1957).

Flea Beetles. Apply rotenone in a 0.75 to 1 per-cent dust at 20 to 35 pounds per acre. Minimum days from last sprays to harvest, one.

Mites, two-spotted, (*Tetranychus telarius*). Apply TEPP, as a 1 per-cent dust at the first sign of infestation (Breakey and Others, 1957); or malathion dust, 4 per-cent at 35 to 40 pounds per acre. Minimum days from last sprays to harvest: TEPP, 3, malathion, 3.

Cyclamen mite (*Steneotarsonemus pallidus*). Use mite-free stock in starting new plantings. Plants may be freed from mites and aphids without injury by immersion for 30 minutes in water heated to 110°F. Packed or tied bunches should be loosened to permit uniform heating. Cool the plants immediately after heating and set out as soon as possible. Strawberry plants may also be fumigated with methyl bromide as a control for mites and aphids. Use 2 pounds of methyl bromide per 1,000 cu ft of space; exposure time, 2 hours at 70°F (Breakey and Others, 1957). The dosage should be lowered slightly at 75°F, and increased somewhat at temperatures lower than 70°F.

Diseases

The strawberry is subject to a number of widespread virus-produced diseases. The grower has no visible means of detecting virus-free plants; hence, the only protection is to use stocks of plants that are substantially free from disease-causing viruses, as well as infesting nematodes. Such plants are now becoming available at a number of nurseries. Virus-free plants have been found for almost all commercial varieties; these are carefully multiplied in enclosures that protect the plants from virus-carrying aphids, and released to the public.

Nematode infestation of the roots of the strawberry may be difficult to detect, so again the use of nematode-free, as well as virus-free, plants is highly desirable.

The following are the recommended methods of treating strawberry plants to free them of root knot and meadow (or root-lesion) nematodes:

(1) Immerse dormant plants for 2 minutes in water heated to 127°F (for the root knot and meadow (or root-lesion) nematodes only).

(2) Immerse dormant plants for 7 minutes in water heated to 121°F (for insects and mites, as well as for plants with root nematodes and those infested with foliar nematodes).

Plants must be held in cold storage at 30°F for at least 2 weeks before treatment to ensure full dormancy; otherwise, they may be killed. Nematode-infested soil should be fumigated before planting, either with di-chloropropene or ethylene dibromide (Darrow and Others, 1957).

Blackberry Mite (Redberry Mite) (*Aceria essigi*). The mite feeds between the drupelets and core of blackberries. Affected berries ripen irregularly and show a characteristic bright red color over part of the berry. For control, apply lime-sulfur solution, 8 gallons (32 degrees

Baumé) per hundred in the early spring, just before the buds swell. A second application may be necessary, using 2½ gallons of lime-sulfur per hundred when the fruiting stems are about 1 foot long (Breakey and others, 1957).

PESTICIDE TOLERANCES FOR CERTAIN FRUITS

The following is a list of official Food and Drug Administration tolerances for various pesticides used on certain fruits. Reference is to preharvest applications. The list is subject to revision; hence, an agricultural officer should be consulted for the latest rulings.

Captan: 100 ppm on apples, pears, and quinces; apricots; cherries; citrus fruits; grapes; peaches and nectarines; plums and fresh prunes; strawberries.

DDT: 7 ppm on apples, pears, and quinces; apricots; cherries; citrus fruits; grapes; peaches and nectarines; plums and fresh prunes; strawberries.

Demeton: 0.75 ppm on apples and pears; strawberries. Grapes, 1.25 ppm.

Dichlone: 3 ppm on apples; peaches.

EPN: 3 ppm on apples, pears, and quinces; apricots; cherries; citrus fruits; grapes; peaches and nectarines; plums and fresh prunes; strawberries.

Ferbam: 7 ppm on apples, pears, and quinces; apricots; cherries; grapes; peaches and nectarines; plums and fresh prunes; strawberries.

Glyodin: 5 ppm on apples, pears, and quinces; cherries; peaches.

Lead arsenate: 7 ppm of combined lead on apples, pears, and quinces; apricots; cherries; grapes; peaches and nectarines; plums and fresh prunes; strawberries. Citrus fruits, 1 ppm.

Lindane: 10 ppm on apples, pears, and quinces; apricots; cherries; citrus fruits; grapes; peaches and nectarines; plums and fresh prunes; strawberries.

Malathion: 8 ppm on apples, pears, and quinces; apricots; cherries; citrus fruits; grapes; peaches and nectarines; plums and fresh prunes; strawberries.

Maneb: 7 ppm on apples; apricots; grapes; peaches.

Methoxychlor: 14 ppm on apples, pears, and quinces; apricots; cherries; grapes; peaches and nectarines; plums and fresh prunes; strawberries.

Nicotine: 2 ppm on apples, pears, and quinces; apricots; cherries; citrus fruits; grapes; peaches and nectarines; plums and fresh prunes; strawberries.

Ovex: 3 ppm on apples and pears; peaches; plums and fresh prunes.

Parathion: 1 ppm on apples, pears, and quinces; apricots; cherries; citrus fruits; grapes; peaches and nectarines; plums and fresh prunes; strawberries.

Tartar emetic: 3.5 ppm of combined antimony trioxide on citrus fruits; grapes.

TDE: 7 ppm on apples, pears, and quinces; apricots; cherries; citrus fruits; grapes; peaches and nectarines; plums and fresh prunes; strawberries.

Thiram: 7 ppm on apples.

Toxaphene: 7 ppm on apples, pears, and quinces; apricots; citrus fruits; peaches and nectarines; strawberries.

Zineb: 7 ppm on apples, pears, and quinces; apricots; cherries; citrus fruits; grapes; peaches and nectarines; plums and fresh prunes; strawberries.

Ziram: 7 ppm on apples, pears, and quinces; apricots; cherries; grapes; peaches and nectarines; strawberries. (Staff, Nat. Agr. Chem. Assoc., 1960).

REFERENCES

Asquith, D., *Farm Chemicals*, **12**(3), 26 (1958).

Bartlett, B. R., and Lloyd, D. C., *J. Econ. Entom.*, **51**, 90 (1958).

Braun, A. J., "1953 Yearbook," Washington, D.C., U.S. Dept. Agr., 1953.

Breakey, E. P., *Wash. Agr. Exp. Sta. Bull.*, **450** (1957).

Clancy, D. W., and McAlister, H. J., *J. Econ. Entom.*, **49**, 196 (1956).

Conners, I. L., *U.S. Dept. Agr. Plant Disease Reporter*, **42**, 165 (1958).

Cox, J. A., *J. Econ. Entom.*, **50**, 455 (1957).

Cressman, A. W., *ibid.*, **48**, 216 (1955).

Cutright, C. R., *ibid.*, **47**, 189 (1954).

———, and Fiori, B., *ibid.*, **48**, 598 (1955).

Daines, R. H., *Agr. Chem.*, **12**(4), 32 (1957).

Darrow, C. M., and Others, *U.S. Dept. Agr. Leaflet*, **414** (1957).

Day, L. H., *Calif. Agr. Exp. Sta. Bull.*, **700** (1947).

de Ong, E. R., Chemistry and Uses of Pesticides, 2d. ed., New York, Reinhold Publishing Corp., 1956.

Dunegan, J. C., *U.S. Dept. Agr. Leaflet*, **406** (1956).

English, H., *U.S. Dept. Agr. Plant Disease Reporter*, **42**, 384 (1958).

Frick, K. E., *J. Econ. Entom.*, **50**, 256 (1957).

Garman, P., *ibid.*, **49**, 521 (1956).

Gast, R. T., *ibid.*, **52**, 9 (1959).

Glass, E. H., *ibid.*, **47**, 1093 (1954).

———, and Fiori, B., *ibid.*, **48**, 598 (1955).

Glass, E. H., and Chapman, P. J., *ibid.*, **48**, 695 (1955).

———, *ibid.*, **50**, 674 (1957).

Grant, T. J., and Others, "1953 Yearbook," Washington, D.C., U.S. Dept. Agr., 1953.

Hamilton, D. W., *J. Econ. Entom.*, **49**, 866 (1956).

———, and Cleveland, M. L., *ibid.*, **50**, 756 (1957).

Hamilton, J. M., and Others, *U. S. Dept. Agr. Plant Disease Reporter*, **41**, 293 (1957).

Jeppson, L. R., and Others, *J. Econ. Entom.*, **50,** 293 (1957).

——, *ibid.*, **51,** 238 (1958).

Keitt, G. W., "1953 Yearbook," Washington, D.C., U.S. Dept. Agr., 1953.

Kienholz, J. R., *ibid.*

Kirby, R. S., *Agr. Chem.*, **12**(5), 41 1957).

Klotz, L. J., and Childs, J. F., "1953 Yearbook," Washington, D.C., U.S. Dept. Agr., 1953.

Madsen, H. F., *J. Econ. Entom.*, **49,** 467 (1956).

——, and Hoyt, S. C., *ibid.*, **50,** 402 (1957).

Madsen, H. F., and Bailey, J. B., *ibid.*, **52,** 493 (1959).

Muma, M. H., *ibid.*, **48,** 432 (1955).

Palmiter, D. H., "1953 Yearbook," Washington, D.C., U.S. Dept. Agr., 1953.

Pickett, A. D., *Agr. Chem.*, **10**(6), 36 (1955).

Porter, B. A., *Entom. Soc. Bull.*, **3**(1), 4 (1957).

Powell, D. and Others, *U.S. Dept. Agr. Plant Disease Reporter,* **42,** 493 (1958).

Rich, A. E., *Agr. Chem.*, **12**(6), 64 (1957).

Riehl, L. A., *J. Econ. Entom.*, **49,** 376 (1956).

——, and Others, *ibid.*, **51,** 193 (1958).

Riehl, L. A., and Wedding, R. T., **52,** 88 (1959a); **52,** 334 (1959b).

Rings, R. W., *ibid.*, **51, 27** (1958).

Scott, C. E., "1953 Yearbook," Washington, D.C., U.S. Dept. Agr., 1953.

Smith, E. H., *J. Econ. Entom.*, **50,** 177 (1957).

——, and Wagenknecht, A. C., *Agr. Chem.*, **14**(4), 51 (1959).

Spencer, H., and Selhime, A. G., *ibid.*, **50,** 364 (1957).

Staff, *Nat. Agr. Chem. Assoc. News,* **16**(2) (1960).

Staff, U.S. Dept. Agr., "Handbook No. 120," 1959a.

——, *Calif. Agr. Exp. Sta. Leaves,* **74–79** (1959b).

Stelzer, D. R., and Fluke, C. L., *J. Econ. Entom.*, **51,** 131 (1958).

Summers, F. M., and Others, *ibid.*, **52, 637** (1959).

Wallace, J. M., and Grant, T. J., "1953 Yearbook," Washington, D.C., U.S. Dept. Agr., 1953.

8. VEGETABLE-CROP INSECTS, DISEASES, AND WEEDS

The application of pesticides to vegetables should always be considered from the standpoint of objectionable residues which might be present at harvest time. Tolerances ranging from a fraction of 1 to 14 ppm have been established by the Federal Food and Drug Administration for many of the pesticides, and others are being added. A few chemicals such as TEPP are not, at present, permitted to show any residue on crops prepared for market. Others, such as ryania and petroleum oils, are exempt from the requirement of a tolerance. Representatives of processing plants, such as canneries and frozen-food factories, should be consulted as to their standards before choosing a pesticide. Weed-control chemicals may also have tolerance limits which must be observed. Since such established tolerances are subject to revision, the latest reports should be obtained from local agricultural officers.

Accidental contamination of vegetables and ornamentals, resulting in injury by drift from herbicides being applied to grain or other crops, has frequently occurred, and should be guarded against. Tomatoes are extremely sensitive, even to deposits on parts of spray machinery previously used for applying one of the hormone sprays, such as 2,4-D (de Ong, 1956). Large areas devoted to lettuce have also been injured by condensed or absorbed residues of insecticides present in the equipment or tank of the spray machinery (de Ong, 1953). To these records, Evans and others (1948) add twelve vegetables which can be killed by 2,4-D and two others (corn and potato) that can be injured. At least two of the crucifers, cabbage and cauliflower, have also been known to be injured by drift from 2,4-D applications.

Pre-emergence applications of herbicides such as Randox, Vegadex, Alanap, and even light dosages of 2,4-D are used on increasing numbers of crops. Dalapon, IPC, and Chloro-IPC are useful for killing grassy weeds, and may act as selective herbicides for certain crops. Petroleum fractions, such as Stoddard Solvent, are used on seedling celery, carrots, onions, and garlic. Potassium cyanate is also recommended as a selective application on garlic and onions 2 or 3 inches tall.

Do not apply TEPP, parathion, EPN, Guthion, demeton, or other dangerous insecticides to the home garden. These are for use only by trained operators who will observe every precaution and assume responsibility.

The effect of insecticides, both from foliage and soil applications, on the flavor of vegetables has been studied by Birdsall and others (1957) as a guide to farmers. The seven hydrocarbon insecticides included aldrin, dieldrin, endrin, chlordane, heptachlor, lindane, and toxaphene, each being supplied by their particular manufacturer. The tests in the study covered four growing seasons and were made on snap beans, beets, cabbage, carrots, cucumbers, onions, potatoes, pumpkin, radishes, rutabagas, squash, and tomatoes. The treated vegetables were evaluated for flavor in the form in which usually consumed. Storage tests were also made on the canned vegetables and on some of the raw vegetables.

Soil treatments were applied shortly before planting at a depth of about 3 inches. Foliage applications were made on all vegetables one month after emergence and repeated until one month before harvest. The dosages used on foliage expressed as pounds of active material per acre, were as follows: 0.25 of aldrin, dieldrin, endrin, heptachlor, and lindane; chlordane, 1, and toxaphene, 1.5. The heavy dosage on foliage was four times that given above for each individual material. The soil dosages were 2 pounds per acre of the active material for all the insecticides, except for chlordane, the dose of which was 4 pounds, and toxaphene, 6 pounds per acre. The heavy dosages were four times the normal dosage.

Of the forty-five significant changes in flavor due to insecticide treatment, only seven were rated desirable. Canned vegetables showed more undesirable changes than when tasted cooked or raw. Of the forty-five significant changes in flavor, nineteen were due to foliage applications and twenty-five to soil applications. Lindane had the largest number of undesirable changes, especially when the vegetables were canned. Of the other six insecticides, but little effect on flavor was noted when both raw and processed series were taken together. Canned beets, to which endrin had been applied, showed a decided darkening of color. Slight increases in the redness of yellow squash, pumpkin, carrot, and rutabagas were noted. Flavor changes noted with heavy applications were usually also found with the lighter ones. Beets, sauerkraut, pumpkin, and rutabagas seemed susceptible to changes in flavor due to insecticide applications, while snap beans, carrots, tomatoes, cabbage, and cucumbers seemed to be more resistant (Birdsall and Others, 1957).

Soil applications to Black Valentine beans of DDT, BHC, lindane, aldrin, dieldrin, and chlordane, at dosages of 5 to 100 pounds of active material per acre, may affect the nitrogen, phosphorus, and potassium content of the plant, and influence the size of the mite population (Rodriguez and others, 1957).

The rate of breakdown in a silt loam and a sandy loam has been determined for lindane at rates of 10 and 100 pounds per 6-inch acre, and aldrin at rates of 2, 20, and 200 pounds per 6-inch acre.

"Lindane was found to break down within 2 weeks after application to a nontoxic compound, which was still detected by the colorimetric method for lindane, but not by bioassay. Two weeks after treatment the quantity estimated by bioassay amounted to 66 percent of that obtained by chemical analysis. Even after 3 years the same ratio was found between bioassay and chemical results. When field samples were analyzed, 3.5 years after the treatment, the quantity estimated by bioanalysis amounted to 46 per cent of that obtained by chemical analysis."

Aldrin was converted to dieldrin, the presence of the latter being shown by chemical analysis. Laboratory experiments showed that 2 weeks after treatment no dieldrin was formed in a loam held at 7°C. In soils, held at 26° or 46°C, 4 to 8 per cent of the recovered insecticides were found to be dieldrin. The peak of dieldrin formation was at 56 days after treatment, followed by decrease (Lichenstein and Others, 1959).

Malathion residue tests on leafy and fleshy vegetables, using 1.75 pounds per acre as dusts, wettable powders, and emulsion formulations, showed a similar deposit, but that from emulsions was reduced the quickest. Rainfall was a factor in removing residues and "in most tests the residues on leafy vegetables remained above 8 ppm for 3 days or longer when no rainfall occurred, and for as long as 14 days on parsley." Parsley washed for 1 minute in tap water showed a reduction in residue from 36 to 3 ppm or lower (Wallis and Others, 1957).

The toxicity of certain insecticides to a group of vegetable-infesting insects has been determined, under existing conditions in Maryland, by Young and Ditman (1959). All insecticides were used in the emulsifiable or miscible form. Amounts of actual toxicant used per acre were as follows: Thiodan 0.28, ethion 0.28, Sevin 0.44, malathion 0.56, Dibrom 0.14, and Trithion 0.26 pound.

Trithion and Thiodan, alone, showed more than 75 per-cent reduction of potato aphids (*Macrosiphum solanifolii*), on both eggplant and tomato. All the treatments except Sevin and Dibrom (an organophosphate compound gave a 75 per-cent or greater reduction of the cabbage aphid (*Brevicoryne brassicae*). The melon aphid (*Aphis gossypii*), on cucumber, showed a 75 per-cent or greater control with Sevin, malathion, Thiodan, and Trithion. Only Thiodan gave significant reduction to the small population of flea beetles (*Phyllotreta cruciferae*). All treatments gave high reduction of the margined blister beetle, potato-leaf hopper, cabbage looper, and the imported cabbageworm. No off-flavors were detected in any of the crops.

The following recommendations and reports on pest control are subject to revision under varying conditions and, hence, should be checked with local agricultural officers. Staff, 1959a; Staff, 1959b; Reed *et al.* 1956.

For the home garden, preference should be given to the less hazardous pesticides such as nicotine sulfate, rotenone and pyrethrins.

ASPARAGUS

Insects

Asparagus Beetle (*Crioceris asparagi*). DDT, 5 per-cent dust at 20 to 35 pounds per acre, or an equivalent amount of active material as an emulsion concentrate, is recommended for this insect. Apply to seedlings only. Rotenone, 0.75 per-cent dust at 20 to 35 pounds per acre, may be used later in the season with a 1-day interval before harvest (Staff, 1959a).

Diseases

Rust. This disease is caused by the fungus *Puccinia asparagi*. The infected tops, which grow up after the cutting season, have a dusty red appearance and when dsturbed give off a cloud of red dust which are the spores. The tops die prematurely, thus weakening the plants from year to year and shortening the life of the field.

Dusting or spraying with sulfur aids in control, and there are also resistant varieties available.

Applications of zineb, 65 per-cent, at 2 to 3 pounds per hundred gallons of water to the acre, have proven more successful than other organic fungicides, under Illinois conditions. Spraying in uncut fields should begin by June 1, and in harvested fields, as soon as the tops are maturing. Repeat the applications every 8 to 10 days until about the middle of August (Linn and Luban, 1958).

BEAN

Insects

Aphids (Various). Parathion, 2 per-cent dust at 20 to 35 pounds per acre; malathion, 5 per-cent dust at 20 to 35 pounds per acre; or nicotine sulfate, 40 per-cent concentrate, 2 pints per hundred gallons are recommended. Minimum days from last spray to harvest: malathion, 1, nicotine sulfate, 3, and parathion, 15 (Staff, U.S. Dept. Agr., 1959b).

Mexican Bean Beetle (*Epilachna varivestis*). Malathion, 5 per-cent dust at 20 to 35 pounds per acre; methoxychlor, same dosage as for malathon; parathion, ½ pound per acre as dust or spray; or rotenone, 0.75 per-cent dust at 20 to 35 pounds per acre are recommended. Minimum days from last spray to harvest: malathion, 1, methoxychlor, 7, parathion, 15, and rotenone, 1 (Staff, U.S. Dept. Agr., 1959b).

Resistance to the insecticidal effect of rotenone by the Mexican bean beetle has been reported from districts in North Carolina. Other materials are now being recommended in its place (Brett and Brubaker, 1955).

Seed Corn Maggot (*Hylemya cilicrura*). Lindane, 75 per-cent wettable powder at $\frac{1}{3}$ to $\frac{2}{3}$ ounce per hundred pounds of seed is prescribed. Heptachlor, dieldrin, aldrin, and endrin may be substituted for lindane, as 75 per-cent wettable powders at $\frac{2}{3}$ ounce per hundred pounds of seed. A seed fungicide should be added to any of these treatments.

Cucumber Beetle, Spotted (*Diabrotica undecimpunctata*). DDT, 5 per-cent dust at 30 to 40 pounds per acre in the seedling stage is recommended. Do not use the straw for feed. For rotenone, use the same formula as for Mexican bean beetle. Minimum days from last spray to harvest: DDT, 7, and rotenone, 1.

Cutworms. DDT is used in the seedling stage, in the same proportions as for cucumber beetle. Apply directly to the rows. Toxaphene dust or spray is added to the soil surface.

Japanese Beetle. DDT, 3 to 5 per-cent dust at 20 to 35 pounds per acre, is used. Do not feed the straw to meat or dairy animals. Methoxychlor, 5 per-cent dust at 20 to 35 pounds per acre may be used. Minimum days from last spray to harvest: DDT, 7, and methoxychlor, 7.

Spider Mites. Sulfur, 90 to 98 per-cent purity, at 15 to 20 pounds per acre on dry limas and kidney beans when used early helps prevent build-up. This may injure at high temperatures. Kelthane at 0.4 pound of active material per acre is used not later than 7 days before harvest.

Diseases

Choose resistant varieties. Caution should be used in applying fungicides because bean foliage is very sensitive. Daines and Others (1957) found that captan injured bean foliage under certain conditions, but the addition of calcium carbonate or magnesium oxide reduced the danger.

Powdery Mildew. This is caused by the fungus *Erysiphe polygoni*. Sulfur is used in control as with spider mites. Apply at the first sign of infestation.

Soil Fungi and Nematodes. Beans are subject to infestation by soil fungi and by the root-knot nematode. The latter is controlled, under Southern California conditions, by dosages of 150 to 200 pounds of methyl bromide per acre. To broaden the field of control, and thus distribute the cost, experiments were made with methyl bromide at heavier dosages to determine the possibility of controling both nematodes and the *Fusarium* wilt fungus (*Fusarium oxysporum f. tracheiphilum*). The methyl bromide, at dosages of 200 to 300 pounds per acre, was chiseled into the soil at a depth of 8 inches, and covered within 15 minutes by polyethylene tarpaulins which remained for 22 hours. Black-eye beans (*Vigna sinensis*) were planted two days later as an assay crop to determine the success of the treatment. The dosages of 200 to 300 pounds per acre controlled the root-knot nematode and the *Fusarium* wilt organism to a depth of 3 feet. The dosage of 300 pounds per acre controlled the fungi *Scerotium bataticola,* but not *Rhizoctonia solani* and a *Stemphyllium* species. Thomason (1959).

BEET

Insects

Cutworms. DDT dust, 2 pounds per acre applied to the soil surface before planting, or toxaphene dust at 3 pounds per acre applied in the same way are recommended. (See restrictions for beet webworm.)

Beet Webworm (*Loxostege sticticalis*). Foliage applications of DDT, 5 per-cent dust; pyrethrins, 0.2 per-cent dust; or toxaphene, 10 per-cent dust, at 20 to 30 pounds per acre are used. Do not apply the DDT or the toxaphene after the appearance of the first leaves to be eaten, marketed, or fed to dairy or meat animals.

Diseases

Beet-Yellow Virus. This is an important disease of table-beet seed plants in the state of Washington. It also attacks sugar beets in the United States and Europe. The green peach aphid (*Myzus persicae*) is the vector of the virus, and control is directed against this insect. Applications of Thimet and demeton proved the most satisfactory in the control of these insects, control lasting for 18 to 24 days after application (McLean, 1957). Malathion may be used on table beets at 1¼ pound of active material per acre. Do not apply within 7 days of harvest.

CABBAGE (BROCCOLI, BRUSSELS SPROUTS, CAULIFLOWER, KALE)

Insects

Aphid (*Brevicoryne brassicae*). For these, apply malathion, 5 per-cent dust at 20 to 35 pounds per acre. Do not apply malathion to broccoli within 3 days before harvest, or to cabbage, brussels sprouts, cauliflower, or kale within 7 days of harvest. Nicotine sulfate may be applied as a 3.6 per-cent dust at 40 to 50 pounds per acre, or as a spray of 2 pints of 40 per-cent concentrate per hundred gallons of water. Do not use within 3 days of a harvest. Parathion, 2 per-cent dust at 20 to 35 pounds per acre, may not be used within 21 days of a harvest, and TEPP, either as dust or emulsion concentrate, ¼ to ½ pound of active material, 3 days before harvest.

Demeton at 0.5 pound per acre, either as a dust or spray, was found by Wene (1957) to reduce the aphid population for 3 weeks; however, reinfestation was beginning by that time. Good results were also obtained with phosdrin and diazinon. Residues of demeton, applied at 0.5 pound per acre, were 0.2 to 0.22 ppm in 64 days from last application to harvest and, in another test, 0.25 and 0.62 ppm for 49 days from application to harvest—all within the permissible tolerance of 0.75 ppm in mature cabbage (Wilson and Van Middelem, 1958). Do not use demeton, parathion, or TEPP in the home garden.

(*Photo, F. E. Skinner*)

Figure 7. Adult Syrphid fly whose larvae attack aphids.

(*Photograph, Doten & Skinner*)

Figure 8. Syrphid fly larva feeding on aphids.

Caterpillars. These include the cabbage looper (*Trichoplusia ni*), imported cabbageworm (*Pieris rapae*), diamondback moth (*Plutella maculipennis*), southern cabbageworm (*Pieris protodice*), cabbage webworm (*Hellula rogatalis*), and salt-marsh caterpillar (*Estigmene acrea*).

In seedling stage, and every 7 days as necessary, apply DDT, 1¼ pound; or toxaphene, 2 to 3 pounds; or rotenone, ¼ pound per acre. DDT or toxaphene is not to be applied to cabbage after the heads begin to form, if any of the outer leaves are to be left on them at harvest. If all outer leaves are strpped from the heads at harvest, then DDT or toxaphene may be appled up to 7 days before harvest (Staff, U.S. Dept. Agr., 1959).

For use after heads begin to form, malathion, 1¼ pounds; or parathion, ½ pound; or rotenone, 0.25 pound per acre are recommended. Do not apply parathion within 21 days, or malathion within 7 days, of harvest. Do not apply parathion in the home garden (Reid and Cuthbert, 1957; Reed and Doolittle, 1956).

Root Maggots (Various). Apply chlordane, 5 per-cent dust, to stem and roots of plants and on soil around the plant when transplanting. The seedbed may be treated before planting, using 5 pounds per acre. Do not aply chlordane to plants past seedling stage.

Harlequin Bug (*Murgantia histrionica*). Before heads begin to form, apply DDT as a 5 per-cent dust. After heads begin to form, use sabadilla as a 10 to 20 per-cent dust at 25 pounds per acre. Do not apply sabadilla within a day of harvest.

Hofmaster (1959) found that, under existing conditions in Virginia, DDT and sabadilla were less effective than other insecticides against adult harlequin cabbage bugs. Sevin, at 0.5 per-cent, and Thiodan, at 0.5 per-cent active ingredient per acre, gave 100 per-cent knockdown in 6 hours or less. Trithion and Dytox (Dipterex) were slower in action, but gave good results. A combination of parathion, 0.25 per-cent, plus toxaphene, at 2.0 pounds of active ingredients per acre, gave better results than either chemical used alone.

Diseases

Clubroot. A disease of cabbage and related plants, this is caused by a slime mold (*Plasmodiophora brassicae*). It is widely distributed over the United States and Europe. The disease is characterized by large swellings of the root system and a weakened and discolored top. Seedlings should be grown in clean soil, and infested fields should be planted with non-susceptible crops. The use of ½ pint per plant of pentachloronitrobenzene solution (3 pounds of active ingredient per hundred gallons) as transplanting water gives some protection.

Cetas (1958) reports successful control in experiments with Vapam

(V.P.M.) when used as a soil drench. A band application of the material at the rate of 1 pint per linear foot of row, diluted with 5 gallons of water, and followed immediately with 1½ inches of water applied as overhead irrigation, resulted in a weed-free band 16 inches wide, satisfactory plant growth, and good control of clubroot. The application was made with one shank of a shank applicator one month prior to setting the cabbage plants.

Black Rot. This is a bacterial-caused disease of central, southern and eastern regions. Use seed grown on the Pacific Coast, which is free from the disease. Rotate crops to avoid growing susceptible crops in diseased fields.

CELERY

Insects

Leaf Tier (*Udea rubigalis*). Two applications half an hour apart of pyrethrins, 0.2 per-cent dust, or DDT, 5 per-cent dust, at 20 to 30 pounds per acre should be made. Do not apply after the bunch begins to form, or the stalk is half-grown.

CUCUMBER

Insects

Cucumber Beetle (*Diabrotica balteata*). Apply cryolite, 50 to 90 per-cent dust, at 20 to 40 pounds per acre. The residue is to be removed by washing or brushing. DDT, 3 per-cent dust, or rotenone, 1 per-cent dust, at 20 to 40 pounds per acre may be used. DDT should not be applied within 7 days of harvest.

Aphids. Apply malathion, 4 per-cent dust at 20 to 40 pounds per acre; nicotine sulfate, 40 per-cent concentrate, 2 pints per hundred gallons; or parathion, ¼ to ½ pound per acre. Minimum days from application to harvest: malathion, 3 nicotine, 3, and parathion, 15. Do not use parathion in the home garden.

Pickleworm (*Diaphania nitidalis*). Apply cryolite (see cucumber beetle); lindane, 1 per-cent dust at 30 to 40 pounds per acre (not to be used if ground is to be used later for potatoes or other root crop because of flavor impairment); rotenone, 1 per-cent dust; or sabadilla, 20 per-cent dust, at 20 to 40 pounds per acre. Remove excess cryolite residue by washing or brushing.

Spider Mites (Various). Apply malathion, 5 per-cent dust; or parathion, 2 per-cent dust, at 20 to 35 pounds per acre. Parathion should not be applied within 15 days of harvest, and malathion, within 3 days. Do not apply parathion in the home garden.

Diseases

Powdery Mildew. Apply sulfur dust, 95 to 98 concentrate. This may cause injury at high temperatures.

Downy Mildew. Apply a weak Bordeaux mixture, a fixed-copper fungicide, or an organic fungicide, except ferbam. Resistant varieties should be grown. Control by the use of a number of antibiotics is shown by Ark and others (1957).

EGGPLANT

Insects

Colorado Potato Beetle. For this insect, apply DDT, 5 per-cent dust; or rotenone, 0.75 per-cent dust, at 20 to 30 pounds per acre. Do not apply DDT within 5 days of a harvest.

Flea Beetles, Hornworms, and Other Worms. DDT, 5 per-cent dust at 20 to 30 pounds per acre, is recommended. Wash or wipe fruit before marketing.

Spider Mites. Apply malathion, 5 per-cent dust at 20 to 30 pounds per acre. Do not apply malathion within 3 days of a harvest.

Diseases

Fruit-Rot Fungus. Use resistant varieties.

LETTUCE

Insects

Aphids (Leaf-feeding). Apply parathion, 2 per-cent dust at 25 pounds per acre; malathion, 4 per-cent dust at 35 to 40 pounds per acre; or demeton as an emulsion concentrate, ¼ to ½ pound of active material per acre. Minimum time from last application to harvest: parathion, 3 weeks; malathion, 10 days for head and leaf lettuce; demeton, 21 days. Do not apply demeton or parathion in the home garden.

Cabbage Looper and Other Caterpillars. DDT, 5 per-cent dust, plus toxaphene, 15 per-cent dust, at 20 to 30 pounds per acre is used. Do not use after the heads begin to form, or on leaves that are to be eaten.

Leaf Hoppers, Six-spotted (*Macrosteles fascifrons*). These are carriers of the virus causing aster yellows to lettuce. Apply DDT, dust or spray, 1¼ pounds per acre; malathion, 1¼ pounds per acre; or methoxychlor 1¼ pounds per acre, either as dust or spray. Do not use DDT after the heads begin to form or on leaves that are to be eaten or fed to dairy or meat animals. Minimum time from last application to harvest for malathion, 10 days; for methoxychlor, 14 days.

Diseases

Mosaic. This is a virus-caused disease that reduces the yields and lowers the quality. It can be reduced by isolation, insect control, and destroying infected plants in seed-growing fields. Aphids spread the disease after it has been introduced in the seed. Prevention by control of aphids is difficult. High-quality seed and destruction of infected plants and wild-lettuce plants (*Lactuca sativa*) will aid in prevention (Grogan and Others, 1955).

Powdery Mildew. This disease is caused by the fungus *Erysiphe cichoracearum*; it attacks both surfaces of the leaf, causing a slight yellowing or browning effect. The disease occurs mostly in the fall and is independent of wet weather. Sulfur-dusting at first sign of the disease, and repeated as necessary, will afford control if the air temperature is 70°F and above. Injury may occur at high summer temperatures (Grogan and Others, 1955).

Downy Mildew. This is caused by the fungus *Bremia lactucae*; it thrives in moist air and at temperatures of 50° to 60°F. The first attack is on the lower side of the leaves, and within a few days the wind-borne spores are being distributed. Control of the disease in Florida is reported with applications of zineb (Parzate), 2 pounds, and maneb (Manzate), 1½ pounds, per acre.

Tipburn. This is manifested as browned edges of the surface leaves and interior of the head. It is not caused by any organism, but by a physiologic disturbance.

Bacterial Soft Rots. These, caused by the bacteria *Erwinia* and perhaps *Pseudomonas*, are transit diseases reported to be causing much loss in Florida. It is thought to be in part due to a lack of proper control of water table and fertilization. A high degree of control of the forms known as "jelly butt" and "slime head" resulted from dipping the lettuce in streptomycin sulfate solution at a concentration of 10 p.p.m. Jelly butt was controlled by painting the butts with a solution of Agrimycin-100 containing 250 p.p.m. streptomycin sulfate (Winfree, 1958).

MELON

Insects

Aphids. Apply malathion, 5 per-cent dust at 20 to 40 pounds per acre; nicotine sulfate, 40 per-cent concentrate, 2 pints per hundred gallons of water; or parathion, 2 per-cent dust at 15 to 30 pounds per acre. The latter is not to be used in the home garden. Minimum days from last application to harvest: malathion, 1, nicotine, 3, and parathion, 7.

Parathion and malathion should not be applied when bees are in the field. Applications should be made late in the evening, after blossoms close, or early in the morning, before they open.

Cucumber Beetle. See Cucumber.

Leaf Miner and Thrips. Apply parathion, 2 per-cent dust at 20 to 30 pounds per acre. This is not to be used in the home garden. It should not be applied when bees are in the field, but very early in the morning or late in the evening. Minimum days from last application to harvest, 14.

Seed-Corn Maggot (*Hylemya cilicrura*). Use lindane, wettable powder, 1 ounce per hundred pounds of seed. A fungicide should be added to this treatment.

The value of an insecticide-fungicide combination treatment as a protectant of the seed of cucumber and winter squash has been shown by Natti and others (1958). Such combinations, regardless of dosage, usually gave better stands than when the fungicide was used alone. Ratios of 1 to 4 and 1 to 8 of insecticide to fungicide gave rather similar results. The dieldrin combination with a fungicide gave a higher total emergence of seedlings than did heptachlor and lindane. The combination treatments controlled seed-corn maggot injury on squash seed, and gave the largest number of normal plants.

Leafhoppers. Apply parathion, 2 per-cent dust at 15 to 30 pounds per acre. Do not use this in the home garden, or when bees are in the field. Minimum days from last application to harvest, 14.

Pickleworm. See Cucumber.

Melon Fly (*Dacus cucurbitae*). The severe attack of this insect on cucumbers and melons in many parts of the world has led to many attempts at control. Steiner (1954, 1955) reported the value of a bait spray composed of a yeast hydrolysate and malathion in relation to passion-fruit production. Later the use of the formula was broadened to include the Oriental fruit fly, the melon fly, and the Mediterranean fruit fly. It is stated that "biweekly applications of 4 pounds of 25 percent malathion wettable powder and one pound of protein hydrolysate per acre in from 5 to 150 gallons of water have generally been found adequate for heavy infestations."

Further tests (Nishida and Others, 1957) of the malathion-hydrolysate bait spray on the melon fly showed that, as a residual spray applied to isolated plants, the baited spray gave a higher kill than the nonbaited. The residual effect of both the baited and nonbaited sprays, however, lasted but approximately 1 to 2 days. In field tests on the melon fly attacking cucumbers and cantaloupes, "there were no significant differences in fly population and fruit infestation between baited and nonbaited plots."

The latent toxicity of a number of insecticides to the melon fly was determined by Sherman (1958). The term *latent insecticide* (Tamashiro and Sherman, 1955) refers to the delayed total lethal effect of an insecticide which, when applied to the larval stage, does not manifest its full action until after the insect becomes an adult. Third instar larvae of the melon fly were placed in jars containing moist sand and the required concentration of insecticide and left for seven days, and then removed to clean sand. "Latent toxicity was shown by aldrin, chlordane, dieldrin, endrin and isodrin but to a lesser degree than to the Mediterranean fruit fly. Lindane, malathion and parathion evinced no latent toxicity to the melon fly."

Spider Mites. Parathion, 2 per-cent dust at 30 pounds per acre, is applied. Time between last application and harvest is 14 days. Do not use parathion in the home garden. Sulfur, 95 to 98 per-cent concentration at 20 to 25 pounds per acre, may be used on honeydews and sulfur-resistant melons.

Parathion and malathion should not be applied when bees are in the field. Applications should be made late in the evening, after the blossoms close, or early in the morning, before they open.

Diseases

Mosaic. This is a disease caused by viruses. Perennial weeds may be harboring the viruses that attack melons and squash. The viruses are also carried in muskmelon seeds and are distributed to other plants. Diseased plants and perennial weeds should be removed and destroyed. Use the recommended measures for controlling aphids (plant lice).

Downy Mildew. This disease is caused by the fungus *Pseudoperononospora cubensis*. Apply Bordeaux mixture or a fixed copper, or one of the organic fungicides, except ferbam or maneb, as directed for foliage use by the manufacturer.

A new variety of cantaloupe, named Homegarden, has been developed which has moderate field resistance to downy mildew and high resistance to the melon aphid *Aphis gossypii* (Ivanoff, 1957).

Powdery Mildew. On melon varieties that are sulfur-resistant, dusting sulfur may be applied at the rate of 15 to 20 pounds per acre. (See the variety named Homegarden under Downy Mildew.)

ONION

Insects

Seed-Corn Maggot. Apply aldrin, 75 per-cent powder at $\frac{2}{3}$ ounce per hundred pounds of seed, or heptachlor, 75 per-cent powder at $\frac{2}{3}$ ounce per hundred pounds of seed. Add a fungicide to the treated seed.

Onion Maggot (*Hylemya antiqua*). Apply dieldrin or heptachlor as a wettable powder slurry, $\frac{2}{3}$ ounce of either, per hundred pounds of seed.

For garden use, heptachlor, ⅛ teaspoon of 50 per-cent wettable powder, is added to a ⅛-ounce packet of onion seed. Shake packet well and add excess powder to the planting furrow. Add a fungicide to the treated seed.

Shirck (1957), during experiments in Idaho for the control of the onion maggot, confirmed the value of seed treatment for mild infestation; for seed onions, better results were gotten by soaking the bulbs before planting. Three insecticides were used as emulsion concentrates, at ¾ pound of the toxicant in 50 gallons of water: chlordane at 75 per-cent, heptachlor at 25 per-cent, and aldrin at 25 per-cent concentration. The best results were obtained with chlordane, followed in descending order by the remaining two.

Onion Thrips (*Thrips tabaci*). For seed and dry onions only. Apply DDT, 10 per-cent dust; toxaphene, 20 per-cent dust; malathion, 5 per-cent dust; or parathion, 2 per-cent dust, at 30 pounds per acre. Repeat applications as necessary every 7 to 14 days apart. The minimum time between last application and harvest for parathion is 14 days, and for malathion, 3 days. Do not apply parathion in the home garden.

At the Winter Garden Experiment Station, Texas, it was found that none of the chlorinated hydrocarbon insecticides when used alone gave satisfactory control of thrips, but combinations of malathion and either dieldrin or heptachlor gave much better control. The dosages used were malathion, 0.625 pound plus 0.38 pound of dieldrin; or malathion, 0.625 pound plus 0.5 pound of heptachlor; or malathion alone, 1.25, in 21 gallons of water per acre (Richardson, 1957).

Diseases

Downy Mildew. This is caused by the fungus *Peronospora destructor*. The disease causes violet-tinted fuzz on leaves and seedstalks, followed by collapsed tissue and death. It spreads rapidly in rainy or foggy weather. Apply zineb, 6.5 per-cent dust at 30 to 40 pounds per acre—or as a spray as directed by the manufacturer.

Smut. This disease is caused by the fungus *Urocystis cepulae*. It attacks only very young plants; hence, the seed may be planted in soil free from the disease and the seedlings transplanted to the field. To grow field-sown onions on infested soil, apply a formaldehyde solution in the furrow with the seed, using a tank with a graduated feed. The formaldehyde solution is made by adding 1 pint of commercial formalin to 8 gallons of water.

PEA (GARDEN)

Insects

Aphid (*Macrosiphum pisi*). Malathion, as dust or spray, at 1 or 1¼ pounds of active material per acre; parathion, ⅓ to ½ pound of active material per acre; or rotenone, 1 per-cent dust at 35 pounds per acre is recommended. Use DDT only before pods form. The minimum time between the last application and harvest is 3 days for malathion and for parathion, 10 days. The latter material should not be used when bees are in the field, nor should it be used in the home garden.

Weevil (*Bruchus pisorum*). Use DDT, as a 5 per-cent dust at 20 to 25 pounds per acre; methoxychlor, 5 per-cent dust at 20 to 25 pounds per acre; or parathion, 1 per-cent dust at 25 to 35 pounds per acre may be used. Minimum time between the last application and harvest, for methoxychlor, 7 days, and for parathion, 10 days.

Diseases

Seed Rot. Use a seed fungicide.

POTATO

Insects

Aphids (Various). Apply DDT, 5 per-cent dust; malathion, 4 per-cent dust; or parathion, 1 per-cent dust; or rotenone, 0.75 to 1 per-cent dust, at 20 to 35 pounds per acre; or nicotine sulfate, 40 per-cent concentration, 1½ pints per hundred gallons. Minimum time between the last application and harvest, for malathion, 3 days, and for parathion, 5 days. The latter material should not be used in the home garden.

The green peach aphid (*Myzus persicae*), under Washington State conditions, has been shown to be difficult to control at the height of infestation, even with the systemic insecticide schraden. Diazinon and schraden, at ½ pound dosages per acre, gave "relatively poor initial kill." But schraden at 1 pound per acre gave "nearly 100 percent control for 3 to 7 days." After the peak invasion of winged aphids, many of the insecticides gave control for from 13 to 17 days (Landis and Schopp, 1958).

Blister Beetles (Various). These are feeders on potatoes and many other crops. Apply DDT, as dust or spray, 1½ to 2 pounds per acre, or toxaphene, 10 per-cent dust, 20 to 30 pounds per acre.

Colorado Potato Beetle and Flea Beetles. Apply calcium arsenate, 25 per-cent dust in lime, 20 to 35 pounds per acre; or DDT, 3 to 5 per-cent dust, at 20 to 35 pounds per acre; or rotenone, 0.75 to 1 per-cent dust, at 20 to 35 pounds per acre.

Leafhoppers (Various). Apply DDT as for the Colorado potato beetle, or malathion, 4 per-cent dust, at 20 to 35 pounds per acre. Minimum time between last application and harvest is 5 days.

Potato Tuberworm (*Gnorimoschema operculella*). Apply DDT as for the Colorato potato beetle. If necessary, repeat at 10- to 14-day intervals.

Wireworms (Various). *Soil treatment before planting,* aldrin or heptachlor, 2 to 3 pounds of active material per acre, as dust or emulsion, should be added. All materials to be disked into the soil 4 to 6 inches deep.

Root Knot Nematode. See Tomato.

Diseases

Scab. A fungus-caused disease, scab is carried on the tuber and also lives in the soil. Growth is favored by an alkaline soil and the use of lime, woodashes, and fresh manure. Use clean seed in soil not affected with the disease. Sulfur may be added as needed to lower the pH of the soil to 4.8 to 5.0 (slightly acidic).

Early Blight. This disease, caused by the fungus *Alternaria solani,* attacks the foliage and reduces the yield. The fungus lives in the soil and is also found on the tuber. Apply zineb, 65 per-cent concentration at 2 pounds per hundred gallons of water, and at 300 to 400 gallons per acre, or Bordeaux mixture or fixed copper as directed by the manufacturer. Use clean seed.

Gerhold (1957) found that, under severe experimental field conditions, control of early blight by zineb was decidedly superior to that from maneb and from captan. The dosages for each of the three fungicides was 3 pounds per hundred gallons for 6 applications at 10 to 14 days apart.

Late Blight. This is caused by the fungus *Phytophthora infestans.* It kills areas on the leaves and stems and infects the tuber, which may rot in storage. The fungus is carried on the tuber.

Clean seed should be used and blight-resistant varieties cultivated. Apply zineb, 65 per-cent concentration, at 1½ pounds per hundred gallons of water, and at 300 to 400 gallons per acre; or other organic fungicide (except ferbam and ziram), as directed by the manufacturer; or Bordeaux mixture or a fixed copper.

A comparison of the value of various fungicides as a control for late blight of potatoes has been made on Prince Edward Island (Canada). Seven applications were made, ranging from July 3 to September 13. The highest yield, 463 bushels per acre, was from the use of a 2 to 1 mixture of maneb and tri-basic copper, and containing a small portion of zinc sulfate. Following in descending order was Dithane M-22 with 461.9 bu; CR-1510 with 440.6 bu; Thioneb 50-W with 437.6 bu; Dyrene 50-W with 435.1 bu; Bordeaux with 431.7 bu; and check with 364.8 bu (Callbeck, 1958).

Virus Diseases. Plant certified seed and choose resistant varieties.

PUMPKIN AND SQUASH

Insects

Pickleworm. See Cucumber.

Squash Vine Borer (*Melittia cucurbitae*). This insect bores into vines and the stem near the crown. Apply lindane, 1 per-cent dust at 20 to 30 pounds per acre, or rotenone, 1 per-cent dust at 20 to 40 pounds per acre. Lindane is not to be used on fields that will be planted later with potatoes because the flavor may be affected. Minimum time between the last application and harvest for lindane is 1 day.

Squash Bug (*Anasa tristis*). Apply sabadilla, 20 per-cent dust at 20 to 40 pounds per acre, or DDT, 5 per-cent dust, to the bugs on soil and under trap boards. Do not apply the latter on plants. Minimum time between the last application of DDT and harvest is 5 days, and for sabadilla, 1 day.

Wright and Decker (1955) in a comparison of the value of various insecticides against the squash bug, found that aldrin and parathion gave good initial kills, but this decreased after 8 days. Dieldrin, at 0.5 pound actual material per acre proved superior to all other insecticides, fewer eggs being laid; nymphs were killed, and adult bugs exposed to 7-day old deposits were all dead in 96 hours. Minimum time between the last application and harvest is 14 days.

SWEET POTATO

Insects

Wireworms. See Potato.

Sweet Potato Weevil (*Cylas formicarius elegantulus*). The larvae of this pest bore through the sweet potatoes and vines. Apply dieldrin, 2 per-cent dust, at 75 pounds per acre in one application, or 40 pounds in each of two applications, at the base of the plants in narrow strips. Minimum time between the last application of dieldrin and harvest is 21 days.

TOMATO

Insects

Root Knot Nematode. Soil fumigation with ethylene dibromide, 83 per-cent, at 3 to 4 gallons of active material per acre is recommended. Apply 7 to 14 days before planting. DD mixture, 100 per cent concentration at 20 gallons per acre, is also used.

Lear (1957) has shown that dibromochloropropane is an effective nematode control and can be safely applied to sites of certain living plants.

It is also effective at much lower dosages than is ethylene dibromide. Plants sensitive to the former material include onions, garlic, sweet potato, Irish potato, and sugar beets.

Effective nematode control is also shown by sodium n-methyl dithio-carbamate when used as a water solution at 4 pounds of active material per gallon. It may be applied by flooding or overhead sprinkling.

Winstead and Others (1958) have shown the practical value of vermiculite instead of liquid application as a carrier of the fumigants D-D and EDB. The latter materials, at the usual acreage dosage, are mixed with the powder in a keg and applied with a fertilizer applicator to vegetable crops.

Colorado Potato Beetle. Apply cryolite, 50 to 90 per-cent dust; DDT, 5 per-cent dust, at 20 to 30 pounds per acre. Minimum time between the last application and harvest for both cryolite and DDT is 5 days.

Hornworm (*Protoparce quinquemaculata*). Apply cryolite, 50 to 90 per-cent, or TDE, 10 per-cent dust, at 20 to 30 pounds per acre; or toxaphene, 10 per-cent dust at 30 pounds per acre. Minimum time between the last application and harvest for cryolite is 5 days, for TDE, 1 day, and for toxaphene, 5 days. See figure 9.

Flea Beetles. Apply cryolite, 50 to 90 per-cent; DDT, 5 per-cent dust; methoxychlor, 5 per-cent dust; at 20 to 30 pounds per acre; or toxaphene, 10 per-cent dust at 30 pounds per acre. Minimum time in days between

(Photo, F. E. Skinner)

Figure 9. Cocoons of a parasitic wasp that attacks Sphinx moth larvae.

last application and harvest: cryolite, 5, DDT, 5, methoxychlor, 1, and toxaphene, 5.

Tomato Fruitworm, Tomato Pinworm and Army Worms. Apply TDE (DDD), 5 per-cent dust, or DDT, 5 per-cent dust, at 30 to 35 pounds per acre. Minimum days between last application and harvest is TDE, 1 day, and DDT, 5 days.

Tomato Russet Mite (*Vasates lycopersici*). Apply sulfur, 95 to 98 per-cent dust, at 30 to 40 pounds per acre; or parathion, 2 per-cent dust at 25 pounds per acre when fruit begins to set. Do not apply parathion in the home garden. Minimum time between the last application and harvest is, for parathion, 10 days.

Drosophila Fly (Vinegar Fly) (*Drosophila melanogaster*). This fly is often abundant in fields of commercially grown tomatoes and deposits eggs in cracks of the fruit caused by handling. The fewest eggs are laid on tomatoes that are slightly green, with abundant amounts on fully or over-ripe fruits. Egg-laying is regulated by temperature, almost stopping at 53°F and rising rapidly at 59°F. Control is achieved through proper handling and applications of pyrethrins, an effective repellent for 24 hours.

Harvested fruit should be removed promptly from the field and not allowed to stand over night. Apply pyrethrins, 0.11 per-cent as a dust, to stacked baskets or boxes in the field, and at the receiving station or at the cannery. Thorough application is essential. No evidence has been found that the pyrethrum dust causes a residue or off-flavor (Stombler, and Others, 1957).

Diseases

Verticillium Wilt. This disease is caused by the fungus *Verticillium albo-atrum*. The fungus works upward in the stem, causing the leaves to turn brown and drop off. Crop yields are reduced in size and quality. Avoid, where possible, growing susceptible crops on the same ground, for the fungus may live in the soil for 8 to 10 years. Plant resistant varieties.

Early Blight. This is caused by the fungus *Alternaria solani*; it produces small, dark-colored spots on the leaves and stems, especially on seedlings in plant beds, and dark brown spots on the stem end of the fruit. Clean plants only should be used for transplanting. Apply Bordeaux mixture or a fixed copper, or organic, fungicide such as zineb. Repeat every 7 to 10 days.

Late Blight. Caused by the fungus *Phytophthora infestans*, this disease causes moist, brown splotches on the leaves, and dead tops. The fruit shows small, water-soaked blotches which spread until the entire surface is covered. In moist weather, a thin, white mold shows on leaves, stems, and fruit. The disease is closely associated with temperature and rainfall, and many attempts have been made to forecast outbreaks by a study of climatic conditions (Hyre and Wilson, 1957). (Use the same chemical control as for early blight.)

Broomrape (*Orobanche ramosa*). This is a flowering plant, parasitic on many crops, including the tomato. Plants severely infested early in their growth rarely produce an economic crop of fruit. The seeds may live over in the soil for years and are stimulated into growth by the presence of a host plant, upon which the parasite feeds. There is a very limited distribution of the plant in California, but it has been known in parts of Europe for many years.

Cultural methods of control have thus far been unsuccessful, but fumigation of the soil with methyl bromide is very promising. Two methods of application have been tried. (1) Methyl bromide at a dosage of ½ pound per hundred square feet has been distributed by a mechanical circulator under a polyethylene tarpaulin. (2) Weedfume, a commercial solution of methyl bromide of 70 per-cent concentration, has been applied to the soil at the rate of 175 pounds per acre of the actual toxicant and chiseled into the soil. The soil is rolled immediately after and covered with a polyethylene tarpaulin for 20 to 24 hours. The edges of the tarpaulin are sealed down. The latter treatment was more successful and less expensive than using the necessary dosages without a tarpaulin (Wilhelm and Others, 1958).

TURNIP

Insects

Aphids. Apply malathion, 5 per-cent dust, at 20 to 25 pounds per acre, or an emulsion concentrate as directed. Repeat as needed. Minimum time between last application and harvest is for tops, 10 days, and for roots, 3 days.

Waites and Van Middellem (1958) found, under Florida conditions, that "turnip tops sprayed three times with malathion at the rates of 10.1, 20.2 and 30.3 ounces active ingredient per acre per application, showed initial deposits of 1.3, 2.1 and 4.5 p.p.m., respectively."

Wireworms (Various). Apply chlordane to the soil surface as a dust or wettable powder at 4 to 10 pounds of the actual toxicant per acre, and work into the top 6 to 9 inches. DDT may be substituted for chlordane in the irrigated lands of the western areas. The latter chemical should be applied at least 3 months before planting. (Soil fumigation may be used as with potato insects.)

Flea Beetles (Various). Apply DDT, 5 per-cent dust; or methoxychlor, 5 per-cent dust, at 20 to 35 pounds per acre. Do not apply DDT to turnips after the first appearance of leaves that are to be eaten, marketed, or fed to dairy or meat animals. Minimum days from last application of methoxychlor to harvest is for tops, 14 days, and for roots, 1 day.

WATERMELON

Insects

Cucumber Beetle. See Cucumber.

Diseases

Anthracnose. This is a fungus-caused disease which is carried on the seed and lives over in the soil. It attacks seedlings at the soil surface, gives a scorched appearance to the leaves, and causes watery spots on the fruits. Plant resistant varieties and use seed fungicides. Apply Bordeaux mixture or a fixed copper, or organic, fungicide except ferbam.

Aycock (1958) found that in North Carolina the commonly recommended seed fungicides did not give satisfactory control of anthracnose on artificially infected seed. The variety Florida Giant, which is very susceptible to anthracnose, was used in all the tests. The seed fungicide Seedox gave almost complete control of the disease and was followed by panogen and Emmi.

REFERENCES

Ark, P. A., and Others, *U.S. Dept. Agr. Plant Disease Reporter,* **41,** 452 (1957).

Aycock, R., *ibid.,* **42,** 134 (1958).

Birdsall, J. J., and Others, *J. Agr. Food Chem.,* **7,** 523 (1957).

Brett, C. H., and Brubaker, R. W., *J. Econ. Entom.,* **48,** 343 (1955).

Callbeck, L. C., *U.S. Dept. Agr. Plant Disease Reporter,* **42,** 108 (1958).

Cetas, R. C., *ibid.,* **42,** 324 (1958).

Daines, R. H., *Phytopathology,* **47,** 567 (1957).

de Ong, E. R., *U.S. Dept. Agr. Plant Disease Reporter,* **37,** 410 (1953).

———, "Chemistry and Uses of Pesticides," 2d ed., New York, Reinhold Publishing Corp., 1956.

Evans, L. S., and Others, *U.S. Dept. Agr. Farmer's Bull.,* **2005** (1948).

Gerhold, N. R., *U.S. Dept. Agr. Plant Disease Reporter,* **41,** 135 (1957).

Grogan, R. G., and Others, *Calif. Agr. Exp. Sta. Circular,* **448** (1955).

Hofmaster, R. N., *J. Econ. Entom.* **52,** 777 (1959).

Hyre, R. A., and Wilson, J. D., *U.S. Dept. Agr. Plant Disease Reporter,* **41,** 616 (1957).

Ivanhoff, S. S., *Phytopathology,* **47,** 552 (1957).

Landis, B. J., and Schopp, R., *J. Econ. Entom.,* **51,** 138 (1958).

Lear, B., *Agr. Chem.,* **12**(8), 40 (1957).

Lichtenstein, E. P., and Schulz, K. R., *J. Econ. Entom.,* **52,** 118 (1959).

Linn, M. B., and Luban, K. R., *U.S. Dept. Agr. Plant Disease Reporter,* **42,** 669 (1958).

McLean, D. M., *Phytopathology,* **47,** 557 (1957).

Natti, J. J., and Others, *U.S. Dept. Agr. Plant Disease Reporter,* **42,** 127 (1958).

Nishida, T., and Others, *J. Econ. Entom.*, **50,** 680 (1957).

Reed, L. B., and Doolittle, S. P., *U.S. Dept. Agr. Home & Garden Bull.*, **46** (1956).

Reid, J. R., and Cuthert, Jr., F. P., *U. S. Dept Agr. Farmer's Bull.*, **2099** (1957).

Richardson, B. H., *J. Econ. Entom.*, **50,** 504 (1957).

Rodriguez, J. G., and Others, *ibid.*, **50,** 587 (1957).

Sherman, M., *ibid.*, **51,** 234 (1958).

Shirck, F. H., *J. Econ. Entom.*, **50,** 577 (1957).

Staff, Agr. Extension Service, "Vegetable and Field Crop Pest Control Guide," Berkeley, Univ. of California, 1959.

Staff, U.S. Dept. Agr., "Handbook No. 120," 1959.

Steiner, L. F., (Hawaii) ARS-33-3 (1954)

———, *J. Econ. Entom.*, **45,** 241 (1952).

Stombler, V., and Others, *J. Econ. Entom.*, **50,** 476 (1957).

Tamashiro, M., and Sherman, M., *ibid.*, **48,** 75 (1955).

Thomason, I. J., *U.S. Dept. Agr. Plant Disease Reporter*, **43,** 580 (1959).

Waites, R. E., and Middelem, C. H., *J. Econ. Entom.*, **51,** 306 (1958).

Wallis, R. L., and Others, *ibid.*, **50,** 362 (1957).

Wene, G. P., *ibid.*, **50,** 576 (1957).

Wilhem, S., and Others, *U.S. Dept. Agr. Plant Disease Reporter*, **42,** 645 (1958).

Wilson, J. W., and Middelem, C. H., *J. Econ. Entom.*, **51,** 175 (1958).

Winfree, J. P., and Others, *Phytopathology*, **48,** 311 (1958).

Winstead, N. N., and Others, *U.S. Dept. Agr. Plant Disease Reporter*, **42,** 180 (1958).

Wright, J. M., and Decker, G. C., *J. Econ. Entom.*, **48,** 250 (1955).

Young, John R., and Ditman, L. P., *ibid.*, **52,** 477 (1959).

9. ORNAMENTALS AND LAWN INSECTS, DISEASES, AND WEEDS

Interest in the diseases and insect pests of flowers has increased very rapidly in the last 15 years, as evidenced both by the number of workers in this field and the published papers in *Phytophathology*, especially in other nonspecialized publications. "Courses in floricultural pathology are taught in at least 13 institutions of higher education in this country." Baker (1958) thus summarizes an excellent review of this phase of phytopathology.

Flower-growers, gardeners, greenkeepers, and commercial operators are being benefited by the progress in pest control, both through the use of chemicals and the development of resistant plants. Highway borders of weeds which obstruct the view and present a fire hazard are now being cleared by the application of herbicides, often followed by burning to remove the dead vegetation. Insect enemies, such as leaf miners, mealybugs, and mites, resistant to standard remedies are for the first time being controlled with little hazard to delicate host plants and at a moderate cost. Snapdragon rust, black spot of roses, and bulb infections are held in check to a greater degree than ever before. The expense of hand-weeding lawns can be largely avoided by preliminary killing of infesting weeds, while dandelions can be easily and quickly eliminated from the lawn by "spot" application with a small paint brush of 2,4-D. In the latter work, care must be taken for susceptible plants—such as tomatoes—to avoid vapor drift or even carriage on the hands. Hand-weeding of seedlings and cuttings may often be done quickly and effectively by the use of properly chosen weed-killers.

New pesticides are coming on the market which offer greater advantages in pest-control work as rapidly as they are adopted by the public. The organic chemicals are largely selective in their application, and thus restricted to a narrow group of insects or plant diseases, necessitating careful following of the directions on the label and any restrictions in its use. The hazardous nature of the chemical pesticides must be recognized, and for that reason, insecticides such as parathion, methyl parathion, EPN, TEPP, and Guthion should be left for professionals to use. Other materials, such as petroleum fractions, copper compounds, and pyrethrum, and the extracts of pyrethrins, are not considered dangerous to handle and may be used freely. In all cases, however, the hands should be washed after using pesticides and, in the case of materials that are somewhat irritating, the eyes should be protected. When using new materials for the first time, it is desirable to consult as to their fitness for the case in question with local agricultural officers or experienced operators; otherwise, they should be used only in a small area for the first time.

With the development of hazardous weed-killers and insecticides and their application by power machinery, especially aircraft, there is the danger of drift to adjoining fields. This is particularly true for seed-growers and commercial florists who have acreages near field crops. Damages amounting to many thousands of dollars have been paid for injuries of this kind. The daffodils (narcissus) and related forms are especially susceptible to injury in the bloom-bud stage. The slightest spotting by even a mild toxic material will impair their natural beauty, and either degrade the crop or render it unsalable.

Before applying toxic chemicals by either ground machine or aircraft, a careful survey of adjoining areas should be made to ascertain if susceptible crops, flowers, and shrubs would be injured.

Fumigation of delicate greenhouse plants and of bulbs is another feature of pest control that has resulted in much injury through use of untested methods, carelessness, or ignoring of the manufacturers' or officials' directions. Dosages and methods of application have been developed for many of the standard fumigants and for other insecticides, such as hydrogen cyanide (HCN), methyl bromide, azobenzene, tetraethyl dithiopyrophosphate, and others in aerosol formations. The fumigation of narcissus bulbs for the bulb fly on the Pacific Coast has now become an established practice, and definite directions issued for the operation including dosages, time of exposure, and operating temperatures, together with the requirements in accessories for the fumatorium. Ignoring such directions has led to costly damage suits.

In no field of chemical control of pests has there been greater progress than in that of the ornamental garden with its abundance of plant varieties, ranging from delicate ferns to shrubs and lawns. Pesticides are used in every stage of growth from the pre-emergence of broad-leaved and grassy weeds to mature trees. Their usefulness ranges from the protection of seedlings, before they emerge, to the sterilization of soil from all plant growth for years.

ORNAMENTALS, INSECTS AND DISEASES

African Violet

The cyclamen mite (*Stenotarsonemus pallidus*), is one of the most difficult pests of this plant to control. McDonough and McGray (1957) have

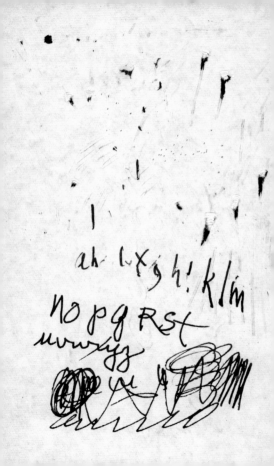

shown the value of the miticide Dimite in checking the mite. Full-strength solutions, as recommended, caused some injury to the foliage, but this was prevented by using half-strength solutions. Plants injured by the mites were frequently attacked by the fungus *Botrytis cinerea.*

Strawberry infestation by the cyclamen mite, however, was best controlled by applications of azobenzene, 2 pounds of active material per hundred; endrin at 0.4 pound per hundred; or Thiodan at 0.5 pound per hundred gallons of spray (Allen and Others, 1957).

Azaleas

These are attacked by both the privet mite (*Brevipalpus inornatus*) and the spider mite (*Tetranychus telarius*). Chlorobenzilate, as directed by the manufacturer, is used. Kelthane is also coming into favor as a control for mites (Jefferson and Pritchard, 1956).

Birch

Borers. The bronze birch borer (*Agrilus anxius*) is a severe pest of the paper birch in Ohio, as is also the flatheaded apple tree borer (*Chrysobothris femorata*). The latter insect is primarily a pest of weak trees; it attacks a wide range of ornamental trees. Preventive applications of insecticides to the trunk and limbs have shown good results from the use of parathion, but more erratic behavior from DDT. The best protection from the birch borer was obtained from two applications of parathion, 6.7 pounds of a 15 per-cent wettable powder per hundred gallons—one on May 31 and the second 30 days later. Control of the flatheaded borer was apparently improved by the addition of a liquid or a polyethylene compound to the DDT spray (Williams and Others, 1959).

Leaf Miners, Galls, and Lace Bugs. Experiments in Connecticut by Schread (1957, 1958) have shown the value of Thimet granules as a soil systemic against the birch-leaf miner (*Fenusa pusilla*), the holly leaf miner (*Phytomyza ilicis*), and the boxwood-leaf miner (*Monarthropalpus buxi*), as well as the locust pod gall maker (*Dasyneura gleditschiae*). In these experiments, the granules were applied to the soil surface and watered in at intervals of 5 to 10 days.

In the 1957 work, the birch-, holly-, and boxwood leaf miners were controlled by applications of Thimet granules beneath the plant and extending outward to the periphery. Dosages used in April, 1957, of 22 or 40 pounds of the active ingredient of Thimet per acre controlled both the first and second brood of the leaf miner. A second treatment, applied in June, did not give as good control of the second brood. The holly leaf miner was effectively controlled in large trees with 4 to 16 ounces, and in small trees with 1 to 2, ounces of Thimet. Most boxwood leaf miners were destroyed with 0.08 to 0.32 ounces of Thimet per plant. Birch trees treated in 1957 were again examined in 1958. Dosages of 10 and 20 pounds of Thimet per acre showed 100 per-cent kill of the first brood of the birch leaf miner, but none of the second brood. The latter did, however, show an 83 per-cent control at the 40-pound-per-acre dosage. Control of the box-wood leaf miner was complete at dosages ranging from 0.16 to 0.32 ounce of actual Thimet per plant. The first brood only of the honey locust pod gall maker was controlled by Thimet. Similar treatments of andromeda and azalea lace bugs were effective (Schread, 1958, 1959).

Bulbs

Insects. The bulb fly (*Lampetia equestris*), the lesser bulb fly or onion fly (*Citibaena tuberculata*), and the bulb mite (*Rhizoglyphus echinopus*) frequently attack the narcissus bulb and to a less extent amaryllis, hya-cinth, lillies, tulips and other bulbs. The lesser bulb fly is considered a secondary infestant, or even a scavenger, but is sometimes a severe pest on onions and bulbs. The eggs are laid near the crown of the host plant near the soil surface. The larvae feed on the interior of the bulb until it is almost entirely consumed, leaving the outer surface of the bulb intact.

Control is achieved by fumigation with methyl bromide in a tight fumitorium at a dosage of 3 pounds per 1,000 cubic feet for four hours, at a temperature bewteen 70° and 80°F and a humidity of 70 to 85 per cent. The bulbs should be piled to permit free circulation of the fumigant. Pre-heating of the bulbs is necessary when the air temperature is below 70°F. Since the egg of the mite is resistant to the recommended dosage, a double fumigation 10 to 14 days apart is necessary.

The fumigating chamber should be insulated to prevent temperature fluctuations and be equipped with heaters to permit temperature control and fans for circulating the fumigant and removing it after fumigation. The interior temperature reading should be visible from the outside dur-ing the process. The fumigant should be removed promptly from the cham-ber, following treatment, either by opening the loading door and starting the fans or removing the load and stacking it in the open.

The *gladiolus thrips* (*Taeniothrips simplex*) is one of the most serious pests of this flower. It feeds on the leaves, stems, and flowers and may be found on the bulbs during storage. Prolonged periods of infestation re-quire the use of insecticides with long persistence. DDT, BHC, or dieldrin applications, as recommended by the manufacturer, are the materials commonly used in control (Jefferson and Pritchard, 1956; Pritchard, 1949).

Diseases. Basal rot of narcissus, caused by the fungus *Fusarium oxy-sporum,* is treated by a dip in dilute phenyl mercury acetate solutions.

Investigation of the practice has shown that the solution is weakened by contact with aluminum or iron tanks, wooden crates, or the soil on the bulbs. Compensation for such loss should be made by addition of the dip solution at regular intervals, or by prevention of contact with iron, wood, or soil (Miller and Others, 1957).

Gladiolus dry-rot disease is caused by the fungus *Stromatinia gladioli*. Young plants are stunted and die, singly and in clumps. Larger plants are not readily killed, but stem and leaf bases are rotted. Corm (bulb) infection first shows as a reddish-brown spot which spreads into a shallow, black rot. The type of attack varies from corm and stem rot to root-rotting. The distribution of the fungus appears to be world-wide.

The fungus is known to live for a number of years in the soil. It grows at a temperature range from 32° to 95°F. Soil penetration is stated to be about 9 inches in the dry season, and about twice as rapidly in the wet season. Sandy soil is conducive to the spread of the disease.

Recommendations for control are as follows: (1) Hand-select lightly-infected stocks. Discard all corms when severely infected. (2) "Dip corms for 5 minutes in Thiram (8.2 pounds active per 100 gallons water) just before planting." (3) Plant in heavy, well-drained, non-infested soil. (4) Before planting in infested soil, apply Thiram mixed with soil, at a rate of 300 pounds of the active material per acre, and drench every 2 months with a water suspension of the same rate. (5) Apply soil fumigants as directed by the manufacturer. (6) "Dig corms as early as practicable and cure rapidly at 80° to 90°F. Clean and store under cool, dry conditions. (Gould, 1958)

Gladiolus susceptibility to atmospheric fluoride is so great that this plant has been selected as an indicator for the presence of this air pollutant in an investigation of the killing of ponderosa pine in the vicinity of Spokane, Washington (Adams and Others, 1956).

Easter lily bulbs are subject to infection by various fungi, *Fusarium*, *Pythium ultimum*, and *Rhizoctonia solani*. The most successful dip-formula thus far developed for treating bulbs as a protection against the fungi is a mixture of two pounds of pentachloronitrobenzene and two pounds of ferbam per hundred gallons of water. Treated bulbs, when planted in clean soil, showed vigorous growth and retained their green color after flowering; basal roots survived, and the harvested bulbs were white rather than yellow. The treated bulbs also averaged at least one more flower than those from untreated stocks (Bald and Others, 1958).

Chrysanthemum

Insects. The chrysanthemum aphid (*Macrosiphum sanborni*) and other species are common pests. Nicotine, is used as a spray or smoke in the greenhouse, and light refined oil emulsion as a carrier for rotenone, nicotine, or pyrethrins, are the common insecticides. These are less destructive to the natural enemies than are the phosphate compounds. DDT is used for the gall midge, and BHC for both the gall midge and the leaf miner. See figure 10 and 11 of aphid enemies.

Diseases. *Botrytis gray mold* and *downy mildew* on chrysanthemum and other plants in the greenhouse are favored by a film of water on the leaves. The spore germinates only where the moisture of the air is condensed into "free" water.

The moisture-holding capacity (relative humidity) of the air may almost double at a rise of 20° temperature. Hence, if the air has a relative humidity of 80 per cent at 70°F and it cools to 50°F, about one-half of the moisture is condensed on the leaves. This film of moisture is sufficient to cause fungus spores to germinate, and new infections are established. To avoid condensation and to keep the plants dry, the humidity should be kept below saturation as a protection against sudden temperature drops. This may be done by balancing the heat and ventilation to keep the warm, humid air moving out at the top of the vents (Baker, 1958).

Daisy Diseases

A hybrid form of the Shasta daisy is grown in the fog belt of the Pacific Coast from San Francisco southward. Aphids and the false chinch bug are the common insect pests, for which the systemic phosphate Phosdrin is used. In the foggier districts, one or more types of fungi attack require frequent applications of zineb plus zinc sulfate.

Gardenia Insects

Common pests are the citrus mealybug (*Pseudococcus citri*), black citrus aphid (*Toxoptera auranti*), two-spotted spider mite, variegated cutworm (*Peridroma margaritosa*), and the hemispherical scale (*Saissetia hemisphaerica*). The mealybug and the mite are controlled by applications of sulfotepp, as an aerosol or as a smoke. Four applications are sometimes necessary to control the scale insect. For aphids, use lindane, parathion, or malathion, as recommended. DDT, as recommended by the manufacturer, is used for the cutworm (Jefferson and Pritchard, 1956; Pritchard, 1949).

Iris

Insects. A common pest is that of the whitefly (*Aleyrodes spiraeoides*). The adult insect is winged, while the larval or nymph stage remains in a fixed position like a scale insect. Fumigation with calcium cyanide is a

(Photograph, Doten & Skinner)
Figure 10. Parasitic wasp ovipositing in aphid.

(Photograph, F. E. Skinner)
Figure 11. Aphid showing exit hole of parasitic wasp.

common method of control. TEPP (TEP) is effective only against the adult stage. Parathion, applied as a spray, is effective against both stages of the insect (Jefferson and Pritchard, 1956; Pritchard, 1949).

Diseases. Crown rot of bulbous iris, caused by the fungus *Sclerotium*, is generally distributed and is especially severe in warm climates. The disease spreads both through the soil and from bulb to bulb in storage trays under warm, moist conditions.

Practical control of the disease is had by soaking infested bulbs for 3 hours in a warm (110°F) solution of formalin, 0.5 per cent. This is followed by careful culling, rotation of planting beds, and sanitary handling. Bulbs partially infected with crown rot may recover after the hot water-formalin treatment or if planted in heavy, well-drained soil under the cool conditons prevailing in western Washington (Gould, 1954).

Rose

Insects. The resistant strains of the two-spotted mite present a serious problem in control recognized for several years. English (1950) found that an aerosol of azobenzene and one of the phosphates (parathion, tetraethyl pyrophosphate, or tetraethyl dithionopyrophosphate) made an effective combination. Azobenzene, being ovicidal, supplemented the phosphates, which were toxic to the mites but not the eggs.

In a further study of the resistant-mite problem, Jefferson and Morishita (1956) found that combining either aramite or chlorobenzilate with azobenzene, and applying as a spray, was slow in action but killed all stages of the mite. There was but little mortality during the first two days, and a complete kill did not occur until the fourth or fifth day. There was also less tendency to bleach pink-colored roses than when azobenzene was used as a fumigant.

Where mites on roses have become resistant to the usual control materials, including azobenzene fumigation, malathion, aramite, chlorobenzilate, and Karathane, a new organosulfur material, known as *Tedion*, is proving helpful on roses, gardenias, and carnations. Applications of this material do not kill the adult mite, but their eggs do not hatch. Very young mites and eggs deposited prior to treatment are killed. Tedion, 25 per-cent wettable powder, is used at the rate of 1 pound per hundred gallons of water, plus a spreader. The material is stated to have a low order of toxicity to warm-blooded animals and, so far as noted, does not injure plants when used as directed (Pritchard, 1958). See Figure 12 of aphid enemy, green lacewing.

Aphids are a serious problem in the spring and early summer—especially in cool springs; by midsummer they may often be held in control by their natural enemies. Nicotine sprays with a spreader, and the more concentrated dusts, are effective and but slightly injurious to parasites and predators. DDT dust, 5 per-cent, may be used where defoliators are present, and may be combined with sulfur as a control for rose mildew if the midday temperature is 70°F or higher. Avoid using sulfur at a sum-

(Photograph, F. E. Skinner)

Figure 12. Green lacewing (Chrysopa), the larva of which feeds on aphids.

mer temperature of 90°F or above. In the greenhouse, nicotine smoke or sulfotepp aerosol, or sprays of TEPP, parathion, and malathion are used.

Thrips entering the greenhouse by the vents are attracted to the opening bloom, rather than the foliage. It is for this reason that residual sprays give unsatisfactory control. Screening the vents with cloth having a mesh of sufficient fineness to prevent passage of the insects interferes with the ventilation of the houses. Cheesecloth, with a mesh of 28 threads to the inch and saturated with an insecticide, was tested at greenhouse ranges in New York. Malathion and heptachlor as 25 per-cent solutions, and dieldrin as a 15 per-cent solution, were applied. Of the three insecticides tested, dieldrin alone gave significant control both with side-screening alone, and with combined top and side-screening. It is therefore recommended for thrips control (Karlin and Others, 1957).

Diseases. The black spot disease, caused by the fungus *Diplocarpon rosae*, produces severe defoliation which is indirectly the cause of much winter injury and low-grade bushes. The attack of spider mites also results in defoliation, thus making them more susceptible to winter injury.

A comparative study has been made in Maryland of the value of various fungicide combinations in the control of this disease. The five varieties of roses used were Red Radiance, mite susceptible and black spot tolerant; Golden Masterpiece and Chief Seattle, both susceptible and readily defoliated by black spot; Peace, black spot tolerant; and Christopher Stone, mildew susceptible. The fungicides used were 3.4 per-cent copper from basic copper sulfate; 3.4 per-cent copper plus 25 per-cent sulfur; 7.6 per-cent ferbam (Fermate) plus 25 per-cent sulfur; 6.5 per-cent zineb; 5 per-cent captan; and 1 per-cent Karathane—which is ineffective against black spot but was included for powdery mildew control. All materials were applied as dusts.

Black spot control on Golden Masterpiece for the years 1954 and 1955 was best with zineb, followed closely by sulfur-copper and sulfur-ferbam mixtures. Captan, copper, and Karathane were decidedly inferior to the previous three. The number of flowers and the total weight of flowers produced closely followed this same order. Winter killing also followed this same order, but less closely. The variety Red Radiance, which is less susceptible to black spot infection, was less affected in flower yield and winter killing than Golden Masterpiece (McClellan and Others, 1957).

A mixture of sulfur, 90 per cent, and ferbam, 10 per cent, is sometimes used as a control of both black spot and rose mildew. The sulfur does not become effective except at temperatures of about 70°F, and may cause some bleaching of petals and foliage injury at high summer temperatures.

Grown gall of Roses is a serious disease in many rose nurseries, especially where the soil has been heavily infested. Partial control on uncalloused rose cuttings was obtained by dipping them for 2 hours in solutions of streptomycin at 500 and 600 ppm respectively. Dusts of the same material were largely ineffective. The variety Burr Multiflora was found to be very resistant to crown gall under field conditions (Ark and Sibray, 1957).

Root-lesion nematode (Pratylenchus vulnus) may cause infestation of rose cuttings growing in infested soil. Striking results in plant growth were obtained by soil fumigation with the following materials, at the dosages indicated: chloropicrin, 33 gallons; D-D, 40 gallons; EDB, 8 gallons; Vapam drench, 40 gallons; or Vapam injected, 40 gallons; all dosages are given in amounts per acre. The degree of control, as expressed in No. 1 grade, ranged from over 400 per-cent improvement for chloropicrin to 290 per-cent for EDB (Sher and Munnecke, 1958).

Dormant rosebushes held in cold storage are subject to a serious mold infection caused by the fungus *Botrytis*. Experiments in the control of this mold have been conducted at the Rhode Island Agricultural Experiment Station, using, fungicides as either aqueous dips, dusts, or in vapor phase, followed by storage for 3 months in sealed plastic bags. Pillar No. 73 roses, after 3-months storage, were treated in March. The plants were trimmed to 24-inch lengths, and the fungicide applied as follows: (1) dip, bundles immersed for 10 seconds, drained, and encased in polyethylene bags, (2) vapor application, chemical mixed with moist sawdust in the bottom of similar bags; (3) dusts, with a rotary hand-duster. The packaged roses were then stored for 3 months at 34° to 36°F. and an average relative humidity of 90 per cent. The effective chemicals, based on both the control of Botrytis and the subsequent season's growth through bloom were Captan (7.5 per-cent dust), Vancide 51 (4800 ppm dip), and Mycostatin (500 ppm dip) (Stessel, 1958).

Weed Control. The control of weeds in rose nurseries varies with the development from cuttings to established plants. Contact sprays, generally speaking, were of limited value. Petroleum fractions alone or fortified with DNOSBP showed but a narrow margin between weed control and plant injury. Emulsions of DNOSBP and solutions of Endothal controlled most types of weeds, with but little crop damage. Contact sprays applied beneath the rose foliage can be used for only a brief period before much top growth of the cuttings. The phenyl carbamates, IPC and others, were effective only at dosages of 10 pounds and above per acre. This was probably because of frequent, heavy irrigation. The urea compounds CMU and DCMU were effective selective soil sterilants for rose cuttings in late-winter or early-spring applications, before the cuttings were well established. Each of these materials was used at a dosage of 1½ pounds in 50 gallons of water per acre. The application, as a wettable powder, was made in early February and controlled all annual weed growth until the first of May. In the spring, after the roses were rooted, they became very sensitive to these herbicides (Day and Russell, 1955).

General-Contact Weed Killers and Soil Sterilants

Chlorates have been used very commonly for all-purpose weed control and as temporary soil sterilants. The hazard of fire from their use has led to the increased demand for boron-chlorate mixtures which are not fire-hazardous and are both temporary and permanent sterilizers, depending on the amount used. Dosage for the mixture is 5 to 6 pounds per square rod as a sterilant, or 2 to 4 pounds dry per hundred square feet for the control of perennial weeds. Both chlorates and boron-chlorate mixtures are used to prevent the growth of vegetation in paths, driveways, and highway borders. They affect the growth of all types of weeds and, used in sufficient amount, will sterilize the soil for two or more years. They may be applied to the soil surface as a solution or in dry form, allowing the rain to dissolve and distribute them downward. Sodium chlorate is preferred because of its quick solubility where fast action is desired. However, because of its fire hazard, when dried on the clothing of the operator, it may be safer to use the boron-chlorate mixture.

Borates are nonpoisonous to animals and humans and for this reason may be used around buildings, playgrounds, and other public places. The toxicity of borates and the rate at which they are leached out of the soil varies with the soil type and the rainfall. The toxicity is greatest in coarse, sandy soils and low in heavy soils. Annual dosages of moderate amounts are preferable to very heavy single ones. Under the semiarid conditions of the southwestern areas, recommendations for annual applications of borate-chlorate mixtures are 10 to 40 pounds per square rod (Crafts and Harvey, 1955). Dosages under Illinois conditions are 6 to 7 pounds per square rod during the growing season, and 4 to 5 pounds in the late fall (Spurrier and Others, 1957). As the chemical builds up in the soil, lighter dosages may be used. Application may be made dry, by hand or with a fertilizer applicator, or as a solution, as directed by the manufacturer. Borates, especially under western conditions, should be used with caution near valuable plants because the leached chemical may cause die back.

Permanent sterilization against all plant growth is possible over long periods of time by the use of arsenical compounds. They are used on fireguards, ditch banks, pole lines, and other industrial locations. They should not be used along highways or on roadsides because of their dangerous nature.

Sodium arsenite is a water-soluble form commonly marketed in "weed-killing" preparations. It is more active in sandy than in heavy soils. A common dosage is 4 pounds of active ingredient per square rod. In sandy soils, this will be leached downward for several inches by the winter rains, killing plant roots on contact, while in heavy soils, penetration may not be more than a few inches, and deep-rooted plants may not be affected. Sodium arsenite is to be used only where the soil is to be kept bare and should not be applied where livestock may be present because it is attractive to grazing animals.

Arsenic trioxide (white arsenic) is much less soluble than sodium arsenite and hence persists longer in the soil. It is not attractive to livestock. The material is marketed as a dry powder and readily distributed by hand or with a fertilizer spreader. It is commonly used as a follow-up after some other type of sterilant. Because of its low solubility, it may not be effective the first year it is applied. To overcome this, it may be mixed with a chlorate, or the organic compound CMU, both of which are active during the first year.

Arsenical compounds are extremely poisonous and must be handled with great care. Avoid letting arsenic come in contact with the skin. Keep livestock from treated areas.

Organic Compounds as Soil Sterilants. Urea compounds, known as *CMU*, and marketed under various trade names, are nonflammable, insoluble powders applied in a suspension in water. Dosages for sterilization lasting over a number of years range from 20 to 40 pounds per acre, depending on the heaviness of the soil. Dosages for annual treatment lasting through one growing season, or perhaps slightly more, will probably range from 4 to 8 pounds per acre. These compounds are so new at this date that accurate data has not been determined.

Two brands of the substituted ureas are Televar W and Televar DW. They are similar in effect, but the former is recommended where the rainfall is less than 20 inches a year and for the heavier soils. Televar DW is for use in sandy soils, where the annual rainfall is more than 20 inches. Both materials are to be applied before the rainy season begins and before a dense growth of vegetation has occurred.

Other organic compounds used as temporary sterilants before seeding include cyanamide and a combination of 2,4-D and IPC. In warm, moist soils, these compounds break down within a few weeks; whereas, in winter they may be effective for months. The use of temporary soil sterilants as pre-emergence applicants is very selective, requiring much care in determining proper dosages and the plants for which they are used (Crafts and Harvey, 1955).

Highway Weed Control

The application of herbicides as a supplement to mowing is now being practiced generally in many states throughout this country. Thousands of miles of highway and road borders are now treated annually in checking weed and brush growth. Power-sprayers are used for applying the chemicals to a narrow border on each side of the highway or road. Chlorates and borates are both used, alone and in combination, as well as the urea compound Monuron. Ammate is applied for brushy growth, and Dalapon for grassy areas, but the hormone compounds 2,4-D and 2,4-T are chosen most frequently. Such applications eliminate many of the unsightly weeds and prevent their spread to adjoining fields, and kill poison ivy and poison oak (Greene, 1957; Zukel and Eddy, 1957). Garmhausen (1956) found, in a three-year program in Ohio, that three sprays were necessary the first year, but only one the third year.

FLOWER AND SHRUB PESTS

Weeds of Flower Seedlings

A comparative test of the value of various herbicides was made in Southern California during December and January, 1957–1958. Test plants used were alyssum, antirrhinum, larkspur, petunia, sweet pea, and verbena. Chemicals used were calcium cyanamide, methyl bromide, Vapam, chloro-IPC pre-emergence dinitro, and two aromatic oils known as Shell 20 and Shell 10. Weeds found in the check plot were nettles, wild radish, lamb's-quarters, volunteer sweet pea, shepherd's-purse, malva, nightshade, nettleleaf, goosefoot, and wire grass.

Methyl bromide was applied under an airtight tarpaulin at the rate of 1 pound per hundred square feet for a 24-hour exposure. A new section was treated every day, the treatment being completed a few days before seeding.

Vapam was applied at a dosage of 0.75 pound per hundred square feet, using a garden sprinkling can, followed immediately by overhead irrigation which wetted the soil to a depth of 2½ inches. Seeding followed one week later.

Alanap at 3 and 6 pounds per acre, pre-emergence dinitro at 6 and 9 pounds, and chloro IPC at 4 and 6 pounds were each applied in 40 gallons of water per acre. Shell oils No. 10 and No. 20 were applied undiluted at 40 gallons per acre.

Methyl bromide and Vapam gave excellent weed control and increased the seed yield of all the varieties of flowers in some instances very decidedly. All the other herbicides except calcium cyanamide gave good weed control, but Alanap, at the 3 pound dosage, and Shell 10 showed less than 50 per-cent control. However, injury to the seed crop of alyssum, antirrhinum, and petunia occurred with both Shell 20 and pre-emergence dinitro. Chloro IPC, at 6 pounds per acre and Alanap were both injurious to the seed crop. It is suggested that Shell 20 and the pre-emergence dinitro might be satisfactory weed-control agents for larkspur and sweet pea (Bivins and Others, 1957).

Growth Inhibitor for Shrubs

In addition to the use of maleic hydrazide as a control agent for grass, it is helpful in checking excessive growth of ivies, honeysuckle, star jasmine, fuchsia, and many other shrubs. The material is marketed as a diethanolamine salt and as a sodium salt powder. Concentration of the actual material as used for application ranges from 0.09 to 0.30 per-cent maleic hydrazide. Careful measurement of the amounts used is necessary because the damaging point for fuchsia, under coastal California conditions, has been found to be 0.20 per-cent maleic hydrazide. However, the damaging point for most shrubs tested ranged from 0.30 to 0.40.

Good growth control resulted from first trimming the plant to the desired shape and letting the new growth cover the trimmed edges before applying the maleic hydrazide spray. The usual effect on evergreens is to produce a more dense and bushy plant by checking the tip bud, resulting in the growth of the lateral buds. Stem terminals of some types of plants may be discolored after application and drop off (North and Others, 1958).

Air Pollutants and Plant Injury

Increasing numbers of reports of injury to ornamentals and various trees have been noted, as a result of expansion of industrial plants and increasing numbers of automotive vehicles in the vicinity of large cities. Arsenical fumes from smelters have in the past been one of the first recognized sources of such injury. The presence of atmospheric fluorides in the vicinity of aluminum reduction plants and other industrial factories have been noted in a number of instances as injurious to vegetation (de Ong, 1946). Measurements of the amounts of gaseous fluorides in parts per billion (ppb) causing plant injury have been made in the vicinity of various industrial centers in the state of Washington. It was found that visible foliar burn was similar with either daylight or darkness exposure. A daily exposure for 8 hours at 1.5 ppb of hydrogen fluoride showed a greater response than when fumigated either 8 hours every third day at 5 ppb, or 4 hours every third day at 10 ppb of hydrogen fluoride (Adams and Others, 1957).

The air pollution over cities, known as *Smog*, is a complex of liquids, solids, and gases comprising more than fifty chemical elements and compounds causing irritation to man and plant injury. "Plant damage is considered to be due to certain intermediate peroxidic products resulting from the chemical combination of unsaturated hydrocarbons with ozone in the atmosphere." Symptoms include discoloration of the foliage of dahlia, spinach, lettuce, and tomato, and a tan streaking of the leaves of grains and grasses (Glater, 1956; Kendrick and Others, 1956).

Nematode Control on Plants by Heat Treatment

A high degree of control of the root-knot nematode (*Meloidogyne incognita*) was shown by a 10-minute exposure at 50°C (122°F) of the bare roots of nematode-infected ornamentals. Following laboratory tests, a demonstration of the efficacy of the head treatment was made on nursery stock in Florida. Tolerance to the hot-water treatment, and the effect on gall formation, as shown by tomato bio-assay, is given for twenty-four types of plants. "Some species showed 100 percent survival without obvious injury, others were completely destroyed, while various degrees of tolerance between these extremes were observed. Succulent herbaceous types were generally damaged most; however, *Gardenia* and *Boxus*, both woody perennials, suffered a high mortality. The larger sized plants were more resistant to treatment, in general." (Birchfield and Van Pelt, 1958.)

LAWN

Insects

A number of different types of beetle larvae (grubs) burrow about an inch beneath the lawn surface, feeding on the grass roots. Among the commonest are the May or June beetle, Japanese beetle, and white-fringed beetle. The grubs and ants are controlled by dust mixtures of the following insecticides, applied with a fertilizer distributor and washed in by sprinkling, the dosages given being for 1,000 square feet: Aldrin, 2.75 per-cent dust, dosage 2¾ pounds; chlordane, 5 per-cent dust, dosage 5 pounds; dieldrin 1.5 per-cent dust, dosage 4½ pounds; or heptachlor, 2.5 per-cent dust, dosage 2.75 pounds. DDT may be used for any of the above grubs, except May beetles, and ants. There is also available a commercial preparation containing spores of the milky disease that is used against the Japanese beetle (Vance, 1956).

Chiggers in the lawn may be controlled by the application of dieldrin, 1.5 per-cent dust, as given for beetle grubs.

DDT at a dosage of 1.2 ounces of actual toxicant in 7.5 gallons of water per thousand square feet of turf controlled various species of leaf-hoppers for 2 months (Kerr, 1957). Heavy infestations of chinch bugs (*Blissus insularis*) in Florida lawns were also controlled for 48 days by a single application of DDT, 10 pounds of actual toxicant per acre (Kerr, 1956).

Diseases

Brown spots and patches in turf grasses are frequently caused by the attacks of fungi. The former, usually known as "dollar spots," are caused by the fungus *Sclerotinia homoeocarpa*. Injured spots are dark green at first and then turn brown or straw-colored. They are usually about 2 inches in diameter, but may grow together to form larger areas. This fungus is most active below temperatures of 80°F. Brown patch is caused by the fungus *Pellicularia filamentosa* (*Rhizoctonia solani*). It causes dark green areas from an inch to several feet in diameter. The fungus thrives wherever high temperatures and humidities prevail. Affected areas turn dark, wilt, and finally become light brown as the leaves die. Both diseases thrive in wet, poorly drained, or overwatered soils. Frequent, close cutting also weakens the plants and makes them more susceptible to attack. Resistant types of grasses have been developed, but since they may also become susceptible to disease, it is desirable to learn of the newer types.

The grass varieties "Washington, Cohansey, and Arlington bent are much more resistant to brown patch than is Metropolitan. Seaside bent is moderately susceptible. Colonial is very susceptible. Washington bent, however, is very susceptible to dollar spot, as is the Toronto strain." Merion bluegrass is resistant to bluegrass leafspot (Lefebvre and Others, 1953).

Chemical control is achieved by applications of a mixture of mercury chlorides, 1 part corrosive sublimate to 2 parts calomel. This mixture is available commercially under various trade names, and their use should be according to the manufacturer's directions. Phenyl mercury acetate and lactate, 10 per-cent active ingredient, at 1¼ ounces to 5 gallons of water per thousand square feet, and applied as a spray, are helpful. Cadmium-containing fungicides, marketed under various trade names, are now being recommended (Lefebvre and others, 1953).

REFERENCES

Adams, D. G., and Others, *J. Agr. Food Chem.*, **4**, 64 (1956).
———, *ibid.*, **5**, 108 (1957).
Allen, W. W., and Others, *J. Econ. Entom.*, **50**, 648 (1957).
Ark, P. A., and Sibray, W. S., *U.S., Dept. Agr. Plant Disease Reporter*, **41**, 452 (1957).
Baker, K. F., *U.S. Dept. Agr. Plant Diseases Reporter*, **42**, 997 (1958).
———, *Univ. Calif. Flower Notes*, **25** (1958).
Bald, J. G., and Others, *Calif. Agr.*, **12**(4), 3 (1958).
Birchfield, W., and Van Pelt, H. M., *U.S. Dept. Agr. Plant Disease Reporter*, **42**, 451 (1958).
Bivins, J. L., and Others, *Calif. Agr.*, **11**(9), 12 (1957).
Crafts, A. S., and Harvey, W. A., *Calif. Agr. Exp. Sta. Circular*, **446** (1955).
Day, B. E., and Russell, R. C., *Hilgardia*, **23**, 597 (1955).
de Ong, E. R., *Phytopathology*, **36**, 469 (1946).
English, L. L., *J. Econ. Entom.*, **43**, 838 (1950).
Garmhausen, W. J., *Nat. Agr. Chem. Assoc. News*, **14**(4), 10, (1956).
Glater, R. A. B., *Phytopathology*, **46**, 696 (1956).
Gould, C. J., *ibid.*, **44**, 711 (1954).
———, *U.S. Dept. Agr. Plant Disease Reporter*, **42**, 1011 (1958).
Greene, W. C., *Down-to-Earth* (Dow Chem. Co.), **13**(1), 14 (1957).
Jefferson, R. N., and Prichard, A. E., *Calif. Agr. Exp. Sta. Leaflet*, **66** (1956).
Jefferson, R. N., and Morishita, F. S., *J. Econ. Entom.*, **49**, 151 (1956).
Karlin, E. J., and Others, *ibid.*, **50**, 56 (1957).
Kendrick, Jr., and Others, *Calif. Agr.*, **10**(8), 9 (1956).
Kerr, T. W., *J. Econ. Entom.*, **49**, 83 (1956).
———, *ibid.*, **50**, 372 (1957).
Lefebvre, C. L., "1953 Yearbook," Washington, D.C., U.S. Dept Agr., 1953.
McClellan, W. D., and Others, *Phytopathology*, **47**, 357 (1957).
McDonough, E. S., and McGray, R. J., *ibid.*, **47**, 109 (1957).
Miller, V. L., and Others, *ibid.*, **47**, 722 (1957).
North, C. P., and Others, *Calif. Agr.*, **12**(6), 7 (1958).
Pritchard, A. E., *Calif. Agr. Exp. Sta. Bull.*, **713** (1949).
———, *Univ. Calif. Flower Notes*, **25** (1958).
Schread, J. C., *J. Econ. Entom.*, **52**, 712 (1959); **51**, 245 (1958).

Sher, S. A., and Munnecke, D. E., *Calif. Agr.*, **12**(9), 9 (1958).
Spurrier, E. C., and Others, *Ill. Agr. Exp. Sta. Circular*, **771** (1957).
Stessel, G. J., *U.S. Dept. Agr. Plant Disease Reporter*, **42**, 396 (1958).
Vance, A. M., *U.S. Dept. Agr. Home & Garden Bull.*, **53** (1956).
Williams, R. E., and Others, *J. Econ. Entom.*, **52**, 255 (1959).
Zukel, J. W., and Eddy, C. O., *Agr. Chem.*, **12**(7), 38 (1957).

10. LIVESTOCK INSECTS, MITES, AND TICKS

Progress in the control of insects, mites, and ticks of livestock, ranges from the early war against the cattle-fever tick and sheep scab, through the research on the sterilization of the male screw fly, to the development of systemic insecticides for use against the bot flies of cattle and sheep. Important among the pests are the biting flies (horn, stable, and horse fly) and the house fly, the pest of the barn and home.

Many effective compounds have been developed, including DDT, lindane, and diazinon for application to the body of the animal or as a residual spray for the barn walls, only to find that, after absorption through the skin, the chemicals might be stored indefinitely in the body tissues or excreted in the milk. Either result, being questionable from the standpoint of public health, has limited the number of insecticides which are recommended as body applications for dairy cows to materials considered harmless for such purposes, including pyrethrins, rotenone, and the organic thiocyanates Lethane and Thanite. The only exception at this time is for methoxychlor as a 50 per-cent wettable powder, a tablespoonful to be applied on the back and neck of the animal every 3 weeks. This should not be used as a spray or dip.

Malathion residues, excreted in milk from dairy cows dusted or sprayed with this material, have been determined by Goulding and Terriere (1959).

One dairy herd received three successive treatments of 4 per-cent malathion dust, followed by an application of a 0.5 per-cent wettable-powder spray. The other herd received a single treatment with 10 per-cent malathion dust. Dusts were applied by hand to the back and flanks of the cows at the rate of 2 ounces per cow. This gave a dosage of about 2.27 grams of active ingredient per cow in the 4 per-cent dust, and about 5.67 grams of active ingredient in the 10 per-cent dust. The 0.5 per-cent spray was applied at the rate of a gallon per cow by means of a power sprayer.

The 4 per-cent dust application was repeated when the herd count of flies averaged thirty flies per side per cow. The 10 per-cent dust and the 0.5 per-cent spray were not repeated, since malathion was detected in the milk after the first treatment.

185

Milk samples consisted of a 2-quart pooled collection of milk from twelve to fourteen cows. One quart of each sample was used for analysis and the other held for reference.

Only two of the ten samples analyzed during the experiments with the 4 per-cent dusts showed a detectable amount of malathion. Changing the control program from a 4 per-cent dust to a 0.5 per-cent spray resulted in a detectable contamination, as did also the 10 per-cent dust treatment.

The following recommendations on pest control are based on those given by the Staff of the Entomology Research Division in Agriculture, United States Department of Agriculture, *Handbook No. 120* (1959). In addition, reviews of recent literature on the development and use of new compounds for pest control on livestock and their surroundings are included. Consult agricultural officers for more recent developments.

Cattle, Beef and Dairy

Cattle Grub (Warble or Bot). Use Rotenone, 5 per-cent dust, 3 ounces applied thoroughly on the back; or 5 per-cent dust, 7.5 pounds per hundred gallons of water, applying 2 to 4 quarts per animal as a spray. Wash or apply on the back with a power-sprayer, 1 to 3 times every 30 days.

Horn Fly. Use pyrethrins, 0.05 per-cent, plus a synergist, 0.5 per-cent, applying 1 to 2 quarts as a mist spray every 3 to 7 days. Organic thiocyanates (Lethane or Thanite) oil solution, 3 to 5 per-cent as mist spray, 1 to 2 ounces daily; or methoxychlor, 1 tablespoonful sprinkled on back and neck every 3 weeks, may be used. Do not use the latter as a spray or dip.

Horse Flies, Stable Flies, and Mosquitoes. Use pyrethrins, 0.05 to 0.1 per-cent, plus a synergist, 0.5 to 1.0 per-cent, applying 1 to 2 quarts as a mist spray every 2 to 3 days. Or organic thiocyanates, as under horn flies, may be used.

Lice. Use pyrethrins, 0.025 per-cent, plus a synergist, 0.25 per-cent; spray animals thoroughly, repeating after 2 to 3 weeks. Or rotenone, 5 per-cent dust, or as a spray with 0.5 to 1.0 per-cent dust, per hundred gallons of water may be used.

Screwworms. Diphenylamine, 35 per-cent (smear 62),* brush or smear on wounds and surrounding areas, twice the first week, and then weekly until healed.

Ticks. Arsenic (As_2O_3), 0.175 to 019 per-cent solution, may be used as a dip (for all animals, depending on size and amount of hair); immerse

---

* Smear 62 or EQ 335: See BEPQ and Entomology Research Branch U.S. Dept. Agr. E-813 (1951).

animals every 14 days. Pyrethrins, 0.1 per-cent, plus a synergist, 1.0 per-cent, applied as a spray when needed; or rotenone, 5 per-cent dust (or 12 ounces per gallon of water) spraying thoroughly, may also be used.

Beef Cattle

Cattle Grub. Dow ET-57, 40 per-cent as a bolus (one 37.5 gram bolus per 300 pounds of body weight), may be applied orally with balling gun or dissolved in water as a drench. Minimum time from last application to slaughter, 60 days. Animals should have access to feed and water before and after treatment. Bayer 21/199, 0.5 per-cent wettable powder as a spray, in a 1-gallon quantity (in one spraying, or in two sprayings 2 to 4 weeks apart if animals are in short coat), may also be used. Minimum time from last application to slaughter, 60 days. Wet the skin all over the body at the end of adult heel fly season. Do not treat sick animals, or calves less than 3 months old; spray animals 3 to 6 months old lightly. Do not use with pyrethrins, allethrin, or synergists.

Horn Flies. Use methoxychlor, 0.5 per-cent emulsion concentrate or wettable powder, 2 quarts as a spray, or 50 per-cent wettable powder, 1 tablespoonful sprinkled, on the backs every 3 weeks or as needed. Tolerance is 3 ppm (in fat). Or use DDT or toxaphene, 5 per-cent in oil, applied as back rubs; one gallon to saturate 20 feet of cable. Minimum time from last application to slaughter, for DDT, 30 days, and for toxaphene, 28 days. Tolerance for DDT, 7 ppm (in fat), for toxaphene, 7 ppm.

Lice. Lindane, 0.03 per-cent emulsion concentrate or wettable powder, may be applied as a spray. Minimum time from last application to slaughter, 30 days. Methoxychlor, 0.5 per-cent emulsion concentrate or wettable powder; malathion, 0.5 per-cent emulsion concentrate or wettable powder, applied as sprays may be used. Tolerance for methoxychlor, 3 ppm (in fat), for malathion 4 ppm. (Do not use lindane on emaciated or lactating animals, or malathion on animals less than 1 month old.)

Screwworms. Use Bayer 21/199, 0.5 per-cent wettable powder, spraying wounds thoroughly and wetting entire body.

Ticks. Lindane, 0.025 per-cent emulsion concentrate or wettable powder, immersed or sprayed thoroughly is recommended. Minimum time from last application to slaughter, 30 days. Malathion, 0.5 per-cent emulsion concentrate or wettable powder, sprayed thoroughly, may be used. Tolerance for malathion, 4 ppm.

Sheep and Goats

Fleece worms. Use Bayer 21/199, 0.25 per-cent as wettable powder; spray thoroughly on and around infested area. Minimum time from last application to slaughter, 60 days.

Lice. DDT, 0.25 per-cent emulsion concentrate or wettable powder, as a dip, or 0.5 per-cent as a spray, may be used. Minimum time from last application to slaughter, 30 days; tolerance for DDT, 7 ppm (in fat). Methoxychlor, 0.25 per-cent emulsion concentrate or wettable powder, as a dip, or 0.5 per-cent as a spray (tolerance, 3 ppm in fat) ; or malathion, 0.5 per-cent emulsion concentrate or wettable powder as a spray (tolerance, 4 ppm) ; or rotenone, 5 per-cent powder (or 1 to 2 pounds per hundred gallons water) may be used, dust or spray thoroughly. (Use DDT but once; others after 2 to 3 weeks, if needed.) Do not use DDT or malathion on milk goats.

Screwworms. See Cattle.

Keds (Sheep Tick). Use Toxaphene, 0.25 per-cent emulsion concentrate or wettable powder as a dip, or 0.5 per-cent as a spray. Minimum time from last application to slaughter, 28 days. Tolerance for toxaphene, 7 ppm. Do not use on milk goats. The following may also be used: pyrethrins, 0.1 plus synergist 1.0 per-cent, immerse or spray thoroughly; rotenone, 5 per-cent dust (or 8 ounces per hundred gallons of water), immerse or apply thoroughly; or malathion, 0.5 per-cent emulsion concentrate or wettable powder, spray thoroughly. Tolerance for malathion, 4 ppm. Repeat treatments as needed.

Ticks. Use toxaphene, 0.25 per-cent emulsion concentrate or wettable powder, as a dip, or 0.5 per-cent as a spray. Minimum time from last application to slaughter, 28 days. Tolerance for toxaphene, 7 ppm. Malathion, 0.5 per-cent emulsion concentrate or wettable powder, as a spray, may also be used. Tolerance for malathion, 4 ppm. Repeat treatments as needed.

Swine

Lice. Use Lindane, 0.05 to 0.06 per-cent emulsion concentrate or wettable powder as a dip or spray. Minimum time from last application to slaughter, 30 days. Use lindane applications only once. The following may also be used: Malathion, 0.5 per-cent emulsion concentrate or wettable powder as a spray (tolerance, 4 ppm). DDT, 0.5 per-cent emulsion concentrate or wettable powder as a dip or spray. Minimum time from last application to slaughter, 30 days. Tolerance for DDT, 7 ppm (in fat). Use DDT only once.

Poultry

Lice or Mites. Use Lindane, 0.5 to 1.0 per-cent emulsion concentrate or wettable powder; spray or paint, covering house, roosts, and nests throughly. Do not apply lindane or nicotine sulfate on birds, or while birds are in the house. Nicotine sulfate, 40 per-cent solution, 1 pint to 150–200 feet, may be used. Paint on roosts only.

Lice Only. Use Rotenone, 1 per-cent dust, 1 pound per hundred birds, applied directly to birds, roosts, and nests. Sodium fluoride or sodium fluosilicate, 100 per-cent dust, applied by the pinch method are also recommended.

Fowl Tick. Use malathion, 3.0 per-cent, as a spray, 1 to 2 gallons per thousand square feet of surface; cover walls, ceilings, and floors thoroughly. Tolerance for malathion is 4 ppm in meat, none in eggs. Lindane, 0.5 per-cent, as a spray, 1 to 2 gallons per thousand square feet of surface, may also be used; cover walls, ceilings, and floors thoroughly. Lindane is not to be applied to birds or in the house.

Fly-Infested Areas

In Barns. Use dipterex, 1 to 2 per-cent dry bait, 1 ounce, or 0.1 per-cent liquid bait, 1 gallon per thousand square feet of surface. Broadcast or sprinkle daily for 3 days, and as needed thereafter. *Do not use any insecticide in milk room, or contaminate animal feed or water.* The following may also be used: Diazinon, 1 per-cent dry bait, 1 ounce, or 0.1 per-cent liquid bait, 1 gallon per thousand square feet of surface. Apply as with Dipterex. Lindane, 0.3 to 0.5 per-cent emulsion concentrate or wettable powder, as a spray on resting surfaces, 1 gallon per thousand square feet of surface. Methoxychlor, 2.5 to 5 per-cent emulsion concentrate or wettable powder, 1 to 2 gallons per thousand square feet of surface, or 1 to 2 ounces per thousand cubic feet as a space spray. Pyrethrins, 0.1 to 0.2 per-cent, plus synergist, 1 to 2 ounces per thousand cubic feet as a space spray.

Outside Barns. Use chlordone, 2 to 2.5 per-cent as a spray, 1 to 2 gallons per thousand square feet of surface. Toxaphene, 5 per-cent emulsion concentrate or wettable powder as a spray, ½ to 1 gallon per thousand square feet of surface; or DDT, 2 to 5 per-cent emulsion concentrate or wettable powder as a spray, ½ to 1 gallon per thousand square feet or cubic feet, may also be used. Cover exterior surfaces, vegetation, manure, and refuse thoroughly. DDT is also used as a space spray.

RECENT DEVELOPMENTS IN PESTICIDES AND THEIR USES

In addition to the recommendations given above, there are other materials registered for use whose residues, if any, are within the tolerances established by the Food and Drug Administration under Public Law 518. New pesticides are continually being developed which, before they can be marketed, must be carefully tested both as to their value as insecticides and their harmlessness to host plants and animals, with residues not exceeding established tolerances. Agricultural officers and manufacturers of pesticides should be consulted regarding new and promising compounds.

Beef-and-Dairy Cattle Fly-Control Experiments

The control of biting flies on beef and dairy cattle has been found to result in satisfactory increases in weight and gains in milk production. The various materials used in such treatment include repellents, insecticides, and synergists. Application is by hand-sprayers or by special devices, applying the material direct to the body of the animal. The studies cover a number of years, culminating with the results of a number of recent surveys.

Granett and Hansens (1956) compared the value of weekly applications of a quart of spray per cow of methoxychlor alone and that of methoxychlor plus butoxy polyproplene glycol (Crag Fly Repellent). A significant reduction in fly numbers (horn, stable, and horse, flies) was noted for both types of spray for from five to seven weeks. An increase in milk production was noted for one day following the use of the first formula, and for two days following the second formula. The increased milk more than paid the cost of the spraying. In a further test of the same spray materials (Granett and Hansens, 1957), applied as dust as well as sprays, the spray applications showed "a marked difference between treated and untreated groups, both in reduction in fly annoyance and increased milk production." The inclusion of butoxy polyproplene glycol in the formula tended to increase the effectiveness of the application. The dust applications were less effective than the sprays.

Bruce and Decker (1958), in a three-year study, have correlated the data on milk productivity and stable-fly population densities and shown that "depressed production [milk] continues for weeks and months beyond the end of the fly season." The intent of the study was not to obtain "maximum levels of fly control but rather in the development of information with respect to the value of various levels of fly control on dairy cattle." Two methods of study were used—the split-herd in which one-half of the herd were sprayed daily with an effective repellent mixture; in the second method, whole herds were treated with repellent sprays, "so selected as to obtain different levels of fly control." The materials used were various concentrations of pyrethrins, piperonyl butoxide, and various repellents. All sprays were applied with hand-operated sprayers at the usual daily dosage of two ounces per animal.

The attacks of biting flies cause the animal the annoyances of pain, loss of blood, interference with normal grazing habits, and use of energy in warding off attacks of flies. This results in decreased milk production, not only in the summer months, but through December. It was also found that, "in general, the treated animals of the split-herd experiments had longer lactation periods and were out of production for a correspondingly shorter period of time than the untreated cows."

The cost of the spray material, it is estimated, would be equaled by a 1 per-cent increase in milk production for six months. Increases in production with the existing fly population of the experiment are possible within a range of 10 to 20 per-cent by the application of a good repellent-spray formulation—a very satisfactory return on the investment (Bruce and Decker, 1958).

Cutkomp and Harvey (1958) have studied the weight response of beef cattle in relation to the control of biting flies. The materials used were applications, by means of a treadle-sprayer, of pyrethrins, 0.54 per-cent; MGK-264, 5.4 per-cent; emulsifier; and petroleum distillate. Later the pyrethrins were reduced to 0.23 per-cent, plus piperonyl butoxide, 2.26 per-cent, and butoxy polypropylene glycol, 55.5 per-cent. Horn fly control was better than 95 per-cent, and that of s stable flies was about 70 per-cent. In 1954, the treated animals showed an average increase per head of 22 pounds more than the untreated, for the 90-day period. In 1955, the average gain for the treated animals over that of the untreated ones, was 41 pounds for the season. In 1956, which was an unusually cool and rainly year, there was no difference in the rate of gain for the treated and the untreated lots. The cost of the spray materials per animal for the 90-day season was $1.14. Allowing a price of 20 cents per pound, this would give a net profit of $3.36 and $10.92 per head in 1954 and 1955 respectively. It is concluded "on the basis of these results, and a study of weather records, that a profitable return from fly biting control may be expected in most years."

Tien-Hsi, Cheng (1958b) reports on the results of experiments on the effect of biting-fly control on weight gain in beef cattle. The materials used were applications, by means of an automatic sprayer, of (1) diethyl-m-toluamide (repellent), 15 per-cent, and methoxychlor, 1 per-cent in water emulsion; and (2) MGK (repellent), 0.4 per-cent, MGK 264 (insecticide synergist), 0.2 per-cent, piperonyl butoxide, 0.1 per-cent, and pyrethrins, 0.035 per-cent in petroleum distillate. It was found that the over-all average gain resulting from all treatments ranged from one-half to two-thirds of a pound per animal per day for the eight-week period.

Automatic Applicators. The use of automatic applicators for applying insecticides and repellents to cattle as a means of fly control has, within the last few years, come into general favor. Both the "Cable Type Back Rubbers" and the treadle machine give control quite comparable to hand and power application, and with a decided saving in expense of operation. The back-rubber type gives protection against the horn fly, but less so against the stable fly, which attacks the legs as well as the body. The treadle machine may be adjusted for various types of sprays; it is less satisfactory for nervous animals. The formulas used include any listed above; methoxychlor, 5 per-cent dissolved in diesel oil, as a very practical one.

Rogoff and Movon (1952) give the following directions for setting up the back-rubber (apparently first recorded in 1950): Two wooden fence-posts, solidly set and braced, are installed about 16 feet apart. A cable, made of a chain, wire rope, or, preferably, three strands of barbed wire wrapped with a fourth wire, is suspended between the two posts so as to sag within about 18 inches of the ground. The cable is carefully wrapped with burlap sacks overlapped and carefully tied. Approximately 1 gallon of the insecticide solution is required to soak a 16-foot length of cable and should be replenished about every 2 weeks with 2 quarts of the formula. No significant skin irritation was seen after 2 years observations of animals treated with the back-rubber. In the case of DDT, there was a much smaller residue in the fat of cattle, using the back-rubber, than from animals sprayed three times with a 0.5 per-cent solution.

Tien-Hsi, Cheng and Vandenberg (1958a) confirm the findings of Rogoff and Moxon in that the back-rubber is more satisfactory in the control of the horn fly than the stable fly. A movable form of the back-rubber was developed in which one end was fastened to a tree or post and the lower end attached to a spring anchored to a concrete block, 8 by 8 by 48 inches in size. The block was also wrapped with burlap, soaked with the insecticide solution, and held in place by wooden stakes. A 12-foot cable was swung from an eyebolt fastened at a 5-foot height on the post, while the lower end was but a few inches from the ground. Distance between the post and block was 10 feet, 3 inches. The slope of the cable and the treated block made possible treating the legs against the stable fly and also against infestations of lice.

Impregnated Cords for Fly Control. Because of house fly resistance to residual deposits of DDT and related compounds, it has become necessary to develop more satisfactory methods of killing flies by the use of chemicals. One successful method is that of cords impregnated with either parathion or diazinon, both of which are quicker-acting than DDT. The treated cords are suspended directly from the ceiling or from horizontal cords (treated), stretched from wall to wall near the ceiling. Dark-colored cotton cords of 3/16-inch diameter are favored as giving longer effective control than those of 3/32-inch diameter. "Cord installation is at the rate of 30 linear feet of cord per 100 square feet of floor." The insecticides found most successful were a 10 per-cent parathion-xylene solution and a 25 per-cent diazinon-xylene solution in which the cords were soaked for 2 minutes. The latter formula is favored for use in dining halls and dairies, because of the lower mammalian toxicity. Such use of treated cords, especially if accompanied with suitable sanitation, gives protection for from 6 weeks to an entire season. To hasten the reduction of large populations of flies, baits of diazinon and of DDVP may be used for a few days (Fay and Lindquist, 1954; Schoof and Kilpatrick, 1957).

House fly Baits. As a supplementary measure for fly control, dry and wet baits of malathion and other phosphate compounds are especially useful in corn meal and molasses or sugar-solution baits, but are not to be used in milk rooms nor allowed to contaminate feed or water. A number of compounds may be used, but diazinon and DDVP are favored because of their quick action and their low toxicity to mammals. The dry baits are conveniently applied with salt shakers, but lack the short residual effect of the wet sprays, which are applied with sprinkling cans. Diazinon or malathion as a dry bait, 1.0 per-cent on sugar, is applied at the rate of 1 ounce per thousand square feet of surface for 3 days, and then as needed. Diazinon, emulsion concentrate or wettable powder, is applied as a wet bait, 0.1 per-cent in water at the rate of 1 gallon per thousand square feet, applied daily for 3 days, and then as needed (Hansens and Others, 1955).

DDVP is used at 0.1 per-cent strength in a 10 per-cent sugar solution, and repeated at intervals of 2 to 5 days at a similar rate as that for diazinon (Kilpatrick and Schoof, 1955; Schoof and Kilpatrick, 1957).

House fly Larvicides. Studies by Sampson (1956) of the comparative value of various insecticides as a control of the house fly in manures have shown satisfactory results by endrin, heptachlor, and lindane, with sprays of 0.125 per-cent concentration of the toxicant, with diazinon a close fourth in the list. Because of the greater mammalian safety of the latter, it is to be preferred. Confirmation of these findings is shown by Wilson and Gahan (1957) during their studies of poultry houses. They also report good results from the application of a dust mixture containing 1.86 pounds of diazinon (wettable powder) combined with 36 pounds of attapulgite and 2 pounds of celite. The mixture was sprinkled from a 1-pint scoop on the manure at 150 mg of diazinon per square foot. This was superior to liquid applications because it prevented liquefaction of the manure.

Dow ET-57, wettable powder, at 1.25 per-cent concentration, applied semimonthly as a spray during the spring and fall, at the rate of 107 ml per square foot, is also an effective agent for controlling house fly larvae in manure (Knapp and Others, 1958b).

Systemic[*] Insecticides Used Against the Cattle Grub (Bot fly)

Systemic insecticides for application by mouth or subcutaneously, as a control for cattle grub, are now being perfected. Roth and Eddy (1957)

---

[*] The systemic insecticide, when applied at one point, may be carried to another part of the animal body with toxic effect to the grub.

were successful in killing the younger stages of the cattle grubs *Hypoderma bovis* and *H. lineatum* with Dow ET-57 but did not kill the mature grubs that were already encysted. The treatment was oral or by subcutaneous injection. Dosages of 25 ml/kg (milligrams per kilogram) to 100 mg/kg gave erratic results. This was thought to be due to the age and number of the grubs at the time of treatment. Further experiments with Dow ET-57 were reported by McGregor and Bushland (1957), who treated a number of steers and heifers by drenching. The dosage of 100 mg/kg gave a 92 per-cent control and prevented encystment of new larvae. Toxicological studies were made by Radeleff and Woodward (1957) of the effect of this chemical on cattle and sheep at dosages of 100 mg/kg and higher. No symptoms were noted of the effect of Dow ET-57 in any of the cattle treated at that dosage, except for one calf of four months age which showed slight diarrhea. Dosages of 125 mg/kg or higher were toxic to yearling and older cattle. No cattle were killed with Dow ET-57, even at a dosage of 400 mg/kg—four times the normal dosage for cattle. A few sheep have been treated with Dow ET-57 at dosages of 100 mg/kg or less without symptoms of poisoning. One yearling ewe receiving 400 mg/kg showed only a mild diarrhea.

Adkins (1957) treated a large number of cattle distributed among four different stations with Dow ET-57. A dosage of 110 mg/kg was used, applied either as a drench or as a bolus (a ball of medicine larger than a pill). The cattle-grub control for the four stations averaged 86 per cent. No apparent difference was noted between drenching and the bolus treatment, but the latter was easier and safer to administer.

Field studies of feed and bolus formulation of Dow ET-57 were made on 479 Hereford steers and heifers at the Kansas Agriculture Station in 1956. All treated animals were given 110 mg of Dow ET-57 per kilogram of body weight. At one branch station, 118 animals were treated with boluses, and showed an average increase of 0.5 grub per animal. The 117 untreated animals showed an average increase of 11 grubs per animal. At one station, 80 head, treated by bolus, showed an average increase of 0.38 grub per animal. Another 80 animals, treated by adding the Dow ET-57 to the feed, had an increase of 0.25 grub per animal. The untreated animals had an average increase of 3.2 grubs per animal. No toxic symptoms were noted in any treated animals, but there was a marked depression of enzyme. "There were no consistent differences among weight gains of the two treatments and the controls within each of the four lots." Further investigations of different feed supplements and methods of ET-57 treatments are recommended (Knapp and Others, 1958a).

Ronnel (Dow ET-57) was administered orally at the Nebraska Experiment Station to 128 Hereford calves, weighing approximately 500 pounds, at the beginning of the tests for the control of the cattle grubs *Hypoderma lineatum* and *H. bovis*. The calves were divided into three groups. Group one received 100 to 110 mg of active ingredient per kilogram of body weight. Treatment was applied on December 4, as a bolus, about 2 to 3 weeks before grubs began appearing on the backs of the untreated animals.

Group two received 92 to 99 mg of active ingredient per kilogram of body weight. Treatment was applied December 18 with a drench prepared by diluting a 50 per-cent emulsion concentrate with tap water to make a 10 per-cent emulsion.

Group three had the same number of calves as group two, and was treated on the same day and with the same dosage. The drench used was a suspension prepared from a 25 per-cent wettable powder of ronnel. Grubs had begun to encyst in the backs of the animals, in both groups two and three, when the treatment was made.

The cattle were examined for grubs and weighed at 28-day intervals from December through May of the following year. Thirty-six animals that received the boluses about 3 weeks before grubs began encysting had an average of 0.5 grubs. The untreated animals averaged 8.6. The drenches were given after the calves had an average of three encysted grubs. The emulsion failed to kill these grubs, and an additional three per animal encysted later. The suspension was effective in killing those already encysted, and less than one additional grub per animal encysted (Jones, 1959).

The phosphorous compound Bayer 21/199 was tested against the cattle grub *H. lineatum* at 1.0, 0.5, 0.25, and 0.1 per cents. The wettable-powder preparations were applied as washes and thoroughly scrubbed into the backs of the animals at the rate of 1 pint per animal. The two highest concentrations gave a complete kill of the larvae, but the 1.0 per-cent was quicker than the 0.5 per-cent. However, all the grubs were dead at the end of the second week, even with the 0.5 per-cent wash. A comparison was then made between the compound 21/199 and the standard recommendation of cube or derris powder (rotenone 5 per cent), 7½ pounds per hundred gallons of water, both applied as sprays. Approximately one gallon of the spray was applied to each animal at 350 pounds of pressure.

Nine infested animals treated with Bayer 21/199 had fifteen second and seventy third instar larvae, or a total of eighty-five. Thirty infested animals treated with rotenone spray had a total of 245 larvae. Bayer 21/199 gave a complete kill of the larvae during the first week. Rotenone killed 84 per cent the first week and a total of 91 per cent within two weeks (Roth and Eddy, 1955).

Further tests were made by Brundrett and Others (1957), comparing Bayer 21/199 with Dow ET-57 as spray applications. The former was used both as an emulsion and as a suspension at 0.75 per-cent, and the latter with similar type of application at 1.0 per-cent. The Dow ET-57 sprays failed to prevent migration of cattle grubs. The Bayer 21/199 sprays were almost 100 per-cent effective in preventing grubs encysting in the back.

A study has been made in Florida by Harris and Others (1959) of the comparative efficacy of Bayer 21/199 and ronnel (Dow ET-57) and the preferred time of application. A single application is desirable, and if possible, it should be late enough in the season to avoid reinfestation.

The cattle used were a mixed lot of beef types, seven to nine months old at the beginning of the experiment on May 6, 1957. The treatments were repeated on a similar number of animals on June 5, July 8, August 22, and September 16, 1957.

Bayer 21/199 was prepared as a 2.5 per-cent spray from a 25 per-cent wettable powder and water. One pint of the dilute spray, containing 11.25 grams of active ingredient, was applied over the back of each animal by means of a hand-sprayer. Ronnel was applied as an oral drench containing 10 ml of the 50 per-cent emulsion concentrate diluted to make 1 ounce of liquid. This was given at the rate of 1 ounce per hundred pounds of body weight.

Bayer 21/199, when applied as a single dermal spray in May, June, July, or August, was significantly more effective than an oral drench of ronnel in reducing the numbers of the cattle grub, *Hypoderma lineatum*, that later appeared on the backs of Everglades cattle. Ronnel, however, was significantly more effective when each was applied in September.

Bayer 21/199 or ronnel applied as early as May was effective in controlling cattle grubs before they reached the backs of cattle.

Miscellaneous Tests with Systemic Insecticides

Drummond (1958) shows the value of a number of systemics against various insects, and the lone-star tick (*Amblyomma americanum*). The compounds were first tested on guinea pigs, and from these the more promising were selected for use by drenching on sheep and goats. American Cyanamid 12/880 at 50 mg/kg killed both nymphal and adult ticks, but was not lethal to sheep and goats; at 25 mg/kg, it killed stable flies and screwworms. Bayer 23/129 at 25 mg/kg was lethal to sheep and goats, but at 10 mg/kg, it killed screwworms and was not toxic to stable flies and lone star ticks. Dow ET-57 at 100 mg/kg killed all screwworms but was not lethal to lone star ticks or stable flies—nor to sheep or goats.

Plot Tests Against the Lone Star Tick

Hunter and Others (1957) found that applications of either dieldrin dust at 0.5, or endrin spray at 1.0, pound per acre would give a marked control of the lone star tick population for at least 4 weeks. This work was done in a hot, dry, dusty district of Texas, and the results might not apply to a humid area.

Blow Fly Repellants

Baker and Schoof (1955) have made a comparative study of the repellency and larvicidal value of various insecticides. The study was conducted in the field under natural conditions. Dieldrin at 0.25 to 2.0 percent and Diazinon and endrin at 0.25 to 0.5 per-cent prevented blow fly infestation for from 26 to 30 days or more, and reduced established infestations from 98 to 100 per cent. Chlordane at 1.0 per-cent was similar in value. Malathion at 0.25 to 0.5 per-cent gave 100 per-cent kill of mature larvae in carcases, but was less effective than dieldrin and diazinon or endrin as a repellent.

The sheep ked (*Melophagus ovinus*) is a common parasite of sheep in the Rocky Mountain district. Sheep are usually grazed in bands of 1,000 to 3,000 head, which makes control by dipping or spraying laborious and hazardous. A method of power-dusting has been developed which has eradicated the parasite from large bands and yet is quite economical. Dusting range flocks with rotenone at 0.5 per-cent has been the common practice, but the treatment does not cause eradication. A number of insecticides, including dieldrin, chlordane, toxaphene, lindane, and heptachlor, have been tested but, of these materials, only dieldrin at 1.5 per-cent has given 100 per-cent control.

Treatment may immediately follow shearing, and flocks have been successfully treated as long as 50 to 70 days later. A satisfactory dust formulation is made principally with pyrophyllite, and containing 2 per-cent light motor oil to reduce fluffiness. The blower is operated so as to give a discharge rate of 2.5 to 3 pounds per minute and should be so arranged that the wind will carry the dust cloud away from the sheep as they pass through the chute. The sheep should be kept moving continuously through the chute, and not allowed to turn back into the holding pen. From 50 to 100 pounds of the dieldrin 1.5 per-cent dust has treated a band of 1,000 sheep (Pfadt and DeFoliart, 1957).

Roth and Bigley (1959) experimented with a series of organophosphate insecticides in the control of the sheep ked. The spray (1958) was applied at a pressure of 250 to 330 pounds at the rate of 2 quarts per animal for both ewes and lambs. Application was made during April, May, and June. The various insecticides were applied at a concentration of 0.1 per cent of the active material.

Korlan (Dow ET-57), Delnav (Hercules AC-528), and Bayer 21/199 gave complete control of the sheep ked. Good results were also obtained with malathion.

Hog Lice and Mange

Tests with malathion at dosages of 0.5 and 0.25 per-cent, as a control of hog lice (*Haetopinus suis*), have shown protection for more than 9 days, while a single application of malathion at 1.0 per-cent gave protection for over 30 days. The spray was applied with a hand-sprayer, using 475 ml (1 pint) per animal. To determine the amount of absorption, if any, two applications of the 1.0 per-cent dosage were applied to pigs at one-week intervals. Analysis of fat, liver, and lean meat from the treated pigs showed malathion contents ranging from none to 0.04 ppm. From these data, it was concluded that malathion was an effective and safe control chemical for hog lice (Johnson, 1958).

Mange infestation of hogs by the mite, *Sarcoptes scabiei suis*, was controlled within 19 days by application of malathion emulsion at dosages of 0.5 and 1.0 per-cent. A detergent wetting agent was used at ½ pound per 25 gallons of water. The bedding and walls were sprayed at the same time to prevent reinfestation. The application was made with a power-sprayer at 50 pounds of pressure, using 1 quart of spray mixture per animal. No gross symptoms of toxicity or skin irritation were noted with concentrations as high as 2.0 per-cent (Raun and Ahrens, 1956).

Poultry Lice, Mites and Ticks

Nicotine sulfate, 40 per-cent solution, applied as a paint to the roosts only, is a common remedy for the control of body lice and the mite, *Dermanyssus gallinae*, which remains on the roost during the day. It should not be applied while the birds are in the house.

The northern fowl mite (*Bdellonyssus sylviarum*), on white leghorn hens, has been controlled by hand-dusting with lindane, 1 per-cent dust at 5 grams per bird. This same concentration of lindane dust also controlled lice when applied on the litter at the rate of 1 pound per 150 square feet.

Malathion, 4 per-cent dust, applied with a rotary duster to flocks on wire roosts at the rate of 4 grams per bird, gave practical control of the northern fowl mite for about 30 days. One pound of this same dust applied to 40 to 200 square feet of litter surface gave prolonged control of the fowl mite. Lindane at 1 per-cent and, also, dusts of malathion at 4 per-cent, applied at the rate of 1 pound per 150 square feet of litter, were effective against the poultry lice, *Menacanthus stramineus* and *Menopon gallinae* (Hoffman, 1956).

The chicken body louse (*Menacanthus stramineus*) and the chicken mite (*Dermanysus gallinae*) have been controlled by spraying the roosts with malathion, 3 per-cent emulsion. This did not, however, give satis-factory control of the fowl tick (*Argas persicus*). Better control of the latter was obtained by a house spray of aldrin, 2 per-cent concentration (Furman and Weinman 1956).

REFERENCES

Adkins, Jr.,. T. R., *J. Econ. Entom.*, **50**, 474 (1957).

Baker, W. C., and Schoof, H. F., *ibid.*, **48**, 181 (1955).

Bruce, W. N., and Decker, G. C., *ibid.*, **51**, 269 (1958).

Brundrett, H. M., and Others, *Agr. Chem.*, **12**(6), 36 (1957).

Cutkomp, L. K., and Harvey, A. L., *J. Econ. Entom.*, **51**, 72 (1958).

Drummond, R. O., *ibid.*, **51**, 425 (1958).

Fay, R. W., and Lindquist, D. A., *ibid.*, **47**, 975 (1954).

Furman, D. P., and Weinmann, C. J., *ibid.*, **49**, 447 (1956).

Goulding, R. L., and Terriere, L. C., *ibid.*, **52**, 341 (1959).

Granett, P., and Hansens, E. J., *ibid.*, **49**, 465 (1956).

———, *ibid.*, **50**, 332 (1957).

Hansens, E. J., and Others, *ibid.*, **48**, 306 (1955).

———, *ibid.*, **49**, 27 (1956).

Harris, E. D., *ibid.*, **52**, 425 (1959).

Hoffman, R. A., *ibid.*, **49**, 347 (1956).

Hunter, G. W., and Others, *ibid.*, **50**, 262 (1957).

Johnson, W. T., *ibid.*, **51**, 255 (1958).

Jones, C. M., *ibid.*, **52**, 488 (1959).

Kilpatrick, J. W., and Schoof, H. F., *ibid.*, **48**, 623 (1955).

Knapp, F. W., and Others, *ibid.*, **51**, 119 (1958a).

———, *ibid.*, **51**, 361 (1958b).

McGregor, W. S., and Bushland, R. C., *ibid.*, **50**, 246 (1957).

Pfadt, R. E., and DeFoliart, G. R., *ibid.*, **50**, 190 (1957).

Radeleff, R. D., and Woodward, G. T., *ibid.*, **50**, 249 (1957).

Raun, E. S., and Ahrens, R. H., *ibid.*, **49**, 140 (1956).

Rogoff, W. M., and Moxon, A. L., *ibid.*, **45**, 329 (1952).

Roth, A. R., and Eddy, G. W., *ibid.*, **48**, 201 (1955).

———, *ibid.*, **50**, 244 (1957).

Roth, A. R., and Bigley, W. S. *ibid.*, **52**, 539 (1959).

Sampson, W. W., *ibid.*, **49**, 74 (1956).

Schoof, H. F., and Kilpatrick, J. W., *ibid.*, **50**, 24 (1957).

Staff, U.S. Dept. Agr., "Handbook No. 120," 1959.

Tien-Hsi, C., and Vandenberg, J. F., *J. Econ. Entom.*, **51**, 149 (1958a).

———, *ibid.*, **51**, 275 (1958b).

Wilson, H. G., and Gahan, J. B., *ibid.*, **50**, 613 (1957).

11. HOUSEHOLD INSECTS AND RODENTS

Protection against insects and rodents in the home, both in urban and rural areas, is greatly advanced over former years. This is due to public recognition of these intruders as disease-carriers, to better sanitation, and to the use of pesticides.

Flies, with their hairy bodies and legs and because of their feeding habits, are ideal carriers of germs. The house fly is known to be the carrier of various forms of dysenteries, typhoid fever, and cholera. Fly-specking also mars the beauty of the home and when abundant detracts from its value. Blow flies deposit their eggs on meat at every opportunity, the only protection being refrigeration, curing the meat, or prompt cooking.

Certain forms of mosquitoes are well known as carriers of the organism causing malaria. One or more forms of fleas are known carriers of bubonic plague. Rodent droppings have been found to be carriers of certain internal parasites that attack man. These are the better-known examples of diseases that may be carried into our homes by these unwelcome intruders.

Sanitary measures, about the home, adjoining areas, and city dumps, have improved following the better understanding of the dangers from such sources. Disposal of waste water from irrigation and proper drainage have eliminated many mosquito-breeding places. Building regulations not only specify the desired volume of air and light in the home but do much to eliminate rodent entrance and the fostering of termites and dry rot.

FLIES*

All common flies except flesh flies are usually found in the home. Flesh flies, feeders on carrion and excrement, and parasites of other insects, may also occasionally enter.

These flies have similar breeding habits but vary in their preference for foods. The house fly and lesser house fly breed in warm, moist organic matter. Such sources may include piled lawn cuttings, compost heaps, leaky garbage cans, manure and offal, and waste materials of fruit and

---

* These include the house fly (*Musca domestica*), lesser house fly (*Fannia canicularis*), greenbottle flies (*Phaenicia* spp.), bluebottle flies (*Calliphora* spp.), black blow fly (*Phormia regina*), vinegar flies (*Drosophila* spp.), and flesh flies (*Sarcophaga* spp.).

vegetables. The larvae of the greenbottle fly or blow fly feed on carrion, manure, garbage, and other refuse. The bluebottle fly and the black blow fly feed on dead animal matter, and are the wool maggots of sheep. The vinegar fly breeds in fermenting and decaying fruits and their products. They are attracted by vinegar, jellies, and pickles, and have become an annoyance on harvested tomatoes.

Fly Prevention

The surest control of flies is prevention of breeding. Begin operations in the early spring with the first appearance of adult flies. The fly population is greatly reduced during the winter. Survivors are largely in the pupal stage—the others having been killed by unfavorable weather, lack of suitable food, or disease.

Well-fitted door and window screens are essential, preferably with the doors opening outwardly. Rust-resistant screen, such as aluminum, copper, or bronze, is preferable in humid climates. The screen mesh for flies is 10 or 12 to the inch, and 16 mesh for smaller insects.

Garbage should be stored in cans with tight-fitting lids. Lawn clippings may be left where cut, spread out thinly to dry, or treated with chemicals. Manure used as fertilizer should be free of fly larvae and pupae. Droppings of poultry and dogs should be buried. Garden compost may be held in a fly-tight box with screened air inlets. Open piles should be covered with a layer of soil after each addition of garden waste. An alternate plan, where the weather permits, is to store the compost dry through the warm weather and add water as needed in the fall.

Control of Fly Larvae and Pupae. Accumulations of poultry manure, lawn clippings, or other organic material infested with the larval and pupal stage of the fly may be treated with a 5 per-cent solution of DDT, either the emulsion or wettable-powder form. The former, however, gives better penetration. Malathion, diluted as directed on the label, may be preferable in the districts where fly resistance has developed. The insecticide should be well distributed in the material where the flies are breeding. (See page 193 for treating large accumulations of manure or vegetable material; page 197 for blow fly repellents on carcasses.)

Control of Adult Flies. Commercial sprays are available for use in hand-sprayers or as aerosols within doors. These usually contain pyrethrins and an activator (synergist), such as piperonyl butoxide, n-propyl isomer, or sesame oil. Close the room and spray for a few seconds; then do not open for an hour or more. Other chemicals used in fly sprays are allethrin, organic thiocyanates, DDT, methoxychlor, and lindane. The latter material is also used in insecticide electrical vaporizers, but is not recommended for use in homes or in rooms where food is exposed or where people work or play.

Surface or residual sprays are applied to the outer walls of the home or outbuildings and may be effective for a number of weeks. They should not be used where children have access to them. Insecticides used for this purpose include DDT (for nonresistant flies), methoxychlor, chlordane, and lindane. DDT and chlordane are not to be used inside dairy barns and milk rooms (see page 189). Lindane and chlordane are not recommended for residual sprays inside homes. Solutions of 5 per-cent DDT and of methoxychlor are available commercially, or higher concentrations may be diluted as desired. Surface sprays may be applied with a spray gun or with a paint brush (Staff, Entomology Research Branch, U.S. Dept. Agr., 1955a; Staff, Univ. of Calif. College of Agriculture, and U.S. Department of Agriculture, 1956).

MOSQUITOES

The mosquito being a water-breeding insect, the first requisite in its control is the elimination of surplus water and chemical treatment of natural ponds, sluggish streams, and marshes. Mosquitoes can and do fly long distances, but frequently when they are abundant, a careful search will reveal them breeding in temporary containers such as tin cans, automobile tires, septic tanks, rain barrels, and watering troughs. Dispose of unnecessary containers, and drain or deepen natural courses.

Control of Mosquito Larvae and Pupae

Where larvae (wrigglers) are found in standing water, apply DDT, chlordane, toxaphene, TDE, or methoxychlor, as 1 per-cent emulsion or oil solutions, over the entire surface. Use these at the rate of 1 ounce per hundred square feet, or about 10 quarts per acre. Lindane, dieldrin, or heptachlor, at 0.5 per-cent emulsion or oil solution, are used at the same rate as above. Commercial solutions at higher concentrations are available and may be diluted with water as desired. These are not to be used where fish are present.

Kerosene, fuel oil, or diesel oil may also be used for applying to water surfaces. Use these at the rate of 2 to 4 ounces of oil per hundred square feet of surface, or 7 to 14 gallons per acre. If there is much vegetation in the water, make the applications a little heavier (Staff, Entomology Research Branch, U.S. Dept. Agr., 1955b).

Control of Adult Mosquitoes

The World Health Organization has sponsored a $500 million campaign to combat the malaria-carrying mosquito throughout the world. Spray applications of DDT are made, especially in all houses where the disease is present. Since it has been found that the mosquito may develop resistance to DDT after a very few years use, lindane and dieldrin are now being used in the same way. Apply surface or residual sprays of DDT, 5 per-cent emulsion; chlordane, 2 per-cent emulsion; or lindane, 1 per-cent emulsion. These sprays will be effective in killing the adult mosquito that alights on the treated surface. Use them on porch ceilings, outbuildings, and on the under surface of foliage near the house—but not within the home. They should not be used where children have access to the sprayed surface or the emulsions themselves. All insecticides are more or less poisonous and must be handled with great care. Wash the hands carefully after using them. Destroy empty containers.

Indoor Sprays. See Flies.

Repellents. Various chemicals, used as a protection against mosquitoes, have been applied to the person or the clothing. The standard is a mixture of dimethyl phthalate (40 per-cent), dimethyl carbate (30 per-cent) and ethyl hexanediol (30 per-cent). Gilbert (1957), during experiments in Oregon with various species of mosquitoes, found that diethyltoluamide was about twice as effective as the standard formula. This material, as a 50 per-cent ethanol solution, gave about 6 hours protection when applied to the skin. Treated clothing retained its repellency for 26 days, but became ineffective after two rinses.

ANTS

Many of the ants entering our homes are native species; however, adjoining much of our coastal areas, the introduced Argentine ant (*Iridomyrmex humilis*) has supplanted them. This species, being prolific and aggressive, usually displaces the native forms and becomes a serious pest. The Argentine ant may differ from other forms in having one central nest with one or more egg-laying queens, and may also have a number of supplementary colonies with or without a queen and located in a dry warm location. During cold or rainy weather, a colony may move into the house, locating near a furnace or other warm, sheltered spot. The thief ant and the red Pharaoh ant frequently also nest in the house. Nest sites may usually be located by watching the ants come and go, especially in the case of trail ants.

Control of Ants

Prevention is better than cure, as with most insects. Repellents, such as chlordane and Strobane plus pyrethrins (Kan-Kil), applied wherever ants enter the house, and to the outer walls from the ground up to, and around, the windows and doors will do much to prevent entrance. Within the house, use a small paint brush to apply the chlordane as a 2 per-cent oil-base solution along the baseboard, window frames, plumbing, and electrical outlets. It may also be applied as a spray or dust, but this should be done very sparingly because chlordane is a toxic compound. Do not inhale the mist or dust. Skin contact should be washed off immediately (Staff, Entomology Research Branch, U.S. Dept. Agr., 1957). Strobane is much less toxic to mammals than is chlordane. It is usually applied as an aerosol, but may also be used as a liquid. Avoid contact of the latter with the skin and do not unnecessarily inhale the mist.

In the garden, chlordane may be applied as an emulsion or wettable powder directly to the soil with a sprinkling can. Use a concentration similar to that for the house repellent. Other insecticides may also be used in the garden, including aldrin, dieldrin, heptachlor, and lindane, as directed on the label. Poison baits and sirups are also of value, but should be used outside the house in connection with a repellent. For the Argentine ant, use only baits with a fraction of 1 per-cent arsenic; otherwise, it acts as a repellent.

YELLOW JACKETS (WASPS) VESPULA

These insects are usually yellow-and-black banded. They may be considered as beneficial because they feed largely on flies, small caterpillars, and other harmful insects. Their severe sting, however, makes them very annoying, and may even cause serious results. These wasps build large nests of a coarse paper-like substance which they prepare from wood fiber. The nest is entirely enclosed except for a small opening near the bottom. Nests may be suspended in the open air or be in the ground.

Wasps may be most readily attacked while in the nest at night. The extension tube of a bellows-type duster or a knapsack sprayer is inserted in the entrance opening and dust or spray blown into the nest. Insecticides used include chlordane, 5 or 6 per-cent dust or a 2 per-cent emulsion; or DDT, 5 or 10 per-cent dust; or a 5 per-cent oil solution. Underground nests may be treated by pouring several ounces of carbon tetrachloride into the opening and then closing with cotton.

Nests suspended in the open may be dislodged into a sack, after first stupifying the yellow jackets by plugging the opening with absorbent cotton soaked with carbon tetrachloride, to reduce the danger of being stung. The nest may then be burned or buried (Staff, Research Branch, U.S. Dept. Agr., 1954).

ROACHES (COCKROACHES)

These insects, because of contamination of food and the sickening odor which they give off, are a serious house pest. Their habit of hiding in small cracks and their nocturnal feeding habit makes them difficult to control. Added to these difficulties is the fact that the German cockroach (*Blattella germanica*) has become quite resistant to the action of chlordane—once the standard control chemical for the roach. Malrin, which is 1.8 per-cent malathion and 3.6 per-cent Perthane, is recommended as the safest material for controlling the German cockroach (Laake, 1955).

Further tests by Jarvis and Grayson (1957) of various insecticides against both resistant and unresistant roaches showed both malathion alone, at 2 per-cent, and malathion plus allethrin, 0.2 per-cent, to be satisfactory control agents. Tabutrex is reported to be an active repellent for roaches.

Sorptive dusts are now beginning to be used as a control for roaches. These dusts kill roaches and termites by physical, rather than chemical, means. The inert dusts, by removing the protective outer layer of wax (cuticle), hasten the death of the insect by desiccation. A study of such dusts, used against the Oriental, German, and brown-banded roaches, showed that, under the conditions of the tests, brands SG67 and SG77 were the most effective.

These two dusts are finely divided, noncrystalline types of silica, formed by the reaction of sodium silicate and sulfuric acid. The resulting compound is a hydrogel which may be washed, dried, and ground to a fine powder. Chemical treatment may further increase the insecticidal action. The dust, when blown over the surface in a very thin layer, kills the insects as they walk over it. Death usually occurs within 2 hours. Dosages for homes and apartments, ranging from $\frac{1}{2}$ to $\frac{3}{4}$ pound, may be applied with a small duster. A visible film of dust should be applied to shelves, cupboards, furnace vents, and other hiding places (Tarshis, 1959).

CLOTHES MOTHS AND CARPET BEETLES*

These insects are notorious for the destruction which they cause to clothing, house furnishings, blankets, upholstery, and carpets, and to wool, fur, and related materials. Moths are especially attracted to clothing that is slightly spotted with food. The moth feeds only in the larval (worm) stage. The webbing-clothes-moth larva spins a silken tube which is attached to the food material. The casemaking-moth larva also spins a tube for its protection, which it drags about as it feeds.

The clothes moth is a weak flyer and may be seen flitting about darkened closets or emerging in dim light from behind furniture that is seldom moved. It is in such situations that the eggs are deposited and the larvae develop. Woolen clothing that is seldom worn—sweaters, socks, mittens, and discarded woolen lined gloves and slippers—is most frequently infested.

* These include the webbing clothes moth (*Tineola bisselliella*), casemaking clothes moth (*Tinea pellionella*), carpet beetle (*Anthrenus scrophulariae*), furniture carpet beetle (*A. flavipes*), varied carpet beetle (*A. verbasci*), and black carpet beetle (*Attagenus piceus*).

Carpet-beetle larvae do not depend upon webbing for protection, but crawl about freely. They are voracious feeders and may be found along the edges of wall-to-wall carpets and other protected places. The adult beetle flies readily and is often attracted to daylight. New infestations may develop through open windows and from adjoining houses, or from bird or rodent nests.

A study of the feeding habits of the webbing clothes moth, the black carpet beetle, and the furniture carpet beetle, made by Mallis and Others (1958), showed little or no feeding upon the synthetic fabrics (nylon, acetate rayon, and so forth); of the natural fabrics, silk, crepe, wool, linen, and cotton percale, only the wool showed extensive feeding; while combinations of wool and the synthetics, irrespective of proportion, showed extensive feeding.

Preventing Injury from Fabric Insects

The most practical protection of clothing against the attack of clothes moths is frequent brushing and airing. The exposure of clothing, particularly dark-colored types, to bright sunshine at air temperatures of 90°F and above is especially effective. Laundering washables and dry cleaning suits and blankets gives added protection. Store clothing and furs in tightly sealed boxes, plastic bags, or chests lined with ¾-inch cedar heartwood.

Use of Chemicals. The use of naphthalene, paradichlorobenzene, or camphor in closets is very seldom capable of developing sufficient concentration of vapor to repel insects. However, in trunks or tightly sealed boxes, it is quite possible to develop sufficient vapor to be repellent or even toxic (Arnold, 1957). Nylen (1956) sounds a warning on the use of paradichlorobenzene with plastics; attention is called to the possibility of its melting into the fabric.

Fluoride sprays and DDT, 4 per-cent solutions, are available for protecting wools. The former will be effective through a number of dry cleanings, but must be renewed after laundering. The manufacturer's direction should be followed closely. A formula known as EQ-53, developed by federal entomologists, may be used in the laundry water or for pest-proofing garments when laying away for the summer. It contains DDT, an emulsifier, and a solvent, and is for sale under various brand names.

Increasing amounts of wool sweaters, blankets, and upholstered furniture are sold under the label, "moth resistant," the guarantee being for a variable number of years. A DDT, 5 per-cent oil solution applied to the upper and under surface of carpets will kill moths and act as a toxic residue. For carpet beetles, a higher content of DDT is necessary to act as a residual deposit. Chlordane, lindane, or dieldrin, at 0.5 per-cent concentration, is effective against both moths and carpet beetles. These latter materials should be used very sparingly in the home (Staff, Stored-Product Insects Section, U.S. Dept. Agr., 1955; Nylen, 1956).

BEDBUGS

These pests may be controlled with DDT, 5 per-cent solution or emulsion, or a 2.5 per-cent suspension of wettable powder. Commercial preparations of various concentrations are available which may be diluted as necessary. They may be applied with a hand or pressure sprayer or even with a paint brush. Space sprays or aerosols will not penetrate into the hiding places. Such applications if heavy may act as residual insecticides, killing the bedbugs as they are exposed to the dried spray.

Pyrethrum sprays are also used to control bedbugs. They should contain 0.2 pyrethrins plus a synergist—1 per-cent or more—such as piperonyl butoxide, sulfoxide, or sesame oil, to increase the toxicity. They do not, however, give as long-lasting protection as do applications of DDT.

Apply the spray to the bed frame, springs, cracks, and crevices. A light mist should be used on the surface of the mattress, and a heavier treatment given to the seams and edges. Avoid prolonged breathing of the mist unless an effective mask is worn (Staff, Div. Insects Affecting Man and Animals, U.S. Dept. Agr., 1953).

Lofgren and Others (1958) have shown that bedbugs from different sources vary decidedly in their susceptibility to DDT, 2 per-cent solutions, while acting as residual insecticides. Lindane, chlordane, dieldrin, and aldrin, as 2 per-cent solutions, were applied to wool cloth patches, which were allowed to dry; part of the bugs were exposed on these patches for 2 hours, and others continuously. In both types of exposure to lindane, all bugs were killed within 24 hours. For the 2-hour exposure, chlordane, dieldrin, and aldrin killed none of the bugs after 24 hours, and a variable number after 48 hours. Of the bugs exposed continuously, chlordane and aldrin each killed 70 per-cent, and dieldrin none, within 24 hours, and 100 per-cent within 48 hours.

Adkins and Arant (1957) have shown that Dipterex acts as a systemic insecticide to the bedbug (*Cimex lectularius*), using the rabbit as the host. A dosage of 14.0 mg per kilogram of weight, given to the rabbit 1 or 2 hours before the bugs fed, killed 50 per-cent of the bugs.

FLEAS

The cat and dog flea (*Ctenocephalides*) is a common pest of pets and an annoyance in the house and often on the lawn. Control recommendations of sprays or dusts of DDT, 5 per-cent, are frequently noted, but these are not as effective as other insecticides. For treatment of pets, one of the safest chemicals is a powder containing 0.5 per-cent rotenone or pyrethrins. These materials paralyze, but seldom kill, the fleas, which should be combed out and killed. Commercial preparations may contain as high as 0.75 to 5 per-cent of these insecticides. Rotenone and pyrethrins are frequently combined with lindane, 1.0 per-cent; or malathion 1.0 to 2.0 per-cent. DDT or chlordane powders should not be used on cats because of the danger of removal while grooming themselves.

For lawn applications, the following amounts of the active materials are to be used per thousand square feet: Dusts—chlordane, 5 per-cent, 1 pound; DDT, 5 per-cent, 1 pound; lindane, 1 per-cent, 2 pounds; malathion, 5 per-cent, 1 pound. Sprays (wettable powders)—chlordane, 40 per-cent, 2 ounces; DDT, 50 per-cent, 1.5 ounces; lindane, 25 per-cent, 2 ounces; malathion, 25 per-cent, 5 ounces. Any convenient amount of liquid may be used for diluting (Vance, 1956).

CHIGGERS

Repellents for impregnating clothing as a protection against the mite *Eutrombicula alfreddugesi*, have been studied by Cross and Snyder (1948). They report that, in addition to benzyl benzoate, there are a number of promising materials, including benzil, 2-thenyl benzoate, *p*-cresyl benzoate, diphenyl carbonate, and 2-thenyl salicylate. The last two were especially durable both in aging and laundering.

The application of insecticides to infested areas is reported as another means of controlling chiggers (*Trombicula*). Traub and Others (1954) had a good control on heavy brush-covered land by the use of dieldrin, and also aldrin, at dosages of 2¼ pounds of active ingredient per acre. Keller and Gouck (1957) reported satisfactory control in woodland with endrin, dosage 0.1 pound per acre, and dieldrin, at 0.5 pound per acre. Vance (1956) recommends dusts for lawns: lindane, 1 per-cent, at 0.5 pound per thousand square feet; toxaphene, 10 per-cent, at 0.5 pound per thousand; or dieldrin, 1.5 per-cent concentration, at 3 pounds per thousand.

For fleas and chiggers, apply the insecticide to the grass. Sprinkle lightly to wash the material down on the grass crown. Leave without sprinkling for a few days, and then water thoroughly. Repeat if necessary.

Handle and store insecticides carefully. Avoid unnecessary contact or excessive inhalation of dust or mist. Wash carefully after the application. Avoid drifting to adjoining property. Allow no children or pets on the lawn during application, or on the treated lawn until carefully washed in and dried (Vance, 1956).

TERMITES AND WOOD BORERS

Termites are destructive feeders on the types of lumber commonly used in construction work. Under favorable conditions of moisture, light, and soil, the western and the eastern subterranean termites (genus *Reticulitermes*) readily attack pine and fir lumber; redwood and certain species of cedar are quite resistant. Sapwood is more readily attacked than heartwood. The damp-wood termite (genus *Zootermopis*) principally attacks decaying wood along streams, but may also be found in moist foundation timbers.

The dry-wood termite (genus *Kalotermes*) attacks sound wood, especially sapwood. It is found in poles, posts, crossarms, and bridge-piling. In the extreme southwestern areas, houses are subject to attack at window frames, doorjambs and rafters.

Prevention and Control of Attack

The subterranean termite is very sensitive to both light and moisture. For this reason, the colony is housed underground—or at least in a dark location. Feeding tubes are sealed tight, and much of the life is spent in an atmosphere of 95 to 98 per-cent relative humidity. The first requisite, then, in protecting a building from termite attack is the proper amount of ventilation and light. Sufficient ventilators should be provided to give air circulation, and a certain amount of light in basements and in crawl-spaces. These measures are also the best protection against "dry rot," which is caused by wood-destroying fungi.

Ebeling and Pence (1957) found that the western subterranean termites tunneled rapidly through moist sand of 50- to 100-mesh size. They could not, however, tunnel through dry sand of small-particle size, because the tunnels collapsed. They could work through dry sand of larger particle size (above 3 mm in diameter) by passing through the interstices. In moist sand, the particles are mixed in the mouth with a gluey substance, and then placed along the walls of the tunnel to make a smooth, tight surface.

"Sand with particles ranging in size so that not more than 5 percent will be retained on a 10-mesh screen and not more than 5 percent will pass through a 16-mesh screen forms an impenetrable screen to subterranean termites." By tamping the sand to reduce the size of the space between the larger particles, more variation is possible in the range of effective particle size. Fillings of the desired range in particle size of sand, crushed volcanic cinders, and finely divided slag (sinter) are being experimented with for sealing off earth fills under porches and steps (Ebeling and Pence, 1957).

A layer of asphalt (⅛-inch thick) to which 1 per-cent of DDT has been added, proved an effective barrier to termites in laboratory experiments. Further trials are in progress where the insecticide-treated asphalt emulsion is applied to the areas inside the foundation, and a 1-inch layer of cinders or sand is applied on the ground in earth-filled extensions of the foundation (for example, patios and porches) (Ebeling and Pence, 1957).

A remarkable difference has been found in laboratory experiments in the effectiveness of insecticides producing 50 per-cent immobility (MPI) and 50 per-cent mortality (MLP). The term *immobile* was applied when the power of locomotion was lost, even though the legs and other appendages might continue to be active for many hours or even days. It was believed that, since with the insecticides concerned death follows any appreciable paralysis, the period required to immobilize the termites might be of greater practical significance than the period required to kill them. If paralysis did not occur quickly, then the termites might possibly burrow through the treated layer, even though many died during the process (Ebeling and Pence, 1958).

When using MPI as the indicator, lindane was the most effective insecticide at all concentrations. But with MLP as the indicator, pentachlorophenol was the most effective insecticide. This was true with a dilution of the latter chemical at all concentrations to as low as 0.01 per-cent, when it was no more effective than lindane. (From the standpoint of practical pest control, it should be noted that pentachlorophenol is not only effective as an insecticide but even more effective as a fungicide. It thus has a dual value in controlling both termites and dry rot.) It was also found that there was little difference in the toxicity of lindane, chlordane, and dieldrin in concentrations ranging from 0.01 to 4.0 per-cent, based either on MPI or MLP. DDT and toxaphene showed much more effect from changes in concentrations, while pentachlorophenol, sodium pentachlorophenate, and sodium arsenite showed striking differences in toxicity due to dilution of the toxicant (Ebeling and Pence, 1958).

The comparative value of various insecticides as a control for the subterranean termite has been conducted by the Forest Laboratory in Mississippi. Three types of tests were used—Ground-board, stake, and building tests. In the first, a 17-inch square of surface soil was soaked with the chemical, then a sapwood pine board 1 by 6 by 6 was laid flat in the center of the treated area. In the stake test, 2 cubic feet of soil was moved to make a hole 15 by 15 by 19 inches deep. The soil was treated with the chemical, and the hole refilled. A sapwood pine stake 2 by 4 by 18 inches was driven to a depth of 12 inches in the treated soil. In both the ground-board and the stake test, it was found necessary to give all of the wood a 3-minute dip of 4.0 per-cent phenyl mercury oleate in white gasoline as a protection against decay. This apparently did not influence termite attack. The third test was made on termite-infested buildings. The chemicals were applied in shallow trenches along the inside and outside of concrete or brick outside treatments were largely around basement entrances.

The wood samples are examined annually, and the degree of infestation, if any, determined. Traces of minor scoring are not considered as infestation. In the building test, a failure is recorded when termites penetrate the treated soil and build tubes over the foundation. "In evaluating these data, it was considered that only formulations giving good results for at least 5 years in one or both types of field tests in Mississippi, can be safely recommended for practical use . . . to protect buildings." (Johnston, 1958)

The results of these tests showed the following insecticides as giving long periods of protection, usually for 5 years and in some instances much longer: Aldrin, 0.5 per-cent in fuel oil or water emulsion; benzene hexachloride, 0.8 per-cent gamma in fuel oil or water emulsion; chlordane, 1.0 per-cent in fuel oil or water emulsion; DDT, 8.0 per-cent in fuel oil; dieldrin, 0.5 per-cent in fuel oil or water emulsion; heptachlor, 1.0 per-cent in fuel oil or water emulsion; sodium arsenite, 10 per-cent in water; trichlorobenzene, 25 per-cent (by volume) in fuel oil (Johnston, 1958).

Slab-on-ground construction is very susceptible to termite attack and difficult to treat; hence, preventive measures are best. The entire surface soil (after grading) of the building should be treated with one of the insecticide solutions at a dosage of at least 1 gallon per 10 square feet—or heavier if gravel or coarse material is used in making fills. Voids in hollow-block foundations should be treated with at least 2 gallons of the toxicant per linear foot of wall. Buildings with basements or crawl-space may be treated by the trench method, without treating the entire soil surface (Johnston, 1958).

Construction on slab-on-ground infestations may be treated by drilling holes in the concrete, at 1-foot intervals, or in the foundation and then forcing in one of the insecticide formulations at the rate of 4 gallons per linear foot of foundation. For buildings with basements or crawl-space, dig a trench 8 inches deep along the foundation walls and around piers, and pour in one of the formulations at the rate of 2 gallons per linear foot of trench. Treat the excavated soil at the same rate (Johnston, 1958).

The dry-wood termite infestation is shown by piles of straw-colored to reddish-brown fecal pellets resembling coarse sand that fall from cracks or holes in infested wood. The fluttering flight of the winged males and females, especially during October, is another indication of their presence.

For light infestations, the operator drills holes in the timbers, probing for the tunnels. When found, they are blown full of dust or liquid fumigants. For general infestation, the buildings may be covered with a large tarpaulin and fumigated with methyl bromide. This is expensive and requires vacating the house for at least two days.

A 10 per-cent emulsion of pentachlorophenol in a light grade of petroleum oil, such as is used to prevent subterranean termite infestation, may also be painted over infested areas, where accessible. The toxic oil penetrates the thin walls of the termite burrow and kills the insects. A thick emulsion is used because it may be applied in a heavy coat, which, as it breaks, permits the oil to soak in. Incomplete control or reinfestation, as shown by fresh pellets, may require a second application. A mask and chemical-resistant gloves should be worn by the operator.

Reinfestation by the dry-wood termite being common, a preventive treatment is desirable. Light coatings over attic surfaces with absorbent clays is being used; however, a more promising material is a dry powdered silica aerogel marketed under the name of Dri-Die 67. Using 1 pound per thousand square feet of attic space, the dust may be applied with a small hand-duster. This treatment is also effective as a roach control (Ebeling and Wagner, 1959a).

Further studies have shown that drywood termites are more susceptible to sorptive than to abrasive dusts. The former can remove the lipoid protective layer covering the insect's body, thus causing a rapid loss of water. The insects lost about 30 per cent of their body weight in water after crawling about over a thin film of dust. Of the various dust materials tested, certain silica aerogels were found to be particularly effective. Other insects, including roaches, fleas, bedbugs, ants, mosquitoes, ticks, and mites, were similarly affected by the desiccating action of the dust.

The addition of certain water-soluble fluorides increases the effectiveness of the dust, especially at high relative humidities. The fluorides present in the silica aerogel particles do not prevent absorption of the wax covering of the insect. Following the absorption or disruption of the wax, the water-soluble fluorides act as contact insecticides (Ebeling and Wagner, 1959b).

A comparative study of the lethality of various types of dusts, including botanicals, talcs, clays, carbonates, diatomites, and the synthetic silica gels and aerogels, have shown the latter to give the shortest killing time— 2 to 3 hours. The lighter materials gave the best distribution in attics (Wagner and Ebeling, 1959).

Powder-Post Beetles (*Lyctus*)

These beetles attack various types of hardwood lumber (oak, ash, and hickory), especially as sapwood. Their work is found in oak flooring and other hardwood finishes, tool handles, tent pickets, and especially on unfinished lumber. Newly cut wood is not attacked but may be while in the dry yard (Johnston and Others, 1955).

Preventive Measures. Infestation during storage can be prevented by dipping rough green lumber for 10 seconds in a cold-water emulsion of DDT, 5 per-cent concentration, or benezene hexachloride, 0.5 per-cent gamma isomer. Either insecticide may be combined with sap-stain preventives at a single dipping. The insecticide applications do not penetrate far into the lumber; hence a second treatment is necessary after the wood is planed (Johnston and Others, 1955).

Finished articles, such as pallets, flooring, and tool handles, may be protected by a 3-minute dip in a refined kerosene or mineral-spirits solution of DDT, 5 per-cent; toxaphene, 5 per-cent; chlordane, 2 per-cent; or lindane, 0.5 per-cent. Products which must be stored outdoors or in moist situations may be protected from decay by adding pentachlorophenol, 5 per-cent solution in a light, refined lubricating oil, to the dip. If the pesticides are dipped in refined white oils, there will be but moderate discoloration of the wood. Treated articles must be thoroughly dry before applying wax or varnish (Johnston and Others, 1955).

Fumigation with methyl bromide may be used for living infestations of hardwood floors. Such work should be done only by licensed and experienced operators. It is necessarily expensive and requires much preliminary preparation, unless the entire house is covered with a heavy tarpaulin; yet, it is the most effective procedure for general infestation, particularly if this is accompanied with termite invasion. Only houses that are well isolated from other buildings should be treated, and they must remain unoccupied for two whole days following fumigation. Occupants of adjoining buildings should be notified of the procedure. Small infestations may possibly be treated by sealing a room very tightly prior to treating, or tarpaulins supported over infested spots might afford a practical method of exposure.

Insect borers are sometimes found in the lumber used for subflooring; when mature, they may cut their way through the hardwood floor and emerge as adult beetles or as wood wasps (horntails). Fumigation is not a practical method of control for borers in subflooring, and should be used only when termites and other borers are present in other parts of the house. Lumber for subflooring that shows any signs of borers should be soaked for at least 12 hours in a 5 per-cent solution of pentachlorophenol and then allowed to dry before use. Subfloors that have been laid, but where construction has not started, may be washed carefully with pentachlorophenol solution, to give full opportunity for penetration. This treatment is also a good protection against the wood-destroying fungi which cause dry rot. For severe infestation, lindane, 0.5 per-cent solution in oil, may be added to the dip. Both of these insecticides are active poisons and should be handled carefully. Dipping tanks should be covered when not in use, and contaminated clothing, laundered before using again.

HOUSE RODENTS

Rats and mice in the home not only destroy and contaminate food, but also injure the building and carry diseases. The usual methods of control are through proper building construction, destruction of nesting places, and the prevention of feeding, wherever possible. Store garbage in metal cans with tight-fitting lids. Eliminate trashy harborages. Repair, rebuild, or build all construction so as to avoid rat and mouse entry. Protect openings into basements and crawl-ways with quarter-inch hardware cloth. Trap any rodents that find entrance into the home or other buildings.

Baiting is the principal recourse for eliminating rodent colonies, once established. Professional exterminators may be called, or with care in following directions, baiting may be done by the householder. In the latter case, the anticoagulant type of poison baits are the safest to handle and require little experience. These are available in commercial form under a number of brand names. It is necessary for the rodent to feed upon them for several days before death occurs. As the name indicates, the material tends to prevent the normal coagulation of the blood; internal hemorrhages form, and the internal organs starve from lack of oxygen. The animals do not develop bait shyness, nor build up a protective tolerance.

The brand Warfarin is marketed as a 0.5 per-cent concentrate in cornstarch and in ready-mixed baits. The brand Pival is formulated at a similar concentration in corn meal, rolled oats, and other baits (de Ong, 1956). A recent type, known as Fumarin, has been developed by the United States Fish and Wildlife Service. It is marketed under a similar formulation in cereal bait. It was found to be stable under long storage, and without rancidity or change in toxicity. No mold growth or insect infestation developed during storage (Robinson and Crabtree, 1956).

REFERENCES

Adkins, T. R., and Arant, F. S., *J. Econ. Entom.,* **50,** 166 (1957).
Arnold, J. W., *ibid.,* **50,** 469 (1957).
Cross, H. F., and Snyder, F. M., *ibid.,* **41,** 936 (1948).
de Ong, E. R., "Chemistry and Uses of Pesticides," 2d ed., New York, Reinhold Publishing Corp., 1956.
Ebeling, W., and Pence, R. J., *J. Econ. Entom.,* **50,** 690 (1957).
———, *ibid.,* **51,** 207 (1958).
Ebeling, W., and Wagner, R. E., *Calif. Agr.,* **13**(1), 7 (1959a).
———, *J. Econ. Entom.,* **52,** 190 (1959b).
Gilbert, L. H., *ibid.,* **50,** 46 (1957).
Jarvis, F. E., and Grayson, J. M., *ibid.,* **50,** 604 (1957).
Johnston, E. R., *Pest Control Magazine,* Feb., 1958.
———, and Others, *Southern Lumberman,* March 15, 1955.
Keller, J. C., and Gouck, H. K., *J. Econ. Entom.,* **50,** 141 (1957).
Laake, E. W., *ibid.,* **48,** 783 (1955).
Lofgren, C. S., and Others, *ibid.,* **51,** 241 (1958).
Mallis, A., and Others, *ibid.,* **51,** 248 (1958).
Nylen, M., *Calif. Agr. Exp. Sta. Leaflet,* **67** (1956).
Robinson, W. H., and Crabtree, D. G., *Agr. Chemicals,* **11**(5), 30 (1956).

Staff, U.S. Dept. Agr., *Div. Insects Attacking Man and Animals Leaflet,* **337** (1953).

———, *Research Branch Leaflet,* **365** (1954).

———, *ibid.,* **390** (1955a).

———, *ibid.,* **386** (1955b).

Staff, *U.S. Dept. Agr. Home & Garden Bull.,* **24** (1955c).

Staff, U.S. Dept. Agr., and Staff, College Agr., Univ. Calif., "Flies," 1956.

Staff, *U.S. Dept. Agr. Home & Garden Bull.,* **28** (1957).

Tarshis, B., *Calif. Agr.* **13**(2), 3 (1959).

Traub, R. and Others, *J. Econ. Entom.,* **47,** 429 (1954).

Vance, A. M., *U.S. Dept. Agr. Home & Garden Bull.,* **53** (1956).

Wagner, R. E., and Ebeling, W., *J. Econ. Entom.,* **52,** 208 (1959).

12. STORED-PRODUCT INSECTS, DISEASES, AND RODENTS

As with fly control, sanitation is the most important measure in the protection of stored products. The beetles, weevils, moths, and decay fungi that attack supplies are only fulfilling their natural function of clearing the land of debris. Without their assistance, we would be overwhelmed by the accumulation. Their activities must be so regulated as to prevent the loss of valued goods.

Food supplies are required to meet high standards of purity before they are admitted to market; for that reason, prevention rather than control is desirable. Indication of insect-feeding is considered contamination just as much as that of the presence of living insects. Fumigation may kill all the insects present in a shipment, but that alone is not usually sufficient, because there may also be the expense of running the load through cleaning machinery or of hand-picking. Grain and other foods with light infestations of mold may possibly be reconditioned and placed in an acceptable grade for human consumption, but only at considerable expense. The use of insecticides, fungicides, and even rodenticides should be planned as an aid to good housekeeping in maintaining a high degree of purity, without the necessity and expense of salvage operations.

Weight Loss Due to Insects. * Grain and other commodities lose value not only by degrading because of contamination but also through loss of weight due to insect-feeding. White (1953) has shown that wheat may lose as much as 20 per cent of the total weight through the feeding of the rice weevil. This loss occurred in 5 weeks' time during the development of the weevil from egg to adult. The temperature during the experiment was held at 80°F, and the relative humidity at 70 per cent.

Net weight loss alone (weight of the molted skins and frass was not determined) due to oxidation-reduction, as brought about by the metabolic

---

* A survey in the Willamette Valley, Oregon, of the insects found in bulk grain in elevators and farm storage lists the following according to their abundance, together with a number of species only rarely found: foreign grain beetle (*Ahasverus advena*), flat grain beetle (*Laemophloeus* sp.), saw-toothed grain beetle (*Oryzaphilus surinamensis*), granary weevil (*Sitophilus granarius*), rice weevil (*Sitophilus oryza*), and red flour beetle (*Tribolium castaneum*) (Swenson and Tunnock, 1957).

processes of the immature forms of the rice weevil in its development, and the weight of the adult weevil, were considered in this work. "This weight was dissipated in the form of heat, moisture and gases, and constitutes a portion of the storage losses usually referred to by grain men as shrinkage." (White, 1953)

Gerberg and Goldheim (1957) found that popcorn kernels, attacked by the Angoumois grain moth had lost 10.1 per cent of their original weight. Cowpeas, confined for 60 days with the adult bean weevil (*Acanthoscelides obtectus*), showed an average loss per pea of 68.7 per cent. Navy beans, confined for 60 days with 50 adult bean weevils, showed an average infestation of 4.2 insects per bean. The average weight loss per bean was 14.7 per cent. A constant temperature of approximately 75°F, and a relative humidity of 50 per cent, were maintained in the rearing chamber.

PROTECTIVE MEASURES

Holding stored grain and dried fruit to a low moisture content is the simplest method of protection from loss by attack of insects, decay fungi, and bacterial infection. The moisture content of 8 to 12 per cent found in standing grain, under the semiarid conditions of the western United States, has been found to give good protection until cold weather checks insect activity. The grain absorbs moisture during the winter, and with the higher temperatures of spring and summer, the danger of insect attack is greatly increased. The moisture content should be uniform, otherwise insects and mold may develop at wet spots. Low temperatures (50° to 55°F and below) are also a protection against insect loss, for pests are almost dormant at this range of temperature.

Infestation of grain in the field by storage-type insects is uncommon, except in the southeastern areas. Newly threshed grain is practically free of insects when stored. Infestation is largely due to the refuse left in storage bins and to scattered grain in and around the storeroom and adjoining buildings.

Moisture Control of Grain as a Protection Against Mold

Laboratory experiments by Tuite and Christensen (1957) in Minnesota, have shown evidence that the present federal regulation (Staff, U.S. Dept. Agr., 1949) of 14.5 per cent for hard red spring and durum wheats, and 14 per cent for all other classes of wheat, are too high for long-time storage (2 to 3 years). Wheat of different classes, nearly or entirely free of fungi, was inoculated with four species of the *Aspergillus glaucus* group (one of the most important of the storage fungi) and stored with moisture contents of 12.2 to 16 per cent at 77°F for 1 to 15 months. Invasion of the wheat by two of the species began at a moisture content of 13.0 to 13.6

per cent, and by the other two species at 14.3 to 14.6 per cent, in 2 months, but within 4 months all fungi had invaded 100 per cent of the seeds. "At moisture contents of approximately 15.5 to 16.0 percent, 100 percent of the seeds were invaded within 1 month." Germination percentage of the inoculated seeds decreased much more rapidly than did that of the noninoculated seeds. It was concluded that "for such long storage periods (2 to 3 years), the safe moisture content limit would appear to be near 13.0 percent rather than 14.0 to 14.5 percent, as specified at present.... For safe storage . . . none of the grain should have a moisture content in excess of 13 percent for a long enough time to permit extensive development of those species of fungi now proved to invade and kill the germs."

Surveys by Tuite and Christensen (1957a) with standing grain showed that the wheat seeds very seldom showed the presence of either spores or mycelia of the storage-fungus *Aspergillus*. "The threshed seeds were invaded by storage fungi much more rapidly than seeds in the heads." Wheat variety or class, geographical location, or weather that prevailed during the harvest season appeared to have no detectable influence on the prevalence of infection of the seed by species of *Aspergillus*. Grain that remained windrowed, shocked, or standing in the field for a month beyond the normal harvest season was essentially free of infection by storage fungi. Evidently inoculum of storage fungi is relatively uncommon in fields of ripe grain, is considerably more abundant in country elevators, and even more abundant in terminal elevators.

It is concluded that the storage of large bulks of grain with variable moisture contents near that at which fungi attack seed will almost inevitably result in fungus growth (Tuite and Christensen, 1957a).

The germs of field corn may be killed and discolored by invasion with the fungi *Aspergillus* and *Penicillium* after 6 to 9 months storage in commercial bins at temperatures above 50°F and 14 per-cent moisture content. There was but little fungus invasion of seeds stored at 12 per-cent moisture. "At 16 percent moisture content, increases in percentage of seeds invaded by fungi and percentage of discolored germs and decreases in germination percentages were slow at 41°, 50° and 59°F. but rapid at 68° and 77°.... At 18 percent content, invasion of the seed was rapid at all temperatures except 41° F." (Quasem and Christensen, 1958)

Dried-Fruit Plants. Dry yards and cutting sheds should be as free as possible from waste and trimmings that may act as food or harbor insects and rodents. Pets should not be allowed in or about dried-fruit storage areas or where fruit is being prepared for drying.

Lug boxes, trays, and other equipment may be sterilized with steam or by the use of chemical disinfectants. Dirt floors in cutting sheds should be avoided.

Personal cleanliness, with frequent washing of the hands and cutting knives, will do much to prevent contamination and ensure high-quality products (Vaughn and Mrak, 1954).

Building Precautions. Plant construction should be so planned that sanitary measures require the minimum effort. The elevation of storage bins on piers reduces the possibility of rodent hiding places. Concrete floors, iron sidings, and ½-inch mesh hardware cloth over openings are helpful. Storerooms may be built ready for fumigation, if necessary. Sacked commodities may be piled on platforms raised 4 inches from the floor, to permit the circulation of fumigation gases. Doors and windows should fit closely and be screened if desirable. Window screening is usually 10 or 12 mesh to the inch. This will exclude the larger flies and moths, but for smaller insects, a 16-inch mesh should be used.

Dust accumulation in mills and processing plants frequently becomes a breeding ground for injurious insects, and spores of decay fungi and bacteria. It also covers residual applications of insecticides and disinfectants and renders them useless. Effective dust-collecting machinery and the use of vacuum cleaners will reduce the danger.

Mills and storage plants should be subjected to a continuous cleaning process during operation. Refuse, trash, and breeding material of any kind must be removed promptly. Emptied grain sacks may be fumigated or removed promptly from the building. Grain bins should be cleaned very thoroughly and all residues removed before storing a new crop. Market grain is to be isolated from feed grain.

Chemical Protectants

Prevention rather than control of insects and fungus invasion has much in its favor. Weight loss and degrading of the commodity begins with the first attack of insects or that of decay fungi. Both can be avoided in part by proper sanitation. Added protection against insect loss is accomplished by the addition of protective sprays or powders that contain insecticides such as pyrethrins and the synergist piperonyl butoxide. Commercial mixtures of these are known as Pyrenone and as Pybuthrins. Application of these materials will generally give protection during the first season of farm storage.

This plan of protection, to be successful, should include a careful cleaning of storage bins, isolation from feed grains, and the application of a residual bin spray. The latter may be either a spray of pyrethrins and a synergist, or a 2.5 per-cent application of methoxychlor, either emulsion or wettable powder, to the walls and floor of the empty bins. The cleaning of the bins and wall-spraying should be completed about six weeks before storing a new crop (Gates and Others, 1957).

TABLE 2

Micrograms of Insecticide per Insect to Give 50 and 95 per-cent kill of Khapra-Beetle Larvae, Confused-Flour-Beetle Adults and Larvae, and Granary-Weevil Adults*

Insecticide	Khapra-Beetle Larvae		Confused-Flour-Beetle				Granary-Weevil Adults	
			Larvae		Adults			
	LD-50	LD-95	LD-50	LD-95	LD-50	LD-95	LD-50	LD-95
Methyl parathion	<0.5	1.4	0.05	0.2	<0.01	0.03	<0.01	0.01
Parathion	<0.5	2.7	0.12	0.7	0.01	0.02	0.01	0.03
Malathion	0.9	3.6	2.25	1.6	0.4	1.1	0.07	0.1
Pyrethrins	0.9	4.2	0.36	1.9	0.09	0.4	0.2	0.8
American Cyanamid 4124	<0.5	2.2	0.8	3.6	0.21	0.7	0.06	1.3
Chlorthion	1.9	8.8	0.58	2.3	0.18	0.4	0.2	0.4
Dieldrin	6.0	>25.0	1.0	3.6	0.17	0.5	0.02	0.07
Lindane	25.0	>25.0	1.0	4.6	0.17	0.8	0.06	0.2
Aldrin	6.5	>25.0	2.0	6.5	0.23	1.2	0.02	0.06
Heptachlor	13.0	>25.0	1.8	8.0	0.1	1.3	0.09	0.2
Allethrin	7.0	>25.0	3.0	15.0	0.27	0.9	2.3	8.4
Toxaphene	>25.0	>25.0	7.8	21.0	0.8	4.5	0.8	1.7
DDT	>25.0	>25.0	20.0	>25.0	0.19	0.4	0.8	2.5
Strobane	>25.0	>25.0	13.5	>25.0	2.3	8.0	1.3	1.9
Phostex	5.0	>25.0	17.0	>25.0	8.3	>25.0	10.2	22.0
Piperonyl butoxide	>25.0	>25.0	>25.0	>25.0	>25.0	>25.0	10.0	23.5
Chlordane	>25.0	>25.0	>25.0	>25.0	>25.0	>25.0	19.0	>25.0
Methoxychlor	>25.0	>25.0	>25.0	>25.0	>25.0	>25.0	>25.0	>25.0
TDE	>25.0	>25.0	>25.0	>25.0	>25.0	>25.0	>15.0	>25.0
Nicotine	>25.0	>25.0	>25.0	>25.0	>25.0	>25.0	23.0	>25.0

* By permission of Vincent, L. E., and D. L. Lindgren, *J. Econ. Entom.*, **50**, 372 (1957).

Contact insecticides, in addition to application to bin walls, are sometimes used on sacks or packaging materials, or used in general sanitation programs. Such applications should always meet established tolerances, if any, when in contact with food for human consumption or on feed for dairy cattle or livestock for market. The comparative insecticidal value of various compounds on stored-product insects is shown in Table 2.

A successful formulation of the protective powder used on grain contains 1.1 per-cent piperonyl butoxide and 0.08 per-cent pyrethrins impregnated on pulverized grain dust. This, when used at the rate of 75 pounds per thousand bushels, left a residue of 13.7 ppm of butoxide and 0.99 ppm of pyrethrins on the treated grain (Wilbur, 1957).

A similar amount of the insecticides may be applied as a water-diluted emulsion, using 4 or 5 gallons of water per thousand bushels of wheat. This leaves a residue of approximately 1.42 ppm of pyrethrins (Wilbur, 1957).

The protectants are applied to the grain between the combine and the truck, either as the grain runs out of the combine hopper into the truck bed, or as it is dumped from the truck into the lifter hopper (Wilbur, 1957).

Unsatisfactory protection can usually be traced to low dosages, incorrect application, or a continuous source of infestation. A high moisture content of the grain may also prevent adequate protection. The Indianmeal moth (*Plodia interpunctella*) may be controlled by the protectant treatment, but both Plodia and the Angoumois grain moth (*Sitotroga cerealella*) are controlled by a surface spray over the grain-filled bin of light petroleum oil, of about 40- or 50-second Saybolt, or the pyrethrin formulation (Wilbur, 1957; Gates and Others, 1957).

Swank and Others (1957) found that applications of pyrethrins and piperonyl butoxide at 10 and 100 mg per square foot, respectively, were actively repellent to adult flour beetles over a period of 3 months. *N*-pentylpthalimide, a product synthesized by the Entomology Research Division, had similar repellent value but, at 200 mg per square foot, was decidedly superior to the former (Swank and Davis, 1957).

Fumigation. The control of insects infesting stored grain, seeds, dried fruit, and nuts by the use of volatile poisonous gases has been a standard practice for many years (de Ong, 1956). Carbon disulfide first came into general use but, because of its explosive hazard, has been largely supplanted, first by hydrocyanic acid, and later by other gases and mixtures of the acid.

Methyl bromide, one of the most popular, is nonflammable at concentrations used in fumigation and least hazardous to the operator. For very large masses of grain, however, mechanical circulation is necessary. Ethylene dichloride, being slightly explosive, is commonly combined with carbon tetrachloride (75 to 25 parts). The two are miscible in all proportions; the mixture has physical properties between those of its ingredients. It is recommended as a fumigant for shelled corn in steel bins at a dosage of 6 gallons per thousand bushels.

A mixture of carbon disulfide–carbon tetrachloride (20 to 80) is used in fumigating wheat in steel bins. The dosage is 2 gallons per thousand bushels at 80°F, and 2.5 gallons at 70° to 80°F (Cotton and Walkenden, 1952).

Ethylene oxide is used both as an insecticide for feed grains and dried fruits and also as a protectant for the latter against yeasts and molds. For the latter purpose it may be combined with propylene oxide to give a higher boiling point (Whelton and Others, 1946).

The susceptibility of the egg, larval, pupal, and adult stages of the rice weevil to various fumigants is reported by Krohne and Lindgren (1958). It will be noted in Table 3 that the egg stage is quite resistant to carbon disulfide and to a less degree to methyl bromide.

The age of the eggs used was plus or minus 1½ days old. "The larvae were half grown (midway between eggs and pupae in age). Adults ranged in age from 2 to 4 weeks. In each test 50 to 60 adults were used in plastic screen cages without food." Exposure time to the fumigants was 2 hours at a temperature of 80°F (Krohne and Lindgren, 1958).

A study of the comparative effect of various fumigants on the germination of seed grains has shown the following results:

(1) *Wheat* germination was not affected by fumigation with hydrocyanic acid, under the conditions of these tests.

(2) Methyl bromide fumigation contributed to decreases in germination as the moisture content of seeds increased from 8 to 14 per cent.

(3) Shortening the exposure period over a range of 2 to 72 hours resulted in increases in germination.

(4) Increases in temperature from 50° to 90°F resulted in decreases in percentages of germination.

(5) "Percentages of germination decreased with an increase in dosages applied when other variables remained constant."

TABLE 3

*Dosages of Various Fumigants Required for 50 per-cent Kill (LD-50) and 95 per-cent Kill (LD-95) of Life Stages of Sitophilus oryza at Exposures of 2 Hours at 80F**

| Fumigant | Percentage of Kill | Lethal Dosage (mg/1) Required for: | | | | LR to R† |
		Eggs	Larvae	Pupae	Adults	
Acrylonitrile	50	1.0	1.0	2.9	2.2	E = L < A < P
	95	1.9	1.9	5.7	3.3	E = L < A < P
Carbon disulfide	50	190.0	48.0	95.0	55.0	L < A < P < E
	95	250.0	70.0	207.0	87.0	L < A < P < E
Chloropicrin	50	7.3	5.6	6.9	7.4	L < P < E = A
	95	19.0	14.2	23.5	20.5	L < E = A < P
Ethylene dibromide	50	0.7	1.7	5.3	3.3	E < L < A < P
	95	1.8	4.4	10.1	7.1	E < L < A < P
Ethylene dichloride	50	197.0	197.0	>270.0	177.0	A < E = L < P
	95	>270.0	>270.0	>270.0	>270.0	
Hydrocyanic acid	50	1.1	3.2	6.4	7.1	E < L < P < A
	95	4.8	6.0	37.0	31.0	E < L < A < P
Methyl bromide	50	10.7	5.8	14.5	7.5	L < A < E < P
	95	18.5	10.1	22.2	13.5	L < A < E < P

* By permission of Krohne, H. E., and D. L. Lindgren, *J. Econ. Entom.*, **51**, 157 (1958).

† Least resistant to resistant

(6) *Barley* germination was not affected by fumigation with hydrocyanic acid, under the conditions of these tests.

(7) Methyl bromide injury from fumigation could be identified as dead seed. Little evidence of retarded emergence was observed.

(8) Dosage, temperature, period of exposure, and moisture content of seeds were the most important variables in contributing to injury from methyl bromide. "Barley was highly tolerant to methyl bromide fumigation under the most extreme conditions."

(9) *Rice* germination was not affected by fumigation with hydrocyanic acid, under the conditions of these tests.

(10) Methyl bromide injury from fumigation could be identified as dead seed. "Little evidence of retarded germination of rice seedlings was observed. Results from germination tests illustrate the interdependence of dosage, temperature, period of exposure, and moisture content of seeds in contributing to seed injury from methyl bromide fumigation. Seeds apparently injured from one fumigation are presumably more subject to injury from a second fumigation." (Strong and Lindgren, 1959)

Tobacco Insects. During the long process of curing to which tobacco is subjected, it is liable to attack from the cigarette beetle (*Lasioderma serricorne*) and the tobacco moth (*Ephestia elutella*). The usual method of control is to fumigate under vacuum or seal the warehouse. A mixture of ethylene oxide and carbon dioxide is used under the former conditions. This fumigant leaves no objectionable odor, but is effective only at a temperature of 60°F and above. Methyl bromide and a mixture of acrylonitrile are both used as fumigants of the sealed warehouse (Caffrey, 1952).

Protectants of Stored Fresh Fruit. The decay of fresh fruits during storage and transit is a serious source of loss.

The degree of cold which can be used safely in cold storage retards the growth of injurious fungi, but not to the extent which will prevent damage. The use of chemical protectants during storage, with few exceptions, has been much less in proportion than those used in protecting the growing crop. This condition is changing, and a larger quantity and greater variety of chemicals is now in use during storage and transit.

Three fungi are frequently mentioned as causing fruit decay, the genera *Penicillium, Botrytis,* and *Rhizopus*. However, the list of decay organisms is far more complex. A study has been made by Adams and Tamburo (1957) of West Virginia apples that showed spot or rot symptoms. "Twenty four different genera of fungi and several kinds of bacteria were isolated." The bacteria and two of the fungi were found to be nonpathogenic. "Species which produced spots or rots on apple fruits were found in four genera not reported previously."

An early recommendation for preventing decay of apples and pears is a 2.5 per-cent solution of copper sulfate for impregnating wrapping papers (Cooley and Acenshaw, 1931). Oiled paper wrappers may, if desired, be used with this copper treatment.

Sodium hypochlorite at from 3,000 to 6,000 ppm has been commonly used as a protectant for tomatoes and citrus fruits, respectively. This compound is also used at 70 to 100 ppm of available chlorine in flood-type machines for precooling peaches. The latter solutions are also sprayed on picking boxes and around packing houses. The sprayed boxes should be stored in closed rooms for several days following the application. Borax or sodium tetraborate has long been used as a protectant of citrus fruit against blue and green mold. The concentration of the solution ranges from 4 to 12 per cent, varying with the temperature range of 60° to 120°F, and length of exposure of 2 to 15 minutes. Exposure to gaseous nitrogen trichloride, in addition to dipping in a borate solution, has been found superior to either treatment used alone.

Sodium *o*-phenyl phenate is coming into common use as a preservative for both citrus and deciduous fruits, and as an additive to the precooling water for peaches.

Apple rot—known as *bull's-eye* due to the fungi *Neofabraea* and *Phialophora malorum,* causes serious losses in the northwestern apple-growing districts. Decay may not become common before December although infection starts during the growing season. Late marketing of the crop is hazardous because of the bull's-eye type of infection. Control has been improved by applications of ziram, 1.5 pounds per hundred gallons of water in the first cover spray for codling moth. A second and more important application is ziram at the same dosage, before the fall rains begin (Kienholz, 1956).

A means of forecasting the development of bull's-eye rot has been developed by Pierson (1958). Sample lots of apples are stored at 60° to 70°F, which shortens the incubation period and permits the forecasting of an outbreak in the crop while held in cold storage. "The time spread in the appearance of symptoms is great enough to permit marketing the parent lot before the disease would normally occur under cold storage conditions."

Laboratory experiments of the post-harvest control of the brown-rot fungus (*Monilinia* (*Sclerotinia*) *fructicola*) on peaches is reported by Szkolnik and Hamilton (1957). The zinc salt Omadine (OM 1563) was found to be decidedly superior to the manganese salt OM 1564, and to captan and micronized sulfur. The antibiotics Mycostatin, Fungichromin, and Oligomycin at concentrations of 100 and 200 ppm gave similar results to that of OM 1563 and without observable injury.

Other experiments in the post-harvest control of brown rot on peaches by Di Marco and Davis (1957) showed the superior value of the antibiotic Mycostatin (Nystatin) and Dowicide A-M 245. Apart from the results as dips, these two materials were also superior in the hydrocooler on field-run peaches. Mycostatin gave equally good control with the rot caused by the fungus *Rhizopus,* as with brown rot. The use of Mycostatin on human foods has not been approved.

McClure (1958) has conducted a series of experiments in the control of brown rot and *Rhizopus* rot on peaches using various low temperatures and chemical treatments. By hydrocooling the fruit in 0.1 per-cent Dowicide A solution, followed by 5 days storage at 40°F, brown rot was reduced 91 per cent and Rhizopus rot 47 per cent.

Ammonia gas fumigation as a control for *Rhizopus* rot on peaches has been tried under laboratory conditions with such favorable results that the method will be tested commercially. Fruit of various varieties and degrees of ripeness were artificially inoculated and stored in wooden chambers. The atmosphere in the chambers was continually circulated during the fumigation. The temperature was held at 70° to 75°F. Ammonia gas (fertilizer-grade anhydrous ammonia) was metered carefully into the chamber over a 6-hour period. Gas samples were drawn at intervals from the chambers, and the concentration of ammonia determined. Variations in the amount of free ammonia in the atmosphere were corrected by the flow rate of ammonia into the chamber. Decay control was determined on both the second and fourth day after inoculation. The total amount of ammonia gas delivered to the 8-cubic-feet chambers ranged from 0.8 of a liter to 5.2 liters.

Inspection on the second day showed 4 per-cent decay for a release of 2.5 liters into the 8-cubic-feet chamber; on the fourth day, the percentage of decay was 58 per cent. Higher releases of ammonia gas gave but slight decreases of decay during the two-day inspection and variable results on the fourth day (Eaks and Others, 1958).

The application of protective fungicides in the vineyard, as an adjunct to post-harvest sulfur dioxide fumigation, has reduced decay in stored Emperor grapes. Captan, B-622, and Crag 5400, applied as dusts or sprays, significantly reduced decay caused by the fungus *Botrytis cinera,* but had slight effect against other fungi that occasionally cause decay during storage. The sprays or dusts were applied at one-month intervals from July to October (Harvey, 1956).

California grapes are commonly fumigated with a 1 per-cent concentration of sulfur dioxide for 20 minutes, followed by fumigations with a 0.25 per-cent concentration of gas at intervals of 7 to 10 days. A study of the value of repeated fumigations did not show a consistent relation between the practice and decay reduction (Harvey, 1956).

Citrus Fruits. Gaseous nitrogen trichloride and biphenyl are in commercial use as a control of the blue-green mold fungi, *Penicillium italicum* and *P. digitatum,* but are only partially satisfactory. Roistacher and Others (1955) established the value of gaseous ammonia for such purposes, and study has begun on methods of releasing small amounts of such gas within citrus-fruit containers. Promising compounds thus far tested include ammonia succinate, ammonium chloride, and ammonium sulfate (Gunther and Others, 1956).

The present practice of shipping citrus fruit unwrapped in fiberboard cartons has led to increases in decay and the need of a volatile fungicide in the container as a protectant. Gaseous ammonia is known to control *Penicillium* decay. It remains to determine the quantity of gas noninjurious to the fruit, but fungicidally effective.

In laboratory experiments, it was found that the best control came from two or three injections of 0.5 or 0.75 gram of hydrous gaseous ammonia per carton on the fifth and ninth days. The fruit container was a telescope-type carton, 10 by 11 by 16½ inches. The gas was released into the carton over a 30-second interval.

The most effective carrier as yet developed for the fungicide is a paper-toweling sheet impregnated with ammonium sulfate, and a second impregnated with sodium carbonate, and then dried. Two sets of these sheets placed in a carton of fruit released ammonia gas in fungicidal quantities. The degree of control of the *Penicillium* decay was influenced by the moisture uptake of the spores prior to fumigation, the sorption of the gas by the container, and the time and quantity of gas injected into the container (Roistacher and Others, 1958).

Ethyl thiocarbamate (C. P. 2229) at 5 per-cent concentration has been shown to be more effective than Dowicide A-Hexamine at 2 per-cent concentration in protecting citrus fruit against decay during storage and in transit. The test fungi used in the experiments were *Diplodia natalensis* and *Phomosis citri,* which cause stem-end rot, and *Penicillium digitatum* and *P. italicum,* which cause green mold and blue mold, respectively (Berry, 1958).

Gamma radiation derived from spent fuel elements from the Materials Testing Reactor at Arco, Idaho, are used in the research on the control of post-harvest diseases of citrus and deciduous fruits. Promising results have been obtained in checking the growth of *Penicillium,* and *Rhizopus nigricans* and *Botrytis cinera.* Dosages are attained by varying exposure time and proximity to source.

The nature of control is apparently not sterilization but rather a prolongation of the period that fruit can be held without spoilage. This period varies with the dosage received, storage temperature, age of the infection, and organism·involved (Beraha and Others, 1957).

Citrus fruits in Florida have long been affected by a serious russeted condition. Affected fruit are smaller than normal in size and of a low grade for packing. Applications of sulfur have been the usual method of control, in the belief that the condition was caused by the rust mite (*Phyllocoptruta oleivora*). An objection to the continued use of sulfur is that it tends to lower the pH of both the surface and the subsoil, thus reducing the availability of certain essential soil materials. Fisher (1957) found, in a series of single applications of zineb in July to different blocks, that the percentage of bright (russet-free) fruit ranged from 95 to 100 per cent. By contrast, the percentage of bright fruit in the untreated block of grapefruit ranged from 11 to 20 per cent, and that of orange 58 to 88 per cent. The dosage of zineb used in the various blocks ranged from 0.65 to 1.31 pounds per hundred gallons of spray, but the degree of control was similar for all dosages. It is suggested that russet may be caused not by mites but by a fungus—*Clasasporium brunneo-atrum*; although the rust mite population was depressed during the applications of zineb. The latter effect of zineb had previously been noted in the control of the mite *Tetranychus hicoriae* on pecans (King and Rosberg, 1956).

Rodent Control

Sanitation standards affecting rodent contamination of wheat, as developed by the Department of Agriculture, are growing increasingly severe for grain in interstate transit. Many cars of the grain, under the new standards, have been condemned and degraded to feed for animals. Low temperatures and desiccation, which are so helpful in combating insects and fungi, are of no value as protectants against rodents. Only the best practices in building construction, elimination of breeding places, and food supplies, and in baiting and trapping are effective.

In addition to the compounds used about homes and food markets (see pages 213–214), there are certain very toxic rodenticides which are for use by professional operators. These compounds include Antu (Storer, 1952; Kreiger, 1952), Compound 1080 (Atkinson, 1953; Potter, 1954), and zinc phosphide (Storer, 1952).

REFERENCES

Adams, R. E., and Tamburo, S. E., *U.S. Dept. Agr. Plant Disease Reporter,* **41,** 760 (1957).

Atkinson, L. L., Calif. Dept. Agr., *Annual Report Bull.,* **42,** 285 (1953).

Beraha, L., and Others, *Phytopathology,* **47,** 4 (1947).

Berry, S. Z., *U.S. Dept. Agr. Plant Disease Reporter,* **42,** 467 (1958).

Caffrey, D. J., "1952 Yearbook," Washington, D.C., U.S. Dept. Agr., 1952.

Cooley, J. S., and Others, *U.S. Dept. Agr. Circular,* **177** (1931).

Cotton, R. T., and Others, *U.S. Dept. Agr. Bur. Entom. & Plant Quarantine,* **EC-24** (1952).

de Ong, E. R., "Chemistry and Uses of Pesticides," 2d ed., New York, Reinhold Publishing Corp., 1956:

Di Marco, G. R., and Others, *U. S. Dept. Agr. Plant Disease Reporter,* **41,** 284 (1957).

Eaks, L. L., *ibid.,* **42,** 846 (1958).

Fisher, F. E., *Phytopathology,* **47,** 433 (1957).

Gates, D. E., and Others, *Kans. Agr. Exp. Sta. Leaflet,* (1957).

Gerberg, E. J., and Goldheim, S. L., *J. Econ. Entom.,* **50,** 391 (1957).

Gunther, F. A., and Others, *Phytopathology,* **46,** 632 (1956).

Harvey, J. E., *ibid.,* **45,** 137 (1955); **46,** 690 (1956).

Kienholz, J. W., *U.S. Dept. Agr. Plant Disease Reporter,* **40,** 872 (1956).

King, D. R., and Rosberg, D. W., *J. Econ. Entom.,* **49,** 404 (1956).

Kreiger, J. H., *Agr. Chem.,* **7**(4), 46 (1952).

Krohne, H. E., and Lindgren, D. L., *J. Econ. Entom.,* **51,** 157 (1958).

McClure, T. T., *Phytopathology,* **48,** 322 (1958).

Pierson, C. F., *U.S. Dept. Agr. Plant Disease Reporter,* **42,** 1395 (1958).

Potter, W. A., *World Crops* (London), **6**(1), 27 (1954).

Quasem, S. A., and Christensen, C. M., *Phytopathology,* **48,** 544 (1958).

Roistacher, C. N., and Others, *U.S. Dept. Agr. Plant Disease Reporter,* **39,** 202 (1955).

———, *ibid.,* **42,** 1112 (1958).

Staff, U.S. Dept. Agr., "Handbook of Official Grain Standards," 1949.

Storer, T. I., *Calif. Agr. Exp. Sta. Circular,* **410** (1952).

Strong, R. G., and Lindgren, D. L., *J. Econ. Entom.,* **52,** 51, 319, 706 (1959).

Swank, G. R., and Davis, D. F., *ibid.,* **50,** 515 (1957).

Swenson, K. G., and Tunnock, A., *ibid.,* **50,** 117 (1957).

Szkolnik, M., and Hamilton, J. M., *U.S. Dept. Agr. Plant Disease Reporter,* **41,** 289 (1957).

Tuite, J. F., and Christensen, C. M., *Phytopathology,* **47,** 265 (1957a).

———, *ibid.,* **47,** 323 (1957b).

Vaughn, R. H., and Mrak, E. M., *Calif. Agr. Exp. Sta. Leaflet,* **26** (1954).

Vincent, L. E., and Lindgren, D. L., *J. Econ. Entom.,* **50,** 372 (1957).

Whelton, R., and Others, *Food Industries,* **18,** 23 (1946).

White, G. D., *J. Econ. Entom.,* **46,** 609 (1953).

Wilbur, D. E., *Agr. Chem.,* **12**(8), 28 (1957).

Appendix

Chemical Names of Pesticides Referred to in the Text

Common or Brand Name	Chemical Name	Function
Acrylonitrile	propene-nitrile	fumigant
Agrox	6.7 per-cent phenyl mercury urea	seed fungicide
Alanap	N-1-naphtyhlphthalamic acid	herbicide
Aldrin	hexachlorohexahydro, endo-xo-dimethano-naphthalene	insecticide
Allethrine	dl-2-allyl-4-hydroxy-3-methyl-2-cyclopenten-1-one ester of dl-cistrans-chrysanthemum monocarboxylic acid	insecticide
American Cyanamide 12008	O,O-diethyl S-(isopropylthiomethyl) phosphorodithioate	insecticide
American Cyanamide 12880	O,O-dimethyl S-(N-methylcarbamoylmethyl) phosphorodithioate	insecticide
Amizol	3-amino-1,2,4-triazole	herbicide
Ammate	ammonium sulfamate	herbicide
Anticarie	40 per-cent hexachlorobenzene	seed fungicide
Antu	alpha-naphthyl thiourea	rodenticide
Aramite	2(p-tert-butylphenoxy)isopropyl-2-chloroethyl-sulfite	miticide
Arasan	50 per-cent thiram (tetramethylthiuram disulfide)	seed fungicide
Arsenic, white	arsenious oxide	herbicide
Azobenzene	azobenzide	miticide
Bacillus thuringiensis	microbial pathogen	insecticide
Bayer 19639	O,O-diethyl S-2(ethylthio)-ethyl phosphorothioate	insecticide
Bayer 21/199 (Coral)	3-chloro-4-methylumbelliferone,O,O-diethyl thiophosphate	insecticide
Bayer 23/129	S-2-(ethylthio) ethyl O,O-dimethylester phosphorodithioic	insecticide
BHC	1,2,3,4,5,6-hexachlorocyclohexane	insecticide
Borax	sodium tetraborate decahydrate	herbicide
Bordeaux mixture	mixture of copper sulfate and calcium hydroxide	fungicide

Chemical Names of Pesticides Referred to in the Text—Continued

Common or Brand Name	Chemical Name	Function
Calcium arsenate	tricalcium arsenate	insecticide
Captan	N-trichloromethylmercapto-4-cyclohexene-1,2-dicarboximide	funcigide
Carbon disulfide	carbon disulfide (carbon bisulfide)	fumigant
Carbon tetrachloride	tetrachloromethane	fumigant
Ceresan M	7.7 per-cent ethyl mercury p-toluene sulfonanilide	seed fungicide
Cetab	cetyl trimethyl ammonium bromide	disinfectant
Chlorbenside	p-chlorobenzyl p-chlorophenyl sulfide	miticide
Chlorobenzilate	ethyl-4,4'-dichlorobenzilate	miticide
Chlordane	1,2,4,5,6,7,8,8-octachloro-4,7-methano-3a,4,7,7a-tetrahydroindane	insecticide
Chloro IPC	isopropyl-N-3-chlorophenyl carbamate	herbicide
Chloropicrin	nitrochloroform	fumigant
Chlorthion	O,O-dimethyl-O-3-chloro-4-nitrophenyl thiophosphate	insecticide
Copper oxychloride	cupric oxychloride sulfate	fungicide
Copper quinolinate	cupric 8-quinolinate	fungicide
Cryolite	sodium fluoaluminate	insecticide
Crag Fly Repellent	butoxy polypropylene glycol	repellent
Cyprex	70 per-cent n-dodecylguanidine acatate	fungicide
2,4-D	2,4-dichlorophenoxyacetic acid	herbicide
Dalapon	sodium 2,2-dichloropropionate	herbicide
D-D	1,3-dichloropropene and 1,2-dichloropropane mixture	fumigant
DDT	dichloro diphenyl trichloroethane	insecticide
DDVP	O,O-dimethyl-2,2-dichlorovinyl phosphate	insecticide
Demeton	O,O-diethyl O(and S)-2-(ethylthio)ethylphosphorothioates	insecticide
Diazinon	O,O-diethyl O-(2-isopropyl-6-methyl-4-pyrimidyl) thiophosphate	insecticide
Dibutyl phthalate	di-n-butyl phthalate	repellent
Dichlone (Phygon)	2,3-dichloro-1,4-naphthoquinone	fungicide
Dieldrin	1,2,3,4,10,10-hexachloro-6,7-epoxy-1,4,4a,5,6,7,8,8a-octahydro-1,4,5,8-dimethanonaphthalene (HEOD)	insecticide
Dilan	2-nitro 1,1-bis (p-chlorophenyl)propane and butane mixture (1-2 ratio)	insecticide
Dimethyl phthalate	dimethyl benzene-o-dicarboxylate	repellent
Dinitro-o-cresol	4,6-dinitro-o-cresol	insecticide
DINOSEB	dinitro-o-secondary butyl phenol	herbicide

Chemical Names of Pesticides Referred to in the Text—Continued

Common or Brand Name	Chemical Name	Function
Dipterex	O,O-dimethyl-1-hydroxy-2,2,2-trichloro-ethyl-phosphonate	insecticide
Diuron (Karmex)	3-(3,4-dichlorophenyl)-1,1-dimethylurea	herbicide
DMC(Dimite)	4,4-dichloro-(methyl benzhydrol)	miticide
DN-111	Dicyclohexylammonium 2-cyclohexyl-4,6-dinitrophenate	miticide
Dow 9-B	zinc trichlorophenate	seed fungicide
Dow ET-57 (Ronnel)	O,O-dimethyl-O-2,4,5-trichlorophenyl phosphorothioate	insecticide
Dri-Die 67	silica aerogel	insecticide
Dyrene	2,4-dichloro-6-(o-chloroanilo) triazine	fungicide
Emmi	ethyl mercuri-1,2,3,6-tetrahydro-3,6-methano-3,4,5,6,7,7-hexachlorophtalimide	seed fungicide
Endothal	disodium 3,6-endoxohexahydrophthalate	herbicide
Endrin	hexachloroepoxyoctahydro-*endo*,*endo*-dimethano-naphthalene	insecticide
EPN	*O*-ethyl-*O*-paranitrophenylbenzenethiophosphonate	insecticide
Erbon	2-(2,4,5-trichlorophenoxy) ethyl,2,2,dichloro-propionate	herbicide
Ethion	tetraethyl methylene bisphosphorodithioate	insecticide
Ethylene chlorobromide	1-bromo-2-chloroethane	fumigant
Ethylene dibromide	1,2-dibromoethane	fumigant
Ethylene oxide	1,2-epoxyethane	fumigant
Ethyl hexanediol	2-ethyl-1,3-hexanediol	repellent
Ferbam	ferric dimethyldithiocarbamate	seed fungicide
Fenuron	3-(phenyl)-1,1-dimethylurea	herbicide
Genite 923	2,4-dichlorophenyl benzenesulfonate	miticide
Glyodin	2-heptadecyl glyoxalidine acetate	fungicide
Guthion	O,O-dimethyl S-(4-oxo-3H-1,2,3-benzotriazin-3-methyl)-phosphorodithioate	insecticide
Heptachlor	1,4,5,6,7,8,8a-heptachloro-3a,4,7,7a-tetrahydro-4,7-endomethanoindane	insecticide
Hexachlorobenzene	hexachlorobenzene	seed fungicide
Hercules AC-528	2,3-*p*-dioxanedithiol S,S-bis (O,O-diethyl phosphorodithioate)	miticide
Holcomb C-326	diisopropyl ester of diethyl dithiocarbamyl phosphorothioic acid	insecticide
Indalone	butyl mesityl oxide, *n*-butyl 3,4-dihydro-2,2 dimethyl-4-oxo-1,2 H-pyran-6-carboxylate	repellent
Isodrin	1,2,3,4,10,10-hexachloro-1,4,4a,5,8,8a-hexahydro-1,4,5,8-*endo*-*endo*-dimethano-naphthalene	insecticide

Chemical Names of Pesticides Referred to in the Text—Continued

Common or Brand Name	Chemical Name	Function
Isolan	dimethyl 5-(1-isopropyl-3-methylpyrazolyl) carbamate	insecticide
Karathane	4,6-dinitro-2-capryl phenyl crotonate	fungicide
Kelthane	1,1-bis(p-chlorophenyl)-2,2,2-trichloroethanol	miticide
Lead arsenate	dibasic lead arsenate (standard)	insecticide
Lethane 384	B-butoxy-B-thiocyano-diethyl ether	insecticide
Lime-sulfur	calcium polysulfide	fungicide
Lindane	hexachlorocyclohexane gamma isomer	insecticide
Malathion	O,O-dimethyl dithiophosphate of diethyl mercaptosuccinate	insecticide
Maleic hydrazide	1,2-dihydropyridazine-3,6-dione	growth inhibitor
Maneb	manganese ethylenebisdithiocarbamate	fungicide
MCPA	2-methyl-4-chlorophenoxyacetic acid	herbicide
Mema	methoxy ethyl mercury acetate	seed fungicide
Merculine	phenyl mercuric salicylate	seed fungicide
Metacide	O,O-dimethyl O-p-nitrophenyl phosphorothioate and parathion mixture	miticide
Methoxychlor	1,1,1-trichloro-2,2-bis(p-methoxyphenyl) ethane	insecticide
Methyl bromide	bromomethane	fumigant
Methyl demeton	O,O-dimethyl O(and S) (2-ethylthio) ethyl phosphorothioates	insecticide
Methyl parathion	O,O-dimethyl-O-(p-nitrophenyl) thiophosphate	insecticide
MGK 264	N-octylbicyclo (2,2,1)-5-heptene-2,3-dicarboximide	synergist
MGK 326	di-n-propyl isocinchomeronate	repellent
Mitox	(See chlorbenside)	miticide
Monuron (CMU)	3-(p-chlorophenyl)-1,1-dimethylurea	herbicide
Nabam	disodium ethylenebisdithiocarbamate	fungicide
Nemagon	1,2-dibromo-3-chloropropane	fumigant
Nicotine	1-methyl-2-(3-pyridyl) pyrrolidine	insecticide
Omadine	zinc salt of 2-pyridinethione 1-oxide	fungicide
OMPA	bis(dimethylamino) phosphonorous anhydride	insecticide
Ovex (ovotran)	p-chlorophenyl p-chlorobenzenesulfonate	miticide
Panogen	methyl mercury dicyandiamide	seed fungicide
Paradichlorobenzene	1,4-dichlorobenzene	fumigant
Para-oxon	diethyl p-nitrophenyl phosphate	insecticide
Parathion	O,O-diethyl-O-p-nitrophenyl phosphorothioate	insecticide
PCNB	pentachloronitrobenzene	fungicide
"Penta"	pentachlorophenol	fungicide
Perthane	1,1-dichloro-2,2-bis(p-ethylphenyl) ethane	insecticide
Phosdrin	2-carbomethoxy-1-methylvinyl dimethyl phosphate	insecticide

Chemical Names of Pesticides Referred to in the Text—Concluded

Common or Brand Name	Chemical Name	Function
Phostex	bis(dialkoxyphosphinothioyl) disulfides (alkyl ratio 25 per-cent isopropyl, 75 per-cent ethyl)	miticide
Piperonyl butoxide	butylcarbityl-6-(propyl piperonyl) ether	synergist
Pival	2-pivalyl-1,3-indandione	rodenticide
Randox	alpha-chloro-N-N-diallylacetamide	herbicide
Ryania	*Ryania speciosa* (botanical name)	insecticide
Sabadilla	*Schoenocaulon officinale* (bot. name)	insecticide
Sevin	1-naphthyl N-methylcarbamate	insecticide
Rutgers 612	2-ethyl-1,3-hexanediol	repellent
Seedox	2,4,5-trichlorophenylacetate	seed fungicide
Silvex	2-(2,4,5-trichlorophenoxy) propionic acid	herbicide
Strobane	terpene polychlorinates	insecticide
Sulfotepp	tetraethyl dithionopyrophosphate	miticide
Sulfoxide	1,2-methylenedioxy-4-(octyl-sulfinylpropyl) benzene	synergist
Sulphenone	p-chlorophenyl phenyl sulfone	miticide
Tabutrex	di-*n*-butyl succinate	repellent
2,4,5-T	2,4,5-trichlorophenoxyacetic acid	herbicide
Tartar emetic	antimony potassium tartrate	insecticide
TCA	sodium trichloroacetate	herbicide
TDE	dichloro diphenyl dichloroethane	insecticide
Tedion	2,4,5,4-tetrachlorodiphenyl sulphone	miticide
1080	sodium fluoroacetate	rodenticide
TEPP	tetraethylpyrophosphate	insecticides
Thanite	isobornyl thiocyanoacetate	insecticide
Thimet (phorate)	O,O-diethyl S-(ethylthiomethyl) phosphorodithioate	insecticide
Thiodan	Hexachloro-hexahydro-methano-benzodioxathiepin-oxide	insecticide
Thioneb 50-W	polyethylene thiuram sulfides	fungicide
Toxaphene	octachlorocamphene	insecticide
Trithion	O,O-diethyl S-p-chlorophenylthiomethyl-phosphorodithioate	insecticide
Vapam	sodium N-methyl dithiocarbamate dihydrate	fungicide
Vegadex	2-chloroallyl diethyldithiocarbamate	herbicide
Warfarin	3-(a-acetonylbenzyl)-4-hydroxycoumarin	rodenticide
Zineb	zinc ethylenebisdithiocarbamate	fungicide
Ziram	zinc dimethyl dithiocarbamate	fungicide

INDEX